D0345241

INTERN

by DOCTOR X

HARPER & ROW, PUBLISHERS, NEW YORK

For ANN, who was there,
and for CHAUNCEY, who ought to have been

Contents

INTERN

The Man on the Spot

This book is a journal of the most critical year in the training of a present-day doctor of medicine: the year that he spends as a hospital intern.

At the very start, I should make clear what I mean by "journal." This is not a memoir or a recollection, but an actual diary, recorded on tape a bit at a time, day by day and week by week, throughout the year of my internship. Parts of it were recorded from the point of exhaustion; other parts reflect the discouragement, the frustration, the depression or the insecurity of the moment. At times I dictated in protest or high indignation; at other times in exultation or excitement. The result is a true and valid document of my internship as I experienced it—a reading of the cards as they fell, for better or worse. There is nothing here which did not indeed happen; inevitably much that did happen was never recorded. The transcript has been edited for coherence and grammar, but every effort has been made to leave the diary unaltered by afterthought or retrospection.

As such, this is a highly personal document. It deals with the things that happened to *me*, with *my* thoughts, *my* opinions, *my* reactions. In regard to details, other interns doubtless had other experiences, thought other things or reacted in other ways. Yet over all, I am convinced that my intern year was representative of intern training in general, not very much better nor very much worse than the training of thousands of fledgling doctors in hundreds of hospitals across the country during the year of my internship . . . or today. The details in this document are unique, but the message it conveys is universal.

At the time of the recording I had no clear idea just what I was going to do with this mass of material when I had finished it, if anything. But I felt that here was a once-in-a-lifetime opportunity to document an extraordinary experience, so fiercely crowded and so rich in its content and implications that it should not be lost. There is no other year in a doctor's life to compare with internship, no year so crucial to his growth as a doctor, no other single year which so powerfully molds and influences his entire professional life. Residency training may be similar, but never quite the same. Practice, still later, is not even remotely the same. There is no going back, no recapturing the world the intern lives in or the life that he lives in that world.

To my knowledge, no such document has ever before been recorded or published. It is not difficult to understand why. Perhaps the greatest initial impediment is time: the intern's work is exhausting, and literally never-ending. Two- and three-day stretches with only a few hours of interrupted sleep are commonplace, and time off, such as it is, must usually be seized for sleeping and regathering energy. Only a previously achieved facility with a tape recorder and a start-stop microphone made this journal feasible for me even to contemplate, much less to accomplish.

But most important of all is the question of propriety. Protection of the confidence and privacy of the patient is the moral and legal obligation of anyone responsible for the care of the sick. This obligation must not be violated; in editing this journal no effort has been spared to conceal all actual names, places, dates and incidents from identification. Because of this commitment, the journal that follows must technically be classified as fiction.

But there are other questions of propriety which I have chosen to ignore or challenge. Over and above the confidential nature of the doctor's relationship with his patient, there is an ancient unspoken code of secrecy surrounding the practice of medicine and the men who practice it. According to this code, what the layman does not know is all to the good; the work that doctors do, the way they do it, the kind of men they are and the way they become doctors must be carefully hidden from public knowledge. I am convinced that this attitude is wrong, and unworthy of the great profession that perpetuates it.

One result of this enforced secrecy is the popular image of the intern. A generation ago he was a dashing, idealistic young hero, incredibly brilliant and selflessly devoted to his work. More recently the page has turned: he is now a cynical neophyte in a corrupt profession, ruthlessly engaged in pushing narcotics, seducing nurses and perhaps performing abortions on the side. The real intern laughs at this nonsense, until he begins to realize that *people actually believe it.* He knows that he is no Galahad—as this journal will demonstrate—nor some sort of hospital Lothario, nor a cynical medical monster either. But then what is he? What motivates him? How does he really feel about the patients he sees, about himself and his work, and about the established practicing physicians with whom he is associated? What is it, finally, that makes a doctor a doctor? How does he learn to become one, and at what cost to whom?

These questions need to be answered. Yet the one man who can *really* answer them—the intern in the midst of his training, The Man on the Spot—has always held back, uncertain of the propriety of answering, and, finally, quietly accepting what seemed to be the lesser of two evils: remaining silent and leaving people in ignorance.

Fortunately, honest answers are finally being demanded. Every year the services of physicians and hospitals are being sought by more and more people, not only for treatment of illness and relief of pain, but for the preservation of good health and the prevention of disease as well. Today 99 percent of our society will sooner or later present itself to some physician, somewhere, for one reason or another, for medical help. Incredibly, the vast majority of people will act on the totally ignorant assumption that the physician they happen to select *knows something about what he's doing: practicing medicine.*

Even more incredibly, these people will *almost always be right* in this blind assumption.

How can this be? How can a doctor's competence be assured? Everyone knows that he has had long years of academic training. During the last two years of his formal medical training the prospective doctor spends a great deal of time seeing patients in clinics and hospitals. He writes up duplicate case histories, makes duplicate physical exams, and then defends his findings and opinions to his doctor-professors. But he never makes a binding decision. At the end of this period he has earned his degree as a doctor of medicine, but he is a doctor in name only. It is during his internship year, the so-called "fifth year of medical school," that he is pounded and sweated into the shape and substance of a competent physician. This year is the proving ground: for the first time he takes upon himself the burden of responsibility, and his handling of it determines his success or failure.

The intern's first duty is to the patient, from time of admission to time of discharge from the hospital. He is literally The Man on the Spot. He lives in the hospital's intern quarters, or very close by, and he does not so much as walk out of the hospital door without first checking out to the intern covering for him. His pay will vary from nothing at all to a pittance. I was paid a relatively generous $125 a month in a hospital where my work varied from 80 to 120 hours a week. I was expected to pay for the meals I took in the hospital cafeteria; the bed in the interns' quarters was free. But income was not a major consideration. The training and experience were.

Of course, the intern (who is not yet licensed to practice medicine) does not work alone. At his right hand is a more experienced resident physician, finished with internship and capable of handling greater responsibility in the special area of medicine in which he is continuing his training. Backing up both intern and resident is the experienced staff physician, either the patient's own attending doctor (in a private hospital) or the doctor appointed to supervise both care of the patients and the work of the house staff (in a charity ward). This chain of command, which exists in any hospital large enough to have an intern staff, protects the patient from inexperienced fumbling to some extent.

But the cardinal law of *"Primum non nocere"*—"First, do no harm"—which has always guided the practicing physician is necessarily suspended during this critical year of a doctor's training. He learns more about medicine in this year than in all the other years combined, and he learns, for the most part, by committing a long succession of colossal blunders and then having them corrected (if possible) by the experienced doctors looking over his shoulder.

Many times the intern *will* do harm. Many times he *will* make things worse instead of better. The intern's triumphs—the brilliant diagnostic coups, the errors he catches in time, the occasions when he makes precisely the right move at the right time to save a life— are precious moments to him; but at the same time he will inadvertently kill the patient who might otherwise have lived, through stupidity, or blundering, or blind inexperience. His triumphs are soon forgotten. His errors he must live with; he cannot be allowed to forget them.

This journal, for instance, does not really convey the depth of Dr. Fred Kidder's wrath the night the medical resident and I nearly killed his patient, old Jerry Dykeman, by giving him a medicine that knocked out the only natural breathing mechanism the old man had left. Very little was said at the time—we were all too busy breathing for old Jerry with a resuscitator until the effect of the drug wore off—but Dr. Kidder was simply furious. We had failed to recognize a treacherous situation and had ignored principles of medicine that we both knew backward. Dr. Kidder never really forgave us that incident for the rest of the year, and he has not let me forget it to this day.

Of course, the profession has not been eager to publicize such incidents, however critical they may be to the education of the doctor-in-training. Such reporting is taboo. As a result, people have never realized that the Jerry Dykemans are the price that they, collectively, have always had to pay for the privilege of having well-trained and competent physicians. Dreadful and frightening as this seems, it is true. People need to understand how a doctor becomes a doctor, what the practice of medicine is all about, what it is that a doctor must put into the game; and, above all, they need some insight into the human limitations upon a doctor's powers.

To understand these things would be to answer a great many ugly questions about the profession of medicine. It would explain why doctors guard their independence so jealously, and regard any move toward political control of their work with such dread. It would explain why doctors feel that their fees are just and equitable, however high or low, and why they resent public criticism so bitterly. It would explain why doctors rally to protect each other from attack whether it is justified or not, why they regard malpractice actions with such indignation, and why they hate the incompetents in their ranks so viciously yet are so slow to censure them—because every doctor is haunted by the knowledge that *next time it could so easily be me.*

My intention in publishing this journal has been to contribute to such an understanding between doctors and the general public. It is the personal account of one doctor in that crucial year of his training in which he crosses the gulf between layman and physician. It seeks to provide at least a glimpse into the dynamic process through which a doctor is made. The journal may horrify and appall some readers and infuriate others. But if it adds in the smallest measure to a better understanding of a great and proud profession, it will have been worth the keeping.

I

Medicine I

There is an old saying among interns that if you can make it through the first month of internship, you have it made. But just how tough that first month will be depends on which service you start with and the resident you draw as your first chargé d'affaires, mentor and nursemaid.

I was unlucky on the one count and fortunate on the other. Medicine I was the toughest service my hospital had to offer, but I was lucky enough to draw a top-notch resident, Dr. Peter Carey. I walked into a mare's nest those first few weeks of my internship. The pressure went on the first hour of the first day and it never stopped until time for rotation to another service two months later.

The biggest problem was orientation. The outgoing interns and residents work right up to 8:00 A.M. on the morning of July 1, the traditional "changeover" day in most hospitals. The new intern is immediately responsible for some twenty or thirty patients already in the hospital. He must learn their problems while taking care of new admissions as well. He must also get to know the other interns and residents, meet all the floor nurses and nursing supervisors on all three shifts and acquaint himself with a frightening number and variety of attending staff doctors.

He does all this in about the first forty-eight hours. After that he just doesn't have time.

I couldn't have done it without Peter Carey's help. Pete had just finished his internship at the hospital and become a first-year medical resident the day my internship began. He was purposely "held over" to help break in the new interns, and he postponed his vacation, weary as he was, until I had at least one foot on the ground.

7

Even so, the first weeks were a blur of confusion, a desperate race to catch up.

Orientation will also be a problem for the reader of this journal. A little background may be helpful:

The Hospital

Graystone Memorial Hospital is a medium-sized, private, metropolitan hospital situated downtown in a city of some 200,000 people but drawing patients from a population area of over a million. Graystone had only about 210 beds at the time of my internship plus an additional 175 beds in the adjacent Children's Division, and the general hospital had no facilities for the care of nonpaying patients, but it was still considered one of the best training hospitals in the entire Southwest. The quality of the teaching and the caliber of the attending doctors were first-rate. All patients at Graystone were under the care of their own private doctors; interns and residents had to earn the confidence of these men before they were allowed much responsibility. Responsibility came more slowly, but supervision and teaching were intense and personal, and often came from experts in the field.

Graystone was seven stories high, the floors organized according to the medical services. The third floor was devoted to surgical patients and postoperative care. The second and fifth were medical floors; fourth had a mixture of medical and surgical. The top floor was reserved for obstetrical patients, and the sixth floor, a flight below, with its splendid panoramic view of the city and the desert and the mountains beyond, was the surgical suite—universally known as the Operating Room or OR.

The first floor was the business floor, home of the switchboard, lobby, admitting office, medical record room and a grubby little doctors' lounge (to use the term loosely) which doubled as a cloakroom. Also on First was the Emergency Room with an ambulance entrance, where outpatients in all degrees of distress were seen, day or night, by the interns on duty, and blocked off at one end were the "temporary" interns' quarters that had been used for seven years. The cafeteria, the laundry and the power plant were all housed in the basement.

Each patient floor had a north and south wing divided by a nurses' station and chartroom. Near the elevator on each floor was a small alcove with ashtrays and soft chairs, used by waiting visitors or lounging patients. Doctors and interns would often pause there for "curbstone consultations," clinical debates or just to rest a few moments.

Also on each floor were the loudspeakers on the wall, the heart of the hospital communication and paging system. It was an inviolable rule that a doctor answer his page immediately, or have it answered for him, no matter what he was doing. We came to hate those loudspeakers, to curse at them, to cringe at the sound of our own names. One of my most indelible memories is of the mournful, slightly nasal voice of the night switchboard operator paging someone late in the evening just as the hospital was settling down for the night. We even learned to interpret from the urgency of the call and the sequence of names being paged just what sort of message would be waiting.

In reviewing this journal transcript years after it was first dictated, I think many readers might be appalled at what seems to be an uncommonly high rate of death and disaster among patients at Graystone Memorial Hospital. This was not the case at all. During my intern year (and subsequently as well) the ratio of patients' deaths at Graystone was consistently *lower* than the national average. The overwhelming majority of patients there ultimately went home healthier and happier than when they were admitted. But the reason this journal sometimes appears to suggest the contrary is easy enough to see. As each section was dictated, I was necessarily recording perhaps 5 percent or less of everything that had actually happened. The run-of-the-mill patients often were never mentioned. I seemed to choose either the cases I felt best about or the ones I felt worst about to discuss . . . and inevitably the ones that hurt the worst of all were the ones we lost.

Graystone was not a new hospital, nor was it particularly old. On sunny days it was a bright and cheerful place. On those rare gray days it was gloomy. At night it had the vague, shadowy aura of impending crisis that settles on any hospital at night. For twelve months it was more home to me than my home was. I came to know which rooms felt cold and drafty, which doors squeaked, which corridor tiles had just been replaced, which elevator was rattling up and down, which doctor was arriving and which one was going home by the sound of voices and occasional laughter echoing up the stair wells. I loved that place and I hated it in those days. Now, quite a few years later, I still feel toward that hospital more ambivalence—more love and more hatred—than for any other pile of brick and mortar I have ever known.

The Services

At Graystone, as in all large hospitals, there is a sharp distinction between the four major divisions of medical practice: Medicine, Surgery, Obstetrics and Pediatrics. Traditionally, the medical service is the diagnostic service, and the specialist in internal medicine—the "internist" who gets so annoyed when patients confuse him with the "intern"—is the specialist in difficult diagnosis and medical therapy. The surgeon must also be a diagnostician, but he is usually called in consultation by the internist when a surgical problem arises. Often the internist and the surgeon work as a team, but they never quite forget their ancient rivalry. The surgeon regards himself as the one who cures with the stroke of the knife, scorning the internist's "pills, promises, prayers and post-mortems," while the internist views himself as the true physician and healer, who turns to the surgeon only when there is cutting and sewing to be done.

Obstetrics, newer to the profession than medicine and surgery, has brought such advances even in the last hundred years that the once-commonplace death of a woman in childbirth is today a major medical tragedy, rarely excusable. Pediatrics is the orphan of the profession; the pediatrician is half-scorned by his colleagues for the seemingly artificial age limitations on his practice. Yet he is also grudgingly respected, because his small patients are very special people with special problems which quite frankly scare the life out of the internist, surgeon and obstetrician alike, and all concerned are glad to have somebody around with the know-how and guts to tangle with the troubles of these most cherished, protected and vulnerable of all patients.

The intern's twelve months are divided among these four major services roughly in proportion to their importance. I spent four months on Medicine, five on Surgery, two on Pediatrics and one on Obstetrics. In some hospitals, an intern will spend one of his surgical months on twenty-four-hour duty in the Emergency Room; at Graystone, because we were short-handed, Emergency Room service was merely added to our other duties.

The Doctors

Every hospital has its own medical hierarchy. Ours was frankly dominated by the doctors from the clinic, located just adjacent to the hospital. The clinic building was far more modern and handsome than the hospital itself, but it used the hospital's laboratory, X-ray and other diagnostic facilities. Radiology, pathology and anesthesia were provided exclusively by clinic doctors.

The Graystone Clinic had some twenty-five specialists in all fields of medicine except obstetrics and pediatrics. Many of these men had enviable national and international reputations. Dr. Armand Fuller, for instance, was a nationally respected cardiologist and served the hospital as Chief of Medicine. The Chief of Surgery, Dr. Nathan Slater, was a past president of the American College of Surgeons and a much-dreaded regional examiner for the American Board of Surgery. Dr. Jacob Compton was engaged in front-line clinical research in the medical control of diabetes.

There was no formal association between the clinic and the hospital, but clinic patients filled most of the hospital's beds, and clinic doctors commanded the lion's share of the intern's time, service and loyalty. Many of the nonclinic or "outside" doctors using the hospital, especially the general practitioners, resented the clinic group, regarding them as a tight little band of arrogant specialists who sought to crowd the general practitioner out of the hospital. But there was no question that the clinic kept the over-all quality of the hospital work on a remarkably high level.

Dr. Slater's resident assistant was the Chief Surgical Resident, responsible for the work of all the other residents in Surgery. On the medical service, Dr. Milton Musser was the Chief Medical Resident, flanked by Dr. Peter Carey and Dr. Randy Brock, who served opposite each other on Medicine I and Medicine II.

And at the bottom of the ladder were the interns. Since there were only five of us instead of the usual ten or twelve, our availability was stretched to the breaking point. The intern's life at the bottom of the pecking order could be miserable and often was. But there was always a certain restraint and dignity involved in pecking an intern; he could be pecked enough but not too much. The result, for us, was the curious sensation of constantly being knocked flat with one hand and gently propped back up again with the other, a feeling that persisted throughout the internship year.

Technically, Graystone did not have its own pediatric service; although the new, modern Children's Division building was just across the street from the older general hospital, it had its own separate administration, and interns from all the hospitals in the city were assigned there for their pediatric training. There was an active obstetrical service in Graystone, however, with its own medical hierarchy, and here again the intern was low man—perhaps lower than on any other service, as is clearly reflected in this journal.

The Duties

In brief, the interns at Graystone were expected to be everywhere and do everything. Our job was twofold: to help the attending doctors provide professional care for their patients and to learn the art and science of medicine in the process. We followed patients from admission to discharge, wrote up their histories, kept their medical records, wrote orders for their studies and medications, and tended to their needs in a thousand different ways. We worked closely with both residents and staff doctors, but we were the ones on first call when trouble came, day or night, and we were expected to deal with it. On duty nights and weekends we did not leave the hospital; it was at those times that we carried the heaviest burden of responsibility, for disasters inevitably occur on nights and weekends, as anyone in medicine well knows.

We were expected to function on all cylinders at all times, but there are only so many hours in a day and so many calories to burn at a given time. I doubt that anyone anywhere works harder, for longer hours at a stretch, carrying more responsibility, than the average hospital intern. But for all his harassment and hurry, the intern *learns*. He absorbs knowledge through his skin. He learns lesson after painful lesson about the quirks and cruelties and surprises of human illness. Even more, he learns hard lessons in humility, patience, compassion and personal integrity.

Of course, with his internship behind him a doctor may change. He may grow fat, or lazy, or rich. He may become greedy, or pompous, or arrogant, or even cruel. He may lower his standards, compromise his ideals or rationalize his dishonesties. Such things can happen in any profession.

But the remarkable fact is that these things very rarely occur among doctors. The lessons of a doctor's internship year have been ground into his very fiber. Most men could not change them if they tried. The diary that follows may show why.

THE JOURNAL, JULY AND AUGUST

Saturday, July 2

The first meeting with the new intern staff was held in the big basement conference room in the Graystone Clinic building, just adjacent to the hospital. It was supposed to be a sort of a briefing session, to introduce the new interns to the staff doctors and vice versa, to announce assignments and call schedules, and to get everybody generally oriented. It was scheduled for 7:30 A.M. on Friday morning so that hospital business could start as usual at 8:00. Ann drove me down to the hospital with time to spare, which was just as well because I couldn't find the conference room and went wandering around the clinic lobby feeling foolish until a couple of people came by who seemed to know where they were going, and I followed them. Even so, I was one of the first to arrive. I already had the dope sheet provided by the hospital personnel office, and I was wearing the prescribed white intern's jacket with the little black badge pinned to my lapel for everyone to see:

_____, M.D.
Intern Staff

Presently others began to arrive: a number of men in business suits, obviously attending doctors; others in hospital clothes with identification badges; still others, apparently clinic doctors, wearing long white clinical coats and looking disgustingly fresh and breezy for that hour of the morning. A few men here and there wore surgical scrub suits, but I found out later that most of the surgeons were already hard at it upstairs and had simply by-passed this conference.

Even without the surgeons, it all seemed very familiar to me, and at the same time frighteningly strange.

Everyone there trouped up for introductions; there must have been three dozen names thrust at me and three dozen handshakes, and I don't remember a one of them. One by one the other new interns appeared. There was Roscoe Herring, a stout and sandy-haired man with owlish eyes behind horn-rimmed glasses and a very pointed nose; and a tall, skinny lad named Hamilton, looking slightly effeminate and decidedly bored with the whole proceedings, with his dainty hands and his wavy hair. Herring was a Pennsylvania man; Hamilton had studied at Nebraska. Presently I saw Floyd Schwartz, the big, black-haired fellow with the squint whom I had met briefly in the personnel office my first day in town. He had studied at the University of Iowa, and was already complaining bitterly about how there would be only five of us interns to cover the whole hospital, when he had been assured at his interview that there would be at least ten, and about how we would all have our butts worked off before we got out of this place.

Then to round out the intern staff Alec Ivy turned up, my old classmate at Hopkins, somehow managing to look very Joe College in his white intern's jacket with button-down, pin-stripe shirt, skinny necktie and gray flannel slacks. I had never known Alec very well at Hopkins, nor liked him very much, but now we greeted each other like long-lost brothers. We were jolly well going to like each other now, and we both knew it. During the next twelve months the five of us were going to be living in each other's laps, and we would get along together whether we liked it or not, and that was that.

Dr. Andrew Case of the Graystone Clinic brought the meeting to order and outlined the things we had to know: the organization of the hospital, the location of patient rooms, our first assignments, our call schedules and the men we would be immediately responsible to. He stood us up one by one and introduced us to the crowd. Next he introduced the resident staff: Pete Carey and Randy Brock, the first-year medical residents, and Milton Musser, the Chief Medical Resident; the whole phalanx of surgical residents: Dr. Olsen, Dr. Barr, Dr. Gloucester, Dr. Mankowitz, Dr. Aarons and a few others not present, including the anesthesia residents who were already upstairs getting the morning operative patients ready for surgery.

Finally he introduced the leading staff men of the hospital and invited their remarks. There was Dr. Armand Fuller, the Chief of Medicine, pink and paunchy, who looked like the last stronghold of entrenched Republican privilege and took five minutes to say that here we all were, just one big happy family, and everything was going to be lovely. There was Nathan Slater, Chief of Surgery, with a face like a hawk and a sharp nasal voice that gave the impression of no nonsense whatsoever. Slater was followed by two aged doctors who remained of the original founders of the clinic and hospital, and then by a whole succession of other staff men.

I don't think any of us heard much of what was said; we just sat there in a little clutch, aware that everyone in the room was watching us, and equally aware that the hands on the big wall clock were getting closer to 8:00 and that somewhere up there a great big hospital full of patients was waiting, and that at the stroke of the hour the five of us would be the interns—the *only* interns—serving that hospital.

Of course, we were all doctors—at least in name. We had all just finished the four-year pull through medical school less than a month before and we all had diplomas and M.D. degrees to prove it. But until now we had always been on the outside looking in. At medical school our part in the care of sick patients, in diagnosis, examination, treatment, clinical judgment, decision-making, second guessing and post-mortem had always been a sort of intellectual exercise. We had been expected to watch and learn, but the interns had always been the fountains of wisdom, The Men with the Answers, the ones who decided what to do and then did it while we debated from the depths of our textbook wisdom whether their decisions were right or not.

Now the tables were turned. *We* were now the interns, and these staff doctors around us were dropping the responsibility into our laps and expecting us to handle it. Now *we* were the ones who would decide what to do and then do it, and God help the patients if the decisions were wrong. And all that vast accumulation of medical school wisdom didn't seem so vast any more. We may have looked confident as hell that morning, but I don't think we were fooling anybody, least of all ourselves.

We were very green, and we were very frightened.

Dr. Case wrapped up the meeting with some fatuous remarks expressing confidence that we would be the best intern staff the hospital had ever had, and then the meeting broke up. Most of the men headed back to the hospital. I trailed along, not even sure just where I was supposed to go now. The switchboard must have found out the meeting was over because when I got to the hospital door the little loudspeakers on the walls were already paging doctors in rapid succession: "Dr. Slater, Dr. Slater; Dr. Meadows, Dr. Meadows; Dr. Brock, Dr. Brock." And then my own name, sharply, twice in a row.

"What am I supposed to do when I get paged?" I asked one of the residents passing by.

"You pick up a telephone somewhere and say, 'What,'" the resident said.

I found a telephone and answered my page. "You have a new admission in 403, Doctor," the girl at the switchboard said. "A patient of Dr. Case's with a penicillin reaction. They want you up there right away."

I reached the elevators and headed up for the fourth floor. My intern year had begun.

Already I am glad I took the time to track down this tape recorder. The way I feel now, if I had to sit and type this all out, it just wouldn't get done. As long as I can lie on my back and dictate, and then turn the tapes over to Ann for typing, it may work out at least partly the way I have in mind. Ann hasn't objected, but she is not exactly crazy about her part in this deal. All she said was, "Well, you'd better keep it brief; I have to hold down a job, too, if you want to eat," and I said, "Haw, haw," and that's where it sits, for the moment at least.

I've spent a day and a half on the medical service now, Medicine I according to the duty roster, Friday night and today until 2:00 this afternoon, and I can see already that this hospital is going to be a real snake pit. It hadn't really dawned on me what it was going to mean to be short-staffed. Now I can see that there is more work to be done here than a full quota of interns could handle, and we are actually going to be less than half-staffed. Everybody has been reassuring us so vigorously that we wouldn't really be expected to cover the whole hospital all of the time that it makes me a little bit suspicious, and I'd swear I got calls from every floor of the hospital last night.

One of the five of us—Hamilton—is on Pediatrics at the Children's Division, which takes him out of the rotation schedule here for the first two months. Alec Ivy and I are paired off on opposite services: I am on Medicine I with Pete Carey, while he is on Medicine II with Randy Brock as his resident. Technically, Medicine III, the outside doctor's service, doesn't have an intern this period, and Milton Musser, the Chief Medical Resident, is supposed to fill in as best he can for both intern and resident. But then Carey has a vacation coming up next month sometime, with Milt Musser covering for him, so the residents are going to be spread as thin as the interns. Alec and I cover our own services during the day and will take Emergency Room calls in alternation when we are both in the house, but nights and weekends the one of us on call has to cover both Medicine I and Medicine II and all Emergency Room work as well. And from the looks of things, this is going to be rough duty.

It is also obvious already that this journal is going to be something different from what I had in mind when I first decided to try to keep it. I had been thinking of recording everything that happened—everything I saw, everything I did, felt or thought, to approach as closely as possible a complete daily record. I can see already that this is ridiculous; there is just too much going on from all sides. There is too much even to remember it to the end of the day, much less get it down on tape. At best I think this is going to be a sporadic diary, dictated by fits and starts in chunks of two or three days at a time if I'm lucky. If I can hit the high spots, get across the things that seem important at the time, and keep it dead honest without pulling any punches, it may still be worthwhile.

I have not told anyone except Ann a word about this little venture, and I don't intend to. I somehow have the feeling that the people at the hospital just wouldn't think too highly of the whole idea. As it is, Ann may tell me after a couple of weeks that I sound like a pretentious ass and suggest that I can the whole idea. And maybe I will.

I got my first call on Friday morning just as the orientation meeting was breaking up (without orienting anybody) and went up to the fourth floor to see the patient. I had kind of hoped there would be some way of sneaking into the work in a leisurely fashion, but I soon forgot that nonsense. When I walked onto that floor, it was like stepping onto a down escalator going sixty miles an hour. We were on our way, and there was no getting off either.

The patient they had called me to see certainly had a penicillin reaction. Dr. Case had given him a shot two or three weeks ago, and now all of a sudden he was one mass of great red blotches from head to toe, with some shortness of breath along with it. Dr. Case had not seen him yet; the man had called earlier in the morning and Case just told him to come to the hospital. I guess he figured the diagnosis from the history and symptoms. There was no history on the man's chart and no orders, and he was just itching something crazy from those hives. It took me an hour to do the history and physical examination and get them written up as I went along, while the man lay there going scratch, scratch here and scratch, scratch there all the while.

These intern's "workups" are actually painstaking medical school-type examinations, and they take forever because you don't dare take a chance on missing a thing. A workup begins with the "chief complaint" that has brought the patient to the hospital, followed by a detailed history of all aspects of his present illness. When that ground has been thoroughly raked and harrowed, you go on to a complete chronological history of all the patient's past illnesses of any sort, going back as far as he can remember, together with a history of the major illnesses of his parents, grandparents and siblings, and an assessment of his social background. Next comes the "review of systems": a careful search for unmentioned symptoms related to the heart and lungs, the urinary tract, the gastrointestinal tract, the nervous system, etc. Then, and only then, you proceed with the actual physical examination . . . which may lead to still further history-taking. I guess an expert and experienced clinician learns to cover what he needs to cover of this ground in fifteen or twenty minutes; but the intern's First Commandment is "Thou Shalt Leave No Stone Unturned," and until we learn which corners can safely be cut when, a complete medical workup can take as much as two hours to finish and record on the patient's hospital chart.

I told this man I was sure Dr. Case would want some medicine ordered right away, and went back to the nurses' station with his chart, trying to think of all the things you were supposed to do for people with penicillin reactions. He had a history of previous heart trouble and his heart was already racing, and with the wheezing in addition I was afraid to order adrenalin for him. The only thing I could think of was cortisone, but I'd never ordered cortisone for any-thing—didn't have the vaguest idea of the dose—and anyway I was scared silly of the stuff after all the precautions and horror stories we'd heard about it in medical school. I tried to call Dr. Case at the clinic, but he hadn't turned up at his office yet, so when one of the other staff doctors turned up—I couldn't remember his name—I asked him what I ought to order for a man in penicillin reaction with hives until I could get hold of his doctor. The guy said, "Well, you can always give him some Benadryl, that can't hurt him, and five minims of adrenalin right along with it, but you'd better wait on the cortisone until you talk to Dr. Case."

So I wrote the order and asked the nurse to give it by injection, and started writing the other routine orders for his care. About this time one of the medical residents turned up on the floor and intro-duced himself. He was a fuzzy-looking guy with receding hair and a crew cut, and a face that reminded me of a gopher; he said he was Pete Carey and would be my resident on Medicine I.

I told him about the new patient and he said, "Well, let's go down and see what he looks like if you've already ordered Benadryl and adrenalin for him." We went back to Room 403, and in about ten minutes Carey did essentially the same work-up that I had taken an hour to do, listened to the man's chest especially carefully, and said to the man, "Well, you certainly have a penicillin reaction, and you'd better be sure to tell anybody who comes at you with a needle any time in the future that you're violently allergic to penicillin, or you could really get in trouble. As it is, it'll probably take a week to get this settled down if we're lucky."

Going back to the nurses' station he told me that I was probably right to wait on the cortisone, but he was sure Dr. Case would want it given, so he ordered a good slug of it, half to be given by hypo and half put into an intravenous infusion.

By this time the nurses on Second had gotten word that I was the new intern on Medicine I and began converging on me with a whole string of odds and ends that needed doing. Dr. Gillies had ordered a spinal tap on a patient in Room 203; there was an intravenous to be started on a patient in 221 (everybody on the floor had had a try at it and nobody had managed to get the needle in); and the man in 216 was complaining of a stiff neck. A dozen different things to do at once. Carey was paged and scurried off somewhere after telling me to meet him after lunch to catch up on some of the old patients on the service—"chart rounds" as he called it. I went down to look at the woman who needed the IV started—it had been ordered the night before, started, and then it infiltrated the vein during the night. The doctor had ordered it discontinued until morning, and then in the morning nobody could find a vein.

The patient was a little old lady of eighty who'd had a stroke and needed intravenous fluids because she couldn't swallow, and God knows they had tried to restart that IV; she must have had seventeen needle holes in her. I spent fifteen minutes systematically going from one extremity to the next with a tourniquet trying to find a vein that looked promising, and finally got the needle into a foot vein and got the IV running again.

Just as I was finishing this I heard my page on the loudspeaker; there was a patient for me to see in the Emergency Room with a scalp laceration. I hustled on down there and found a young man who had been hit on the head by a brick that fell off a hod his partner was carrying. It had laid open a two-inch flap of scalp that had bled all over everything. Knocked him silly for a few minutes, but no evidence that he'd really been unconscious. The Emergency Room nurse had started to clean the guy up already, but he was still a mess, with hair, dirt and little chips of brick embedded in his scalp and a fresh bleeder starting every time you touched him.

It took me half an hour to get him sewed up, with the guy complaining bitterly all the while about all the beautiful hair I had to shave off in order to get to him. I didn't do a very good job, but I got the skin closed and the bleeding stopped. I was trying to decide whether to admit him on one of the doctors' services for observation for intracranial injuries (I kept thinking of the guy we saw back at Hopkins with the brain hemorrhage, who had quietly passed out on the way home from the doctor's office after having a scalp laceration sewed up, fractured his skull on the curb when he fell and subsequently died of the skull fracture) when I heard my page, and the operator asked me if I knew that I should have been making rounds with Dr. Gillies on Fifth since 9:00 (it was now 10:30) and that he had called down three times asking where I was. So I told the nurse to take the guy over to X-ray and get skull films and make him sit around the Emergency Room for an hour by the clock before she let him go on about his business, and to arrange for his regular doctor to take a look at his suture line the next day.

So then I scurried up to Fifth and found Dr. Gillies along with Carey and Randy Brock and two or three others I didn't know, just finishing teaching rounds for the morning, discoursing about how you can distinguish between the jaundice caused by a hepatitis and the jaundice that comes from a stone plugging the bile duct. Dr. Gillies was a tall, skinny guy with glasses and a Boston accent; I later learned that he was the clinic's whiz-kid on liver disease. He gave me a fishy stare when I turned up, and then went on with his dissertation without a pause. I thought of apologizing for being late and telling him what had held me up, but then I thought, What the hell, if he can't figure it out for himself there's no point to making a big issue out of it. But I still felt plenty silly, my first day in the place and I didn't even know there were supposed to be rounds (I'm sure they were mentioned at the orientation meeting, but I just didn't hear it).

Presently Dr. Gillies suggested going down to the cafeteria to continue the discussion over coffee, but Pete took me aside and said, "We'd better skip coffee this morning because we've got too much to do. There's that spinal tap in Room 203. Have you ever done one before?"

I actually had, a couple of times, during my stretch on anesthesia at Hopkins in third year of medical school, but I said, "Not very many, and I'm not sure of the technique. Maybe I'd better watch you do this one." So he said, "Fine, let's go do it," and we went down to Second again. While he was doing it he briefed me on a couple of other problem cases on the service and then told me casually that six new admissions were expected during the afternoon, which appalled me. By the time he finished and then took me in to meet a couple of other patients in the near vicinity it was lunch-time and we agreed to meet later on Second and go over the rest of the patients on the service.

Went down to the cafeteria for lunch and got nicked 85 cents—sorry, 88 cents, there's a 3 percent sales tax in this miserable state—for a scoop of chicken à la king on a gob of mashed potato, a piece of pie with ice cream on it and a cup of coffee. Apparently the second cup of coffee is free; I hope this sort of generosity isn't going to break the hospital cafeteria up in business. I made a mental note to bring sandwiches for lunch from now on and just buy soup and coffee from the cafeteria; a buck a day for lunch five days a week and on duty weekends would blow about a third of my monthly stipend right there. I think I'd rather eat peanut butter and jelly sandwiches and live it up with a steak at home once a month. I don't know yet what the bite will be for dinner, but probably worse. Anyway, I'll be eating dinner at home when I'm off duty, and on duty nights I may just skip it, since I gather that there will usually be new admissions sitting around waiting to be worked up by dinner hour and I may just feel like working on through until I finish them.

Also, Roscoe Herring (who was as disgusted at the price of lunch as I was) was saying that the cafeteria is thrown open every night for "midnight supper" starting about 10:30 P.M. and ending at 2:00 A.M., to catch the nurses going off the 3:00-to-11:00 shift and the nurses coming on from 11:00 to 7:00, as well as any vagrant doctors who may be wandering around the place at that hour of the night, and that this particular spread is free for anybody. Herring claimed that all they put out for midnight supper was cold cuts, bread, butter, milk and some kind of hot slumgullion made up of whatever nobody would eat at lunch and dinner thrown into a pot and heated up. But you can eat one hell of a lot of cold cuts at 11:00 at night if you haven't had any dinner, and as far as the hot pot goes, I guess you can tell by the smell whether you want to eat any of that or not.

Anyway, after lunch I met Pete Carey on Second, and we sat down and went over the charts of about twenty patients who were in the house. He said not to worry about these old ones because he would follow them. I should pay more attention to the new admissions. His dope about new admissions was slightly wrong; there were eight, not six, starting at 1:30 in the afternoon, and about the time I had four calls in fifteen minutes about new patients and figured one hour per patient to do a work-up I was beginning to wonder why we had a bed down in quarters for our duty nights. It didn't sound as if I was going to get into any bed that night.

I just tackled them as they came, and there was nothing very exciting about any of them—about half came over directly from the clinic with fairly complete work-ups already done by the clinic doctors, so that I had at least some idea what the hell they were doing there—and what with one or two more calls from the Emergency Room, I finished working up the last new patient at 9:30 P.M. About 5:15 I ran into Alec Ivy on Fourth, wearing a big fat grin and saying, "Well, boy, it's all yours; I'm leaving," and I just grunted at him and said to myself, That's fine, son, you go right ahead and leave because you've got the weekend coming up and I hope you sweat.

By 9:30 all of a sudden everything stopped; all the new patients were worked up and Pete said, "Well, I'm going to sign out to you and go home" (he lives in the Harmon Apartments across the street from the hospital), "but be sure to call me if anything happens that worries you." Then he suggested that I could save myself calls after I went to bed by making sleeper rounds on all the floors before I turned in. "Those nurses will kill you if they can," he said. "They'll wait until midnight on some patient who doesn't have a sleeping pill ordered and then call you up and ask you what to give him."

I took his advice and made rounds of all the floors and then went down to see if Herring's word about midnight supper was true. It was. Cold cuts, and a hot pot of cooked-up leftovers. The only one down there that early was a young fellow who introduced himself as Dr. Morton Silver, a partner of Dr. Abraham Isaacs on the Medicine III service, an outside doctor. He was munching on a chunk of salami and drinking a cup of coffee when I turned up, and I said, "Jesus, what a day," and he just grinned and kept munching his salami. This was at 10:30 at night. After a while he said, "You going to turn in now? You're lucky. I've still got seven house calls to make," and he picked up another chunk of salami and took off, chewing on it.

I went up to the interns' quarters, feeling completely beat, and decided to luxuriate in a long hot shower since the hospital was paying for the water. It was delightful. The only trouble was that I got paged twice in the middle of it (they have a speaker in the interns' john, for God's sake!), so it was kind of a frantic shower. Both calls were for sleeping pill orders, and both of them were from floors that I had just left a half an hour before after checking to make sure that there weren't any patients that didn't have any sleeping pills ordered. But it does give you a feeling of importance to be the only guy in the whole hospital that the nurses can call to find out whether they can give some patient a grain and a half of Nembutal or not.

I'd heard that the loudspeakers were turned off at 11:00 P.M., so I thought, Aha! This is the time to hole up and get some sleep. Floyd Schwartz, the intern on Dr. Slater's service, Surgery I, was stretched out on a couch in the interns' lounge with his scrub suit still on, watching the late show on TV. He didn't seem inclined to talk so I hit the sack.

Then about 1:00 A.M. I started getting sleeper calls. All three of the floors that had medical patients must have called at least twice each between 1:00 and 4:00 A.M., with the calls nicely arranged so I'd just get to sleep after one before the next one came. You got the impression that those night nurses (who come on bright, fresh and cheery at 11:00 P.M. and work their eight-hour day until 7:00 A.M. and then go home) thought you were sitting there poised by the telephone just waiting for them to give you a jingle. Somebody—I think it was Randy Brock—had made some sour remark that the new interns had better start getting nasty about sleeper calls from the first night on, make themselves so enormously unpleasant about these things that the night nurses would shrink from calling, or else they would keep you awake all night every duty night with this sort of thing. I'd passed the comment off without much thought at the time, but after last night's performance I wonder if maybe he wasn't just quoting chapter and verse of the gospel.

A little after 4:00 A.M. there was a call from the night nursing supervisor telling me that a patient of Dr. Fuller's had just been admitted as an emergency, probably acute heart failure with pulmonary edema (lungs filling with fluid), and that Dr. Fuller had called in to ask the intern and resident to see the man. Apparently Fuller hadn't actually seen the patient, just talked to him on the phone and told him to get on into the hospital. I got my pants on and went up to the fifth floor and discovered that the nurses were actually trying to resuscitate the man. I could hear him wheezing and gurgling all the way down the hall. He was about sixty, propped bolt upright in bed with a pillow clutched around his middle to support him, barely conscious, and gasping as if every breath were his last. His face was gray and his lips were purple and at first glance I thought, My God, he's had a seizure, because he was oozing white, foamy stuff from his mouth and drooling it all over his nightshirt. Then I realized that this was pulmonary edema with a capital P; this guy was actually filled from the mouth on down with this foamy, watery stuff that was just rolling up out of his lungs.

Somebody had had presence of mind enough to get a suction machine into the room, and I didn't stop to get any history; I just grabbed the suction tube and shoved it into his nostril and down his windpipe and sucked out a whole batch of this bubbly stuff, which of course sent him into a paroxysm of choking and coughing and turned him even bluer. His heart was pounding at about 140 a

minute, and he was taking a gasp about every second. I told the
night nurse that she'd better get Dr. Carey over here pronto because
this guy was in trouble, and then stuck a stethoscope on his chest. It
sounded like Niagara Falls in there. All I could think of was to suck
the stuff out, get tourniquets on his legs to cut down on his venous
return and order an ampule of Aminophyllin to be given IV (intravenously) at once. I did think to ask if he'd ever had digitalis
(the old classical medicine to help improve the efficiency of a failing
heart) before, and he shook his head kind of hopelessly, so I ordered
up a couple of ampules of injectable digitalis to be given IV right
after the Aminophyllin. The nurses had an oxygen mask on him,
but it had twisted around so it was feeding oxygen to his ear. I
pulled the mask off and substituted a nasal catheter and turned the
tank oxygen up full blast.

Carey turned up a few minutes later, and asked me what I'd
done. He ordered a sixth-grain of morphine in addition and sucked
the guy out again, only he didn't fool around about it; he must
have gotten that tube a foot down into the guy's lungs and got up
an immense quantity of a vile-looking mixture of bubbly foam,
mucus and blood. I had to hold the man's head during this procedure while a nurse secured his arms, and I thought he was going to
take right off the bed when that suction tube went down, but he
turned a little pinker afterward, and a few minutes later he wasn't
foaming all over the bed any more and seemed to be breathing a
little more slowly and easily.

Pete and I left the nurse in attendance and went down to the
chartroom. He called Dr. Louis Franklin (Dr. Fuller's sidekick) and
told him the situation (I listened in on another line), and Franklin
sounded as though this were just part of the workaday world to
him, said we were doing just fine, and to call him back if the man
didn't seem to be responding well and he'd come over, but he
thought he'd bail out pretty well, and said we'd better hold up on
another dose of digitalis until 7:00 or 8:00 in the morning, but to
take an electrocardiogram right then to be sure the man hadn't had
a coronary to kick this thing off. Pete and I did the electrocardiogram
together, and it looked to me like a coronary on the tracing, but
Pete said, no, that was just the pattern you saw with an oxygen-
starved heart muscle, and that my heart would be starved for oxy-

gen too if it was beating 130 times a minute and trying to push blood through a soggy sponge of a lung like that guy had.

We sat tight with the man for about an hour and a half, and by 5:30 A.M. he was coming around remarkably well and Pete thought we could take the tourniquets off and set up an oxygen tent instead of the catheter so the oxygen wouldn't dry out his nose and throat so badly. By now the man was able to give a history. It seems everything had been splendid until he suddenly woke up at 3:00 in the morning and couldn't get any air. He got up and sat by the window for a while, but things seemed to be getting worse so finally he had called Dr. Fuller in desperation. It looked like another dose of IV digitalis at 8:00 and another sometime later in the day would be the ticket, but Pete ordered more morphine for 8:00 and suggested we leave further orders up to Franklin or Dr. Fuller when they came in for morning rounds.

By this time it was almost 6:00 Saturday morning and I was so keyed up I decided that going back to bed was hopeless. It was broad daylight outside, so I went down to quarters and took another shower and changed clothes (I had sweat clean through my shirt and undershirt, and had this man's slobber all over both sleeves of my jacket). I turned up at the cafeteria at 7:00 just when it opened and had ham and eggs for breakfast, figuring I'd earned something more than the bowl of Wheaties I had been planning on. I was a little surprised to find about 10 of the clinic doctors turning up there about 7:15, and one of them asked me if I'd been up all night, and I said, well, that just depended on how you looked at it, and he just grinned.

I had an hour to kill before morning rounds so I went in to see Mr. Keller, the man with the penicillin reaction (he was still itching but not quite as violently, and the wheezing was gone). There were also half a dozen other people on the service that I hadn't seen the day before. Also wrote my work-up on the man with pulmonary edema and checked him again, found him sleeping like a baby in the oxygen tent with his heart rate converted to 80 per minute and his respirations about 20.

At 9:00 I turned up on Fifth for teaching rounds with whoever was supposed to conduct them. At 9:15 Dr. Boyd Pickering, the clinic dermatologist, appeared, but he didn't have any patients in the house so he just sat down with us in the fifth floor alcove and started describing some exotic skin disease called pityriasis rosea. Milt Musser, the Chief Medical Resident, was there and he seemed to be intent upon sneering at dermatology as the most useless of all medical specialties. Dr. Pickering didn't take offense, but he didn't seem too interested in what he was talking about either, so we folded up rounds about 9:30.

Pete and I were both off for the weekend, so we went looking for Alec Ivy and Randy Brock to break them in on the problems of the service. I was just plain pooped and plenty glad to get out of there about 10:15 when Ann turned up in the parking lot outside the intern quarters to pick me up and take me home.

Tuesday, July 5

I'm really getting a ridiculously easy start on this internship, I guess, since yesterday was a holiday and the hospital was on "holiday routine"—which means emergency coverage but no formal rounds, no scheduled surgery and only emergency lab and X-ray services available so that nothing much could be ordered. I guess Alec had a bitch of a weekend; he looked kind of gray when I turned up at 8:00 Monday morning, and he gave me a hasty run-down on the patients on my service and what had gone on with them over the weekend. He asked me if I'd had a good weekend, and I told him I'd been too fagged out to do anything but sleep almost all day Saturday until suppertime and then again after supper until Sunday morning. Ann and I had planned to paint the bedroom on Sunday, because the wallpaper in there was huge pink cabbage roses on a blue background, and Ann had said when we rented the place that I could take my choice between those roses and her; one or the other was going to go. We got one of the four walls painted and then saw it was going to take two coats to cover them up, and got discouraged and quit around noon on Sunday. Also, we had a new electric stove which Ann had never used before, so we had a raw lunch and a burnt dinner.

After Alec had briefed me and started off on his rounds so that he could leave by 10:00 for the Fourth of July holiday, Pete and I made our own rounds and caught up on a couple of loose ends. Mr. Keller with his penicillin reaction is responding to treatment all right, but Dr. Case still thinks he is going to be in for another three or four days. The man with pulmonary edema looks and sounds like he's ready to run the mile against anybody; apparently once his heart rate slowed down on the digitalis, the changes in the electro-cardiogram reverted to normal, so he definitely hasn't had a coronary.

With the little free time I had between rounds and Emergency Room calls I just reviewed charts. There were no admissions on Monday until about 4:15, and then three people came in back to back, none of them critically ill but all admitted for diagnostic studies Tuesday morning. I worked them up one by one, and found it was still taking me between sixty and ninety minutes to do an admission work-up—careful medical history and physical examination, written out in the chart along with the initial orders. Somehow I'll have to slice the time; Pete tells me there are sometimes ten or fifteen admissions in an afternoon, and if I take an hour apiece this is going to be impossible.

One of the patients Monday afternoon was a forty-year-old woman named Cora Baker, skinny as a beanpole with skin stretched across her cheeks like a skeleton. She had been losing weight for several months, a total of over sixty pounds. It was about all she could do to lift her head off the pillow; she had to pause and catch her breath between sentences as I took the history. She had been sent over by her doctor somewhere in the central part of the state for Dr. Orville Peterson to diagnose. Peterson hadn't seen her when she was admitted, but she was obviously a sick cookie; the more history I took, the more baffled I was at just what in hell *was* wrong with her. At Hopkins they used to call cases like this "ETKM"— Every Test Known to Man—and I didn't know whether I should sit down and order up everything I could think of that might be helpful (which was plenty) without checking with Dr. Peterson or simply outline in my admission note what I thought ought to be done. When I saw Pete later I told him I was whipped on this one, didn't even know where to start with her, and he said I could always assume that Dr. Peterson would want chest X-rays, a routine blood count and sedimentation rate, a fasting blood sugar, a blood urea nitrogen test and stomach X-rays, so I couldn't go too far wrong ordering those things as soon as possible.

A couple of messy lacerations kept me busy in the Emergency Room during the evening, and after midnight supper I went around to all the floors and made an issue about this business of calling me every hour on the hour for sleeping pill orders. Went down the Cardex file on each floor with the night nurse who had just come on and tried to cover every patient before going down to turn in. It paid off. I had only two pill calls all night and those were from the OB floor where there wasn't any intern coverage.

But I had a mean one drop in my lap about 1:30 in the morning, also from the OB floor. There was a woman up there that Dr. Flagg had delivered about 8:30 in the evening who started to bleed heavily, and someone needed to see her. Dr. Flagg was across town at St. Christopher's Hospital delivering a pair of twins and just couldn't leave right then, and had asked if one of the house staff would take a look at this woman until he could get there.

So I rolled out of bed and struggled into my pants, trying to wake up and remember all of a sudden, right now, just what in the hell you were supposed to do about a woman who started a uterine hemorrhage five or six hours after delivery, and my mind was a blank. All I could think of was Ergotrate and Pitocin (drugs which cause the uterine muscle to contract), and I had no idea of the dosage of either, since in medical school everybody always insisted that you didn't have to pay attention to dosages there because you'd learn all those icky little details during internship. I grabbed the *Merck Manual* off the desk in my room and tried to leaf through it and find something about post partum hemorrhage while I waited for the elevator to come down, but I couldn't even find the right pages; I was still punchy from sleep and couldn't get my mind to function, so by the time I got to the seventh floor I was damned near in a panic state myself.

I was hoping maybe this was just some nervous nurse scared by a little blood on a pad, but no such luck—this woman was bleeding, I mean she was really gushing. She was just blanched out; her lips looked about the same color as her cheeks. She was conscious, but her pulse was fast and I couldn't even get a blood pressure reading, and she was panting for air and trying to sit up in bed, half-confused and picking at the bed sheets the way I had seen a couple of people do at Johns Hopkins when they were dying and knew it. Her uterus should have been down in a hard knot just above the pubis, but instead it was the size of a watermelon and so soft that I could hardly tell the uterus from the rest of her abdomen. I stood there and thought, My God, she's just going to exsanguinate with me standing here holding her hand.

Then one of the night nurses, bless her soul, said, "Doctor, I brought the shock blocks [wooden blocks used to elevate the foot of the bed to help combat shock] down here in case you might want them," and suddenly it dawned on me that it wasn't the bleeding I had to worry about right then, that this woman was in *shock*, and I said, "Yes, let's get those blocks under the foot of the bed." So two nurses shoved the shock blocks under the end of the bed while I lifted it up, tipping the woman's feet up at about a 30-degree angle. Then I started massaging her belly, trying to get the uterus to clamp down a little bit, and sent a nurse out to get an IV setup, and started trying to remember what you do for shock instead of what you do for post partum hemorrhage. By now I was scared silly, and mad at myself as well; for all the dozens of times I had read about shock and what to do about it, I had never actually *seen* or *treated* a patient in shock, and at the moment I couldn't think of a damned thing.

Then in a minute or two the nurse turned up with 1,000 cc's of 5 percent glucose water in an IV jug and said, "Doctor, if you're going to want to order any blood for this lady, maybe you can draw the blood sample for typing and cross-matching before you start the IV going," and again this gal saved the day—I hadn't even thought of a transfusion. I said, "Yes, I'm going to want three units of blood on an emergency cross-match," and then proceeded to draw the blood sample for the blood bank to use for typing and cross-match and started the IV going. I knew about plasma expanders like dextran, but I was a little scared of them, and the woman was looking a little better now that her feet were tilted up, so I told the nurse to put some Pitocin in the IV, and when she said, "How much do you want in there?" I said, "Well, hell, enough to clamp that uterus down," and went back to the nurses' station with her. She told me they usually put an ampule of Pitocin in 1,000 cc's of glucose, so I said, "Fine, go ahead and do that," even though I didn't have the vaguest idea how much Pitocin there was in an ampule. An orderly came up to take the blood sample down to the blood bank, and I told him to snap it up, we needed the blood in a hurry.

About this time Dr. Flagg walked in, a great big burly guy who looked like a prize fighter. I told him what I thought was going on with his patient and what I'd ordered, and he said, "Okay, that sounds fine, but maybe a little ephedrine will speed things up," and ordered that, too. I hung around a while until Dr. Flagg said, "Well, thanks, Doc, sorry I had to bother you," and so I started for the elevator to go back down to bed again. I was still shaking. The corridor was dark and a nurse went padding by me with her rubber-soled shoes squeaking on the tile as I waited for the elevator, and I heard a couple of patients snoring through their open doors, and I think it really slammed home to me then for the first time that *I was the intern in this place*, I was *responsible* for these people and what happened to them. A nurse had bailed me out on this one, but that woman would have been dead in another fifteen minutes if *somebody* hadn't come up with the right answers, and I was the guy everyone expected to provide the right answers in a pinch. It suddenly hit me that there were going to be a thousand pinches like this to deal with before I got through, and maybe the attending doctor would turn up in time and maybe he wouldn't, and maybe there would be a good, sharp nurse on hand to bail me out and maybe there wouldn't.

Just thinking about it gave me the chills. God help you poor people if you're stuck with me in a pinch, and God help me, too. It won't do any good to dredge up the right answers in fifteen minutes if that happens to be ten minutes too late. When I got down to quarters I got out my Cecil's *Textbook of Medicine* and spent an hour and a half reading the section on the diagnosis and treatment of shock. When I finally turned in at 4:00 A.M., I still couldn't get to sleep for beans.

I got up in time for breakfast Tuesday morning and then went up to the fifth floor early. The place was already swarming with doctors; after the long holiday weekend everybody was bustling around trying to make up for lost time, I guess. I almost had to fight

my way in to the chart rack. I saw Dr. Case and asked him what he
planned to do with Mr. Keller and his penicillin reaction, and he
said he thought he could go home. Dr. Peterson was also there,
looking at the chart on Cora Baker, the skinny woman who had
come in Monday with the history of weight loss. He had written a
whole pageful of orders in addition to the ones I had written. I
made some inane remark about Mrs. Baker looking like a sick
woman to me, and Dr. Peterson looked up at me through his gold-
rimmed glasses and said, "Well, Doctor, they often are when they
come into this place, but it's how sick they are when they leave that
counts, isn't it?" and went back to his writing.

I met Carey, who looked harried (and who also looked as if he
had just crawled out of bed), and he said, "I hope you're bright and
cheery this morning," and I said, "Why?" and he said, "I just
checked at the admitting desk and found out we've got seven new
patients scheduled for admission today, so get set to work."

The first one came in about 10:30, and after that there was a
steady stream of admissions. I didn't have to worry about spending
a dollar for lunch because by lunchtime it was pretty clear that if I
wanted to get home at all tonight I was going to have to run my
butt off right down to the deadline. I finished up about 7:45 P.M.,
and for the life of me I can't remember one single clear thing about
anyone I saw all day, except for one little old lady who was so stone-
deaf that I had to shout at her to get through at all, and then every
time I shouted she would say, "Well, for heaven's sake, young man,
you don't have to *shout* at me," in a piercing voice that must have
carried clear up to the operating rooms. I never did find out what
she was doing there; for all I could tell, she thought she had just
checked into the Desert Wind Hotel. She was Dr. Van Wert's patient, and he had just seen her in the clinic before she came over
here. Maybe he knows.

Wednesday, July 6

This was a "short day," coming up in the middle of the week
instead of Friday because of the holiday throwing off the routine.
Nothing very much to record, except that I spent most of the day
going around finding out who it was that I admitted yesterday.

Only three new patients today, none of them very interesting. It still takes forever for me to work them up, but at least I'm not scared to walk into their rooms any more. It still seems that I get a little farther behind each day. I complained about this to Carey today, and he seemed to think it was hilariously funny. I still keep plaguing him about almost every new admission, asking him what to order and what not to; I imagine Pete is getting pretty bone-weary of this by now, but so far he hasn't complained about it.

Oh, I forgot to mention that I had to get to the hospital extra early this morning to attend the Wednesday morning breakfast conference Dr. Case plans to have with the interns each week. It has to be at 7:00 A.M. to free the surgical interns for their first scrubs about 7:30. This is supposed to be a gripe session, with Dr. Case there all sweetness and light to hear our troubles and find solutions to our problems. This morning, though, nobody was very eager to register complaints. Case is a kind of formidable little cuss, anyway, with black hair and rimless glasses and piercing little black eyes and a face like a mole. He's the only bachelor among all the clinic doctors, and likes to fly down to Acapulco for long vacation weekends two or three times a year. But when he fixes you with those beady little eyes and speaks in that clipped, authoritarian little voice of his, he isn't exactly the sort of guy you feel you can open your soul to.

At this breakfast conference everybody beefed about the shortage of interns, and Case pointed out that everybody was disappointed about that, but that happened to be the way things had turned out this year. The hospital would make every effort to see that we weren't overworked. I brought up these hourly piss calls that come from the floor nurses all night long and found out that the other guys were being tormented by the same thing. Case seemed puzzled, said, no, that couldn't be happening; the night nursing supervisor is supposed to be screening calls and letting through only those she feels she herself can't deal with. We pointed out that it didn't seem to be working out quite that way in practice. He said he would talk to the night supervisor again; if sleeping pill calls came from anyone else, we should refer them back to her then and there. He didn't sound as though he thought this would do much good, though.

One of the new admissions today was a Mr. Sperling, a patient of

Dr. Case's with a rapidly progressing anemia. I was sure they would want to transfuse him on the spot—his admitting blood count came back with a hemoglobin level of 5 grams, about a third of what it ought to be—but Carey said, no, a transfusion now might screw up his diagnosis for another couple of months, and he thought Case would want to have a gastric analysis and a bone marrow tap and a few other odds and ends done before doing anything about the anemia. I suppose that's a valid reason, although the man was awfully weak and short of breath, and I wouldn't like to be walking around with 5 grams of hemoglobin very long if it were me or my patient.

Friday, July 8

Friday again, and it's hard to believe that this is the beginning of the second week.

The days have seemed extremely long, but that's partly illusion. When I have a night on call I don't get out of the hospital at all; one day runs right into the next, and when I'm running all night long (like last night), a "day's work" starts at 8:00 A.M. one day and ends at 5:00 P.M. or later the next, which certainly gives the impression of working a thirty-six-hour day.

Some things have changed, at least a little. I'm not quite as tense as I was a week ago. I still get a knot in my stomach every time I go to see a newly admitted patient, but once I'm there looking at him I'm not so much at a loss as I was at the beginning.

The day started this morning with a medical conference scheduled for 7:30 A.M. This is one of the big medical meetings of the week in this town; lots of staff doctors turn up for it and we've been told that all the house staff are expected to be there. Pete Carey didn't show up, however, nor did Peterson, with whom I was supposed to make rounds afterward. I spent half the meeting worrying about whether I ought to be there or up in the hospital making rounds with Dr. Peterson.

The conference today was conducted by a little weebie named Ned Stern. He presented a lady patient with Addison's disease—chronic failure of the adrenal glands. Apparently Stern was presenting the case for opinions and advice, but most of the discussion was monopolized by a big-cheese surgeon named Meadows who insisted on asking a whole bunch of irrelevant questions. Dr. Stern ended up without getting much help from anybody. He did give us a brief review of body-fluid balance which was more or less helpful, though; these patients get their fluids and electrolytes all out of whack. I guess you have to be pretty sharp to treat them at all.

After the conference I found Carey and Dr. Peterson just starting rounds on Fifth. With them was Peterson's flunky in the clinic, a tall, brown-haired, flabby-looking guy named Harry Smithers. We sat down in the alcove on Fifth for a while and talked about ulcerative colitis, since it seems that Dr. Peterson has about four cases in the house now. One is a seventy-five-year-old hermit who lives off in the desert somewhere, a miner or prospector or something of the sort. It's a little strange for a man his age to have ulcerative colitis— the kind of "nervous bowel" that gives people chronic diarrhea with ulceration of the bowel lining and sometimes quite a bit of bleeding. But this old man has it, and has it pretty bad. He hasn't any family to take care of him so he's running up a horrible hospital bill here, and the surgeons want to take his colon out because they don't think his disease is going to quiet down with just medical treatment. They insist he's going to die without the surgery, in spite of the fact that he'd have a hell of a time taking care of a colostomy by himself out in the desert if they did operate. We wheeled him over to Dr. Smithers' office in the clinic building and proctoscoped him, a good way to get a look at the inside of an ulcerated colon, if you happen to want to.

Got back on the floors a little while later. Didn't have too many new admissions scheduled, but I've been worrying about how to follow up on the patients I've already admitted. I find that I don't actually remember them very well unless there's something very exciting going on. Even when I get around to see some of the patients myself I don't follow them as well as I should, and get caught flat-footed by things that have transpired since I last saw them. There are so many patients and so many little details to remember about each one.

Last night I went along with Dr. Fuller to see one of his coronary patients on evening rounds, and learned a few things about coro-

nary disease and also about Dr. Fuller. He told me why a change in
heart sounds in a coronary patient is significant. It sometimes tells
you that the patient is going into heart failure a few hours before
outright symptoms of failure turn up. Dr. Fuller is one of the big
cheeses at the clinic and usually only makes rounds on the VIPs
(according to one of the nurses). Dr. Franklin is his younger, do-the-
dirty-work partner. Pete says that if I ever have an evening call on a
heart patient it would be best to call Franklin and not Fuller unless
Fuller specifically asks to be called.

I've also learned that there are rounds and then there are rounds.
"Business rounds" are the job of the interns and residents: seeing
each patient on the service once a day at least, writing progress
notes on their charts, seeing that things that the staff doctor wants
done get done, keeping an eye on temperature charts, carrying out
special procedures and so on. These are housekeeping rounds; there
isn't any set time for them, but if you don't get them done in the
morning, the new admissions catch up with you in the afternoon
and you end up making rounds at midnight, which nobody loves.

On "teaching rounds" we see the patients the staff man thinks
will be interesting, and may spend a whole hour discussing one
patient. "Grand Rounds" are special, high-powered teaching
rounds conducted by a chief of service or some other big shot, with
the attending staff, the house staff, medical students and everybody
else trailing along. I don't know if Graystone has formal Grand
Rounds every week or just when some visiting fireman is in town.

Anyway, with twenty or twenty-five patients on the service, I'm
having trouble keeping up. I keep catching myself thinking that the
next guy up, namely, the resident, will take care of this or that; it's
hard to realize that I'm supposed to be the intern in charge of
things. I also get confused figuring out how far to go, what the
patient's doctor will want. I'm sure that I'm not taking on as much
responsibility as I should be with the patients. So instead of rushing
around trying to see everybody at once, today I went down to the
second floor after I left Carey and reviewed charts on three or four
patients I have there in detail, going back to the first orders and
work-ups written when they were admitted, looking in on the patients, checking to see what changes in orders ought to be made,

and in one or two cases writing a progress note. But the resident had already been there first, and it took so long for four patients that I almost missed lunch completely.

The only new admission today was Mr. Casey, a seventy-nine-year-old man with hypertension who had had a stroke—not a very serious one, apparently. He has partial paralysis of his leg and arm on the left side; no other disturbance at all. He's a pleasant old man. This time, instead of walking into his room medical-school fashion with chart and paper in hand to take down his history as I heard it, I just asked him questions and examined him and went back to the nurses' station to write it up. This seemed to work pretty well; I remembered most of what I saw and heard and got my work-up whittled down to three pages instead of my usual four. I don't think I missed anything significant, but we'll see.

[*Post hoc*: I didn't know then what a perfectly incredible volume of minute detail a doctor learns to remember in taking a patient's history and examining him. Reviewing later sections of this diary, I am amazed that I not only still remember *precisely* what certain patients said but remember even the tone of voice, the expressions on their faces, sometimes even the color of pajamas they were wearing. And these are patients I have neither seen again nor even thought of for years.]

As for Mr. Casey and his hypertension, there wasn't much for me to do but put him on a low-salt diet and order some studies I was pretty sure his doctor would want. It sounded as though he has some active urinary tract infection, and his hypertension has never been treated, so I started the ball rolling by ordering kidney function studies and wrote for an ophthalmology consult.

After that I did a sternal marrow puncture on Mr. Sperling, Dr. Case's patient with anemia, so he can decide if the man has leukemia. This procedure involves using a local anesthetic to numb the skin over the breast bone and the nerve fibers of the bone sheath, and then using a little saw-toothed needle to bite a one-millimeter hole through the bony plate so that a specimen of marrow can be sucked into a syringe. The sucking-up process is quite painful for a fraction of a second; Mr. Sperling gave a gasp and said it felt like his chest was caving in momentarily, but it passed very quickly. I was scared silly the first time I did one of these things at Hopkins, but this one went fine. Pete drifted in and seemed impressed that I had any idea what I was doing.

Unfortunately, I didn't impress him as much with another little procedure I did later. A patient had come in, a young colored man, for a twenty-four-hour admission for a spinal tap. I wasn't even sure what his doctor was looking for. The guy apparently had had a skull fracture about six months ago and has been having headaches ever since. He also has what sounds suspiciously like a history of syphilis. So I did the spinal tap on him—or rather, I tried. After three stabs without success, and with the patient complaining bitterly all the time, Pete walked in and hit the spinal canal on the first try, then left me to collect the samples of spinal fluid and do the pressure readings. There must be some trick to this procedure that I just don't grasp. As long as a resident is looking over my shoulder it goes just fine, but when I try one solo I get nowhere. Maybe next time I'll do better.

I'm walking into my first weekend on call now, and I dread it. I just don't know what to expect, with a straight stretch of duty from 8:00 A.M. Saturday until 5:00 Monday afternoon. Alec Ivy looked pretty ragged last Monday, but I haven't had time to talk to him about it. If next Monday is like last week, I'll be getting off a lot later than 5:00 P.M., too, and Bill and Irene McNabb are coming to dinner that night. We may dine fashionably at 10:00 P.M., which Ann will love.

Monday, July 11

I am too damned tired to try to dictate very much about what happened this past weekend; in fact, right now I'm so tired and disgusted it wouldn't break my heart if I never saw the inside of that place again. There seems to be some sort of idea that the interns have a completely unlimited supply of energy and ought to be bright, chipper, interested and eager to please no matter what the hour or what the call. I don't think there was a single two-hour stretch from Saturday morning until Monday evening that I didn't have a call of some sort about something, and everyone is put out if you don't sound as though you are just delighted to rush right up there and do what they want done.

I suppose I shouldn't be irritated, but it's just the damnedest thing: a nurse will drag you out of bed at 2:00 A.M. to see a new admission, and when you get up on the floor, there the nurse is, all fresh and cheerful, saying, "Good morning, Doctor! How are you feeling this morning?" And then she's offended when you grunt and shuffle past her with your head full of fog and bags under your eyes, wondering just how the hell else she expects you to be feeling at 2:00 in the morning besides lousy. Anyway, the whole weekend was a rat race, and those damned cheerful night nurses didn't make it any better.

[*Post hoc*: I know now that night nurses are invariably this way, and it irritates me just as much today as it did back then. Some things in medicine don't change.]

Part of the trouble with the weekend was the nature of the chores, too. I'm beginning to recognize a distinction between "clean" calls and "dirty" calls. The clean calls are the quick, pleasant, interesting things that you handle without any great trouble or stress, get them cleaned up and have done with them. The dirty calls are the ones that put the heat on you. They can tie you up in hours of hard work and worry and fretting. I had a good example of a dirty call Saturday afternoon about 2:00 P.M. when the nurse on Third asked me to come up and look at one of Dr. Larry Bowler's postoperative tonsil cases. The only scheduled surgery on Saturday mornings is tonsillectomies, and Bowler had done this little four-year-old girl about 7:30 A.M. Apparently she had seemed to be doing all right, and then all of a sudden vomited up a stomachful of blood and went into shock.

I went up there, and the child really looked lousy. It was even hard to rouse her, and there wasn't any question but that she was bleeding. I checked and found out the nurses had already put in a call for Dr. Bowler at his office, but when I asked them to get some blood drawn for typing and cross-match and to start an IV, they said they thought I'd better do it because the child was so small they weren't sure they could find a vein.

I stewed for a solid half-hour trying to get a vein one place or another, sticking needles into the poor child and finally getting enough blood to get the typing and cross-match going, but I couldn't get the IV started. The poor child was frightened to death, screaming most of the time and thrashing around, so I finally asked her frantic mother to please go on out and wait somewhere else. Then I got two nurses and said, "Now you hold this child down so she can't move, or I'm never going to get this thing going." So they all but sat on the poor kid and held one arm out straight and still, and I finally got the needle into a vein and the IV running. About that time the child gave a lurch and rolled over and vomited another stomachful of blood all over my jacket sleeve and the bed and her hair and the floor and the nurses' uniforms, and the nurses tried to hold her head over the edge of the bed so she wouldn't aspirate any of the stuff into her lungs—and I hung onto that needle for dear life and by some miracle kept it in her vein.

By then it was 3:30 and the transfusion blood had arrived from the blood bank, so I had them start a unit going into her, and her blood pressure picked up rapidly. Dr. Bowler turned up in the midst of all this, a little, skinny, nervous-looking guy with dark red hair and freckles and the coldest, meanest-looking blue eyes I ever saw in my life. He took a look down the child's throat (though what he saw down there with all that black stuff in her mouth beats me), and then all he had to say was, "Christ, Doctor, why didn't you just take her back up to the OR and put a couple of stitches in back there?" and stomped off to call the anesthesiologist to come take her upstairs. I spent the next two hours sweating it out and thinking, My God, suppose the kid should die now; maybe I should have taken her upstairs even though I've never done a T & A (tonsillectomy and adenoidectomy) before and have no idea what the hell to take a stitch into when one of them starts bleeding. I suppose I should have called for a surgical resident first off and dumped the whole thing in his lap, but all I could think of was the child in shock and getting that miserable needle into a vein.

Anyway, that's what I mean by a "dirty" call. I had about five of them back to back on Saturday evening and Sunday morning, and then a batch of new admissions on Sunday afternoon, and another batch starting about noon on Monday, and right now I couldn't remember who I saw or what I did for them even if I wanted to.

Teaching rounds this morning were supposed to be with Dr. Pickering, the clinic dermatologist, but he is on vacation, so we made them with Dr. Gillies instead. He's a tall, thin, well-spoken man with a crew cut, a long nose and a very high opinion of himself. He's Dr. Howard Tuckerman's junior partner and the clinic's specialist on liver diseases. Their service in the hospital is rather light now, with only a few patients in the house. We went to see an old man whom someone had asked Gillies to see in consultation to evaluate for surgery.

Gillies did a very skillful job of it, showing us how an expert can take a thorough medical history in about five or ten minutes. Then we did the physical examination together. I had a chance to see the physical signs and hear the heart murmur that goes with mild aortic valve disease, rather than the severe kind I'd seen in medical school. After we had seen the man, Gillies sat us down in the alcove on the fifth floor, and we talked about what we had found. One of the urologists was planning to take out the patient's prostate gland and wanted Gillies' opinion of the surgical risk on account of the heart disease. Gillies wrote his consultation note on the chart while we talked; he didn't seem to have any great worries about the threat of surgery. We are supposed to have these discussions as part of teaching rounds every day. Naturally the interns are expected to contribute. So far I've had little to say, but maybe that will change as I feel my way along.

Had two admissions today, both of them quite interesting. One was an old lady who has had multiple sclerosis for a number of years. She was Dr. Gillies' patient, and he came in while I was examining her and showed me how easy it is to pick up the telltale physical signs of that disease right at the bedside. The woman wasn't in any grave trouble, but she was kind of a depressed little creature, and very weak.

The other patient was a woman with undiagnosed pain in her abdomen. Her gall bladder was taken out several months ago, but she still has the pain in her abdomen; she just doesn't have a gall bladder to blame it on now, so this one may turn out to be a diagnostic problem. I thought of the possibility of a hiatus hernia, or a stone in her common bile duct. The trouble is, she's one of these women who go screaming and crawling up the wall if you pinch her toe. I couldn't be sure whether she was raising a big howl about nothing at all or whether she was actually having some trouble. She's a very pleasant lady—no trouble with that—but I wasn't convinced that she was really suffering too much. Nor was I sold on her history of heart pain. She said she used to have pain in her chest when she exerted herself, until the doctor told her it was probably from her heart. Since then she simply hasn't exerted herself, period. So now there's no way to tell whether she has pain from her heart or not.

I saw another of Dr. Peterson's ulcerative colitis patients today, and my-oh-my what a sad-looking creature *she* was. Pete Carey says she has the typical "colitis personality." She's a skinny, withdrawn little woman with great big sad eyes, sitting and heaving deep sighs, terribly depressed and terribly depressing. All through my examination she kept telling me how worthless she was, how she was only thirty-seven years old but looked fifty (which was perfectly true), how her chest wasn't any good, and how her fingernails weren't any good, and how she supposed she could go home from the hospital, but she knew she'd be right back in again, etc., etc., etc. I got out of there as fast as I could. Looking back over the record, I found that Dr. Peterson had been seeing this woman and treating her for three or four years with no basic improvement. She still has the colitis; she just gets better or worse from time to time, and the one time the colitis really cleared up for a while she got a peptic ulcer instead. And it looks like this might go on for another forty years.

Later Pete and I were joking about the psychiatrists' theories about ulcerative colitis, but when you see patients like this one you can't help but wonder if these people aren't simply trying their best to flush their gastrointestinal tracts down the john, or throw them up in the sink, as the case may be.

Wednesday, July 13

I got two or three calls during the night for sedation orders on patients I wasn't responsible for who were admitted by Dr. Brock. We've been having steady trouble in this respect. Dr. Brock is the medical resident covering Medicine II along with Alec Ivy. He's a tense, hyper-hyper sort of guy who just worries constantly that things aren't going to be done exactly the way they're supposed to be done, so he's been working up the patients admitted on the "uncovered service" as well as his own—which, of course, is exactly what the admitting doctors on Medicine III are hoping someone will do. They've all been *told* that Medicine III isn't supposed to be covered by house staff during this month and next, so they are supposed to write up their own histories and physicals on the patients, and write their own orders and take calls. The interns and residents are only supposed to see those patients in cases of crash emergency, but either Randy Brock or I have been working up all the patients on that service as well as our own because the attending doctors aren't doing it.

We had a house staff conference with Dr. Case this morning at breakfast and discussed this problem, but he didn't give us too much satisfaction. He just said it wasn't supposed to be this way, and that we should let him know of any specific cases, which struck me as a dandy way for an intern to get a staff doctor good and pissed off at him. Later I was talking to Dr. Van Wert about it. He's another clinic doc, a pompous young guy with horn-rimmed glasses who Has All The Answers, or else sure lets on that he has. He just sneered at Case's "solution." "Don't be silly," he said. "The doctors on that service will let you keep on doing their work for them just exactly as long as you let them get away with it. If you want it to stop, just refuse to go near their patients and let *them* get hauled out of bed."

Well, it sounds fine, but I'm still low man around here, and I've got to live with the staff doctors. So we may just have to work our butts off for a while to get things done that somebody has to do.

One note of cheer: it seems the hospital Powers That Be were caught by surprise when they got only half the interns they expected this year, and there's been a big beef to the Board of Trustees that maybe the stipend was too low. So Case reported that the Board had voted to increase the stipend from $75 per month to $125 per month "in order to be more realistic," beginning the first of July next year. Floyd Schwartz nearly choked on his eggs and started complaining bitterly that that didn't help *us* any, so Case let him bitch for a couple of minutes and then got a sneaky little smile on his face and added that the Board had also voted to make the increase retroactive to July 1st of this year as well. So we should each get another $50 a month for our troubles.

And that is just as well, too, because Ann and I have been living on practically nothing the last few weeks. When we turned up in this town with our household goods in a rented trailer, we had about $300 in our pockets. Ann had no job yet, and I may not be paid before the first of August. Our rent is only $65 a month, but we really got slugged when the landlady demanded the first and last month's rent in advance before she would sign a year's lease, and we found out we had to buy an electric stove if we wanted to cook.

Anyway, the news about the pay raise brightened the day considerably. After rounds this morning I managed to break away from the hospital (for the first time in two weeks) long enough to go out and get a haircut, without feeling that I was spending our last dime.

I was supposed to do a spinal tap on the lady with multiple sclerosis today, but she decided she didn't want an intern to do it, so Pete did it instead. I might have tried to talk her into it—"poozy-woozy" is what Pete calls it—but she was very apprehensive, and I would have fouled it up for sure. Later, Pete said, "Sometimes you run across a patient who won't let anybody but Dr. Tuckerman himself do a spinal tap. Even Gillies won't do."

"So then what do you do?"

Pete shrugged. "Write it on the chart and tell Tuckerman. He can usually talk them into letting the resident do it, at least, but it isn't a good idea for the intern to crowd it too much. That's the way malpractice suits get made."

At lunch they paged me for two new admissions, nothing urgent, but the patients were in. The first one was Mrs. Blomberg, quite a problem from the standpoint of medical management. This woman has a massive carcinoma (a form of cancer) of the colon, and was admitted because of pain, particularly in her anus and rectum, which she ascribes to hemorrhoids. Most of the clinic docs follow the policy here of telling a patient about a cancer that is present, but not necessarily telling the whole story of it. This woman is convinced that her cancer was cured six months ago when the surgeons

took out a twelve-inch segment of colon, so now it's her hemorrhoids that are hurting her. Of course, she indeed has hemorrhoids,
too, but she's been taking a triple dose of Seconal every night at
home to get to sleep, and uses morphine by mouth, a grain at a
time, and even that doesn't hold the pain. The nurses remember
her from her last admission because she gave them such an unpleasant time, so they're not happy to see her back. Dr. Fuller,
who's following the patient, told them that there's no particular
reason to hold back on the morphine, or any other medication,
because pain relief is the only thing left to offer the woman. She
may have another month to go, but not much more; with that kind
of cancer spread all over the inside of her belly there isn't a damned
thing left to do but wait.

Here again I didn't know quite what to order when I first saw the
patient. Her clinic chart hadn't come over yet. I was astounded at
the amount of morphine she'd been taking—I thought she meant a
grain in all in the course of a day, and she meant a grain at a time
every three hours! At least I did make the diagnosis without any
help. Her liver filled up half her abdomen, and she's had jaundice
for the last ten days. That and the severe pain didn't leave much
doubt. Also, she looked *sick,* a lot sicker than she thought she was.

Tuesday, July 19

It seems like only a day or two since I brought this up to date,
but I see it's been almost a week. It's just incredible how days run
into days; a day on, with duty that night and the next day all seem
to run together into one day, and since I have duty both Thursday
and Friday nights when I have the weekend off, *that* particular
"day" runs from Thursday morning at 8:00 until Saturday morning
at 10:00—about a fifty-hour day, but still just one day by intern's
reckoning, since I've been sleeping catch as catch can and can't
honestly see a hell of a lot of difference between daytime and night-
time any more.

Thursday morning we made rounds with Dr. Fuller, since Dr.
Franklin was on vacation. Right now there are more patients with
diagnostic problems on the service than critical illnesses. Mr. Sperling is a case in point. He's the old man about seventy who came in

with extreme anemia, and he has been through a whole series of studies that have turned up just about nothing. The lab work has been negative, the bone marrow biopsy I took was negative, and he still has only one-third the red blood cells and hemoglobin he should have. This is Dr. Case's patient, and we have thought of all sorts of possibilities—leukemia, tuberculosis, you name it. Dr. Case had Fred Kidder see the man, and I've heard that he had some obscure ideas about what might be wrong, but I don't know what they were.

And then there was Mr. Casey, the little man with the stroke, who handed us a nice fat jolt when a survey X-ray of his chest showed a little half-inch mass in the middle of one lung. So now the big question: is it carcinoma? And if it is, did this stroke come about because of spread of the cancer to the brain? Sometimes you feel you're just standing there wringing your hands waiting for something to happen.

I've gotten better acquainted with Pete Carey these days. He's a funny guy, very pleasant and helpful, but spastic about his job as medical resident and extremely careful to make sure that all the wheels are well greased. He knocks himself out to be diplomatic when he's correcting me, which Brock does not. Brock, I find, is an inscrutable one. We get along all right, but I don't particularly like him yet and I'm not sure I ever will.

First pay checks came through Friday, covering from the first to the tenth of July. For me, a whole $39.68. The business office hasn't gotten the word about the increase in stipend, I guess. I feel as though I've already worked three months for that juicy tidbit.

Friday was slower than usual; I even got an hour's nap after lunch and a couple of hours to study up on reading EKGs. I happened to be in the first floor lounge when Dr. Horace Goodfellow walked in—I gather he's one of the big-cheese obstetricians in the city. He and his sidekick Ben Boggs handle about 70 percent of the deliveries at Graystone, and we had a chance to talk for a moment. He said he was pleased to see me reading sitting up, because when you see an intern reading lying down he generally isn't reading.

There were a whole succession of calls all night Friday; I might as well not have gone to bed. Outpatients, pill calls, everything. About 5:00 A.M. Saturday the OB nurse called and said, "Doctor, we have a woman in labor up here who's hysterical and we can't do anything with her." So I dragged myself out of bed and went up there. When I walked in the woman's room she gave me a murderous look and said, "Oh, for God's sake, what do *you* want?" She wasn't crying and she wasn't hysterical; she was just plain snotty, just as thoroughly unpleasant as she could possibly be. I checked her, to a chorus of insulting remarks about my morals, my manhood and my sex practices, and found she wasn't doing anything with her labor so there was no problem there. The urge to be snotty right back was just about overwhelming, but I kept my big mouth shut, just told her everything was fine and to take it easy.

I had planned to use the weekend off to catch up on the journal, but Saturday when I finally checked out to Alec and got out of there I wasn't any more ready to sit down and dictate words of wisdom than to fly. I must have looked as ragged as I felt. Ann turned up in the car at 10:00 A.M. Saturday to pick me up, with a picnic lunch and a change of old clothes packed in the back of the car, and said, "Come on, buddy, we're going to get out of town for a while."

It was a beautiful, sunny warm day, so I said, "Okay, fine, you drive," and curled up for an hour's nap or so. When I woke up we were quite a way north of the city, driving over a back road through some of the high, dry, mountain country with its long-needle pines and deep canyons and clean, sharp air and its little streams not yet quite dried up. We stopped for lunch at a spot where the trees were so thick you couldn't see the sky, with a mountain stream and pool that made me hunger for a fishing pole. Until dark we just moseyed around that country, catching an occasional incredible view down and out across the desert, and yet being in glorious mountain country at the same time.

We decided to hole up in a motel instead of going back to the city for the night, and found one that looked halfway respectable, but I guess we didn't. Until I walked in to register I hadn't even given a thought to the fact that all we had for luggage was an empty sandwich bag and a rolled-up wad of dirty underwear. So naturally we drew the fishy stare from the motel keeper, which made me sore and gave Ann the giggles, and the guy was still further confused by the "Doctor" on the registration card and the Maryland license plates, so finally I just figured, Hell, Dad, you add it up any way you want to, and handed him the ten bucks he asked for and moved the car down to the cabin. We slept in until 10:30 next morning, spent some more time exploring the mountain country, and got back to the city in time to have dinner at home and take in a movie Sunday night.

Well, it's amazing what rest and change can do. When I left the hospital Saturday morning I was just good and damned sick of it. By Monday, I was actually looking forward to the day and week, even though Alec looked like he'd been dragged through the wringer over the weekend. It also looked like he'd spent most of the weekend admitting patients onto my service. There must have been fifteen names I didn't recognize on the chart rack with Medicine I tags on them, so I spent most of Monday and Monday night as well as today catching up on them and seeing the new people coming in. We have thirty-two patients on the service now, and starting in after a weekend off is almost like starting the internship all over again.

I did learn that Dr. Peterson has decided that Cora Baker, the skinny woman who had been losing weight so rapidly, has sprue, a kind of defect of food absorption that can be corrected by eating huge quantities of the B vitamins, and he has started her on treatment. She still looks as though she'd just been exhumed, but she insists she feels better already after a couple of days' treatment.

Mrs. Blomberg, the woman with the cancer of the rectum, is having a terrible time with pain—she's taking enough morphine at a time to drop a mule in its tracks, and it doesn't seem to faze her a bit—and she has all the bigwigs at the clinic in a stew, for some reason. She came in as Dr. Fuller's patient, but Dr. Slater has been seeing her and following her too, and today they had Cal Cornell, the neurosurgeon, in to see her about doing a nerve-cutting operation in her spine to reduce the pain. Apparently Cornell didn't think much of this idea, and had what amounted to a big fight with Dr. Slater about it in the chartroom after he'd seen her this afternoon. I got in on the tail end of it, but Slater seemed to be mad as hops and stomped off down the hall saying something about how if Cornell wouldn't do it, he'd do it himself. Cornell, who is a great big cadaverous moose of a man, sat staring at the woman's chart for ten minutes, muttering to himself, and then slammed it down on the desk without even finishing the note he had started writing in it. So I don't know exactly what is up with Mrs. Blomberg.

Monday, July 25

One thing that bothers me is that I seem to be so busy working up new patients all the time that I don't have much chance to dig into the real diagnostic problems and follow them through. A patient comes in who looks interesting, and I work him up, and the next I hear of him is three days later when his diagnosis is established and his treatment begun and all the fun is already over. Pete says we've had an exceptionally heavy month of admissions, and that it shouldn't keep up this way indefinitely. I hope he's right, but I don't see any reason to think so.

What went on last week tends to blur together, but a few things stand out sharply. Saturday afternoon and evening, for instance, I ran into a real sleeper. It wasn't exactly a medical problem, as it turned out, and it was a patient of one of the outside doctors on Medicine III, so I wasn't really supposed to be seeing the patient at all. But the floor nurse called me about 2:00 in the afternoon to come see this patient of Dr. Flagg's, a teen-age girl who was bleeding so badly she needed attention and nobody could seem to get hold of Dr. Flagg. He'd seen the girl in his office in the morning and sent her into the hospital for admission.

She was a cute little thing, about fifteen years old, with glossy black hair and blue eyes, apparently very much impressed with being in the hospital and getting all this attention and being visited by handsome young interns and all that. She was also doing a whale of a lot of vaginal bleeding; the floor nurse said she'd just put on a double pad when she called me, and it was already soaked through, and it had been going this way ever since she'd gotten into the hospital an hour and a half before.

According to the girl, the bleeding had just started out of a clear blue sky about a week after her last menstrual period had ended, and I couldn't dig out any history to suggest why she was bleeding so much. She seemed to be giving a straightforward history, and didn't seem to hedge in answering my questions, and when I asked her if she thought she might be pregnant, she said, "Well, no, you see I'm not married." I told her I knew that, but all the same was there any possible remote chance that she might be, and she looked right at me and laughed and said, "Well, I certainly don't see how," so I went ahead to examine her. No answers there either; she looked like a perfectly healthy, normal specimen to me, and when I called the floor nurse to help me do a vaginal exam with a sterile glove, the girl didn't seem to object, although she obviously didn't like it very much. This was the first time I had ever done this kind of examination under quite these circumstances, with the patient in bed instead of on an examining table with stirrups. There was blood all over the place, and I might just as well not have bothered because I couldn't feel a damned thing. I guess I was just too worried about hurting the girl or something.

While I was in the middle of this, Dr. Flagg walked in, a great big ox of a man about six foot four who weighed 250 pounds and had a hand like a sledge hammer. He put on a sterile glove and shoved his hand in there as if he were reaching for her tonsils, which she *really* didn't like, and brought out a fistful of gucky, clotted stuff and then turned to the nurse and said, "Better get her some Ergotrate right now and then call Anesthesia; it's sitting right there and I'm going to have to scrape her out."

By this time I wanted to know just what *was* going on, so I followed along, and as it turned out the "it" that was "sitting right there" was a two-month fetus that this girl was trying to miscarry. In the operating room I could see what Dr. Flagg had felt, sitting half in and half out of the mouth of the uterus. He just pulled it out with sponge forceps and then did what seemed to me a sort of haphazard curettement of the uterus, but the girl wasn't bleeding a bit by the time they took her back down to the floor. The whole thing kind of shook me up; I felt like a perfect ass, because when I thought about it later, I realized that any idiot should have known that there's only one thing likely to make a fifteen-year-old girl bleed the way that girl was bleeding, regardless of what she tells you.

And speaking of what patients tell you, I am fast learning that they will sometimes tell you the *damnedest* things, and in dead earnest, too. During this weekend Peterson admitted a very weird lady with a most bizarre tale. She had pain in her belly, she said, and her story was that she had an abdominal aneurysm. Furthermore, she said, she had had malaria. She also said that last December she'd had worms crawling out of her anus, that she felt something down in her stomach moving around, and that the pain in her belly felt like somebody had a rope around her underneath the skin and was pulling it tight on her. What I am supposed to make out of a medical history like that I don't know. I have the funny feeling that that babe just got into the wrong kind of hospital.

Oh, yes, one tough one turned up Sunday night quite late, a little three-year-old girl who was brought in from a ranch about eighty miles away, admitted for Dr. Case and Dr. Peterson to take care of, only neither of them knew anything about her at all. Her name was Sharon Bibble, and she looked like a ghost, no color in her face or lips or anything. Several large black-and-blue marks on her legs and arms, and a temperature of about 104. That one I could almost diagnose from the door of the room; after I'd checked her I called Dr. Case and told him I thought we had a leukemic little girl, and when he came in later he confirmed my impression. Of course, we tried to get some blood for examination to clinch it, and had a terrible time getting a needle into the kiddie—she was sick, but she could still fight. I haven't seen the blood count report yet, but I know what it's going to be. Next step will be a bone marrow biopsy, the next step God knows what. She was perfectly well three weeks ago, by the account, so this has moved in fast and she may just not be with us very long.

Wednesday, July 27

Yesterday was the fastest, hardest-working day I've put in at the hospital yet—lasted the longest and had the most going on at once. I suppose that looking back over the past month my only real complaint is that I'm constantly, chronically, unremittingly tired. I haven't felt really fresh and rested since I walked into the place a month ago, and I can't see any reason to think that things are going to get any better the rest of the year. Summer is supposed to be the light time of year; during the winter I'll be on Surgery, a bad season for that service. The "off every other night and every other weekend" sounds fine, but I never get off until 7:00 P.M. or so, and weekends I'm too fagged out to do anything. On days when I have the overnight duty, the day starts at 8:00 A.M. and goes on until 1:00 or 2:00 in the morning, not a nice steady pace but always this sort of jagged, frantic, everything-happening-at-once business, with always more to do than I can do well and always an interruption (or maybe five). And then at 2:00 A.M., if I do sack, I can almost count on anywhere from one to six calls before 6:00 in the morning, and almost always *some* damned thing about 6:00 that closes out even sleeping in until breakfast.

Yesterday was a good example; very little specific I can remember even now. I saw Dr. Case and checked the blood count report on little Sharon Bibble, and she has lymphatic leukemia. Case said not to torment her with a bone marrow study; it would add nothing to the diagnosis. He's starting her on cortisone, and in a day or two will fill her up with packed red blood cells (whole blood with the serum centrifuged off so they get the most red cells possible in the smallest possible volume), and we start the long downhill road with that little girl.

So I ran all day yesterday, and was up almost all night, and spent today feeling bushed as bushed could be. I didn't really give a damn today whether school kept or not; it's an awful temptation on days like this to get sloppy, and you can't afford to do that. So this was another evening of getting home just dead after two days of solid work.

Saturday, July 30

Not much new to report. Pete has been sick since Wednesday with some kind of bug, propped up like the King of Siam in a private room on the fifth floor with orders not even to stick his nose out of the door until Van Wert, who is taking care of him, says he can. Personally I think he just ran out of starch; he's been looking pretty ragged this last week, as have all of us. So since Wednesday Milt Musser has been sort of halfheartedly covering for him, although Milt has enough of his own work to do. I stick my head in Pete's door once or twice a day to keep him posted on things, and maybe he'll be back on the ball by Monday.

Tuesday, August 2

The first of the month was a break point for some of the guys on
other services, but not for me; I stay on Medicine I just as I have
been, and Alec Ivy stays opposite me on Medicine II.

Pete is back in the saddle, for which I am thankful enough. The
doctors on this service do a great deal of talking about keeping the
load light, but when it comes right down to it, they all want the full
treatment and expect the *other* guy to keep the load light. There's a
certain amount of work that has to be done with every patient, and
if there's an intern staff working, the attending doctors just don't do
it. We end up doing the routine work and miss out on the participation and follow-up.

At 5:30 A.M. this morning I was called to see an old man who was
being brought to the hospital by ambulance with a stroke, or so the
story went. This was a patient of Van Wert's, a Mr. Mangano;
apparently he's the patriarch of quite an influential clan, judging
from the sons, daughters, grandchildren, brothers and sisters, etc.,
who swarmed into the hospital on the heels of the ambulance. Dr.
Van Wert called before I had even seen the patient and said the old
man had had some kind of cerebral vascular accident during the
night, leaving him with one-sided paralysis, and that there wasn't
much for me to do except to see that he was getting air all right and
order a special-duty nurse on the morning shift.

Well, that was fine, and everything went just dandy, at first. The
old gentleman had a fresh paralysis of the right arm and leg, but
was conscious and able to smile at me with the left side of his face
and even thank me for my attention. The trouble was, just as I was
finishing my exam (which wasn't very rigorous) he took a great gasp
of air and clutched at his chest with his left hand and turned blue,
groaning "It's-a hurt, it's-a hurt!" and thrashing around so fiercely
that I thought he was going to throw himself out of bed.

I didn't know what was up, but it didn't look good, so I buzzed
for a nurse and ordered some morphine and a tank of oxygen. Mr.
Mangano kept groaning and clutching his chest; he was a skinny
little man, about eighty years old, but with amazing strength, and I
remember thinking that if I'd ever seen a classical picture of a

patient having a coronary in bed, this was it. It was a half-hour before I dared leave the bedside, but by then the morphine began to hook in and he quieted down and the oxygen brought his color back, so I asked the nurse to see if the lab girls could get me an emergency EKG while I went to call Dr. Van Wert.

It was the sort of comedy of errors you run into every now and then when you're really trying desperately to reach a doctor in a hurry. I phoned Van Wert at home, but his wife said he'd left for the hospital half an hour ago and certainly ought to be there by now. The switchboard assured me that he hadn't turned up yet, but sometimes stopped by to see patients at St. Christopher's Hospital on his way to Graystone. St. Christopher's paged him and got no response, so I tried his office at the clinic while the Graystone switchboard began paging him vigorously. Then I got suspicious, because I remembered that Dr. Van Wert was one of the boys who was always turning up very early, around 7:00 or 7:15, for breakfast in the cafeteria. I ran down there (after a full thirty minutes on the telephone), and there he was, big as life, finishing up his second cup of coffee. All the loudspeakers on the basement floor had somehow shorted out during the night so he hadn't heard his page, although he'd been there for over twenty minutes.

Mr. Mangano was getting blue again, and the lab girl was just finishing the EKG. The poor man certainly had had a massive stroke, and now the cardiogram tracing showed that he had had a massive coronary thrombosis as well. Van Wert rolled him over on his side, reached in with his fingers and pulled his tongue out (which made him turn considerably pinker in about a minute) and then used a nasal catheter to suck a whole bunch of dirty-looking mucus out of his trachea. After we had worked on him for about an hour we turned him over to the special nurse and to his son, who wouldn't stay out of his room, and as we walked back to the chart-room I said, "Well, at least he's still breathing." And Van Wert said, "Yes, but not for long, my boy, not for long, I'm afraid. But you did all you could do. Just keep him full of morphine and keep his airway open and I'll write IV orders and we'll see."

A few minutes later I got paged for another new patient. This was a boy coming in on Fifth with hepatitis (a dangerous virus infection of the liver). Dr. Peterson was supposed to be his doctor, but it was Dr. Fred Kidder who came in with him. Apparently Dr. Kidder was about to leave on a two-week vacation and was turning the boy's care over to Dr. Peterson and Dr. Smithers. The boy was about seventeen, name of Rusty Barnes, a very nice, unassuming youngster. He had had "flu" about two weeks before but hadn't told anybody about it because he was trying to get a four-wheel drive rig ready for an endurance run that was coming up with a club he belonged to and he said he was afraid his folks would make him quit if they'd known he was sick. Finally, yesterday, he had apparently looked kind of funny to them, and then this morning his skin, the whites of his eyes and everything had turned bright yellow and his urine was the color of coffee. He even had a funny, sweetish smell about him, and his father had put him back to bed and gotten hold of Fred Kidder, who'd come to see him at home.

The story sounded funny to me, at least on the basis of what I had read and heard about hepatitis, and I spent a long time taking a history from the youngster, wondering about aromatic solvents and paint thinners he might have been using on the car, but there wasn't anything I could get hold of there. While I was working him up, Dr. Peterson came in, saw him and reassured his parents, who were standing around wringing their hands and getting in everybody's way. Apparently Rusty is an only child; the mother looked like a typical strong-willed matron, and his father was a quivering heap of inadequacy if I ever saw one, a little, mousy guy about half the size of his son, who didn't seem entirely sure of just what was going on. The boy will have to be in isolation, of course. Peterson didn't think there was any likelihood of carbon tetrachloride poisoning or anything of the sort here, just straightforward hepatitis, and ordered up a batch of liver-function studies for base lines, but it seemed to me he was unnecessarily gloomy when he talked to the boy's parents, telling them that Rusty was a very sick boy, and that we'd have to watch him closely. He didn't look so sick to me; the last I saw of him about 11:30 A.M. he was wisecracking with one of the student nurses and leafing through a hot-rod magazine.

Two other admissions early in the afternoon, and then things slacked off and I actually got out of there by 5:30 P.M. for my night off.

Our inventory is down to about twenty-five now on the service. Everybody was worried that Pete had infectious mononucleosis, but his lab tests came back negative, and he bounced back too quickly for that. We've gotten into real Southwestern summer heat now— hot, hot days with a sun that could fry an egg before it hit the ground, although it cools off sharply after sundown. Graystone is air conditioned, sort of, indifferently and sporadically, so that one end of a corridor is cold as a deep freeze while the other end feels like the Sahara. Maybe nobody wants to take his chances on which room they might get at the hospital. Anyway, there does seem to be a lull around the place. Schwartz says even the surgical schedules are off this week.

Mr. Mangano survived his day of admission, to everybody's amazement, and is still surviving, even though he loses contact with things from time to time. At least he's not having any more pain, and once in a while is able to cough up some junk from his chest so that he doesn't have to be sucked out all the time.

One patient I've been seeing a lot of but haven't mentioned is a little old lady named Hattie Stevens. It goes to show you that you can't always believe what you see, I guess. Hattie is a sweet, soft-spoken, naïve little lady who came in on Peterson's service because of stomach and bladder trouble, but proved to have a galloping hypertension. Never known before, but there for sure: a blood pressure level of 280 over 190 on admission, almost constant, pounding headaches, vision failing rapidly in a matter of months and so on. I got a look at her eye grounds with my ophthalmoscope, and it was a wonder to me that she could see anything at all; her retinas were just covered with hemorrhages and scars from older hemorrhages. Peterson fiddled around for a few days with phenobarbital and rauwolfia to drop that pressure down, but it didn't budge, so he called Franklin in to take over the case, and we have been using a succession of bigger and bigger guns to get the blood pressure under control.

I thought everything was going along fine: headaches had stopped, pressure was at least in reasonable shape, blood nitrogen level was coming down, vision improving, everything dandy. **Dr.** Franklin has seemed pleased with her response, but after we got away from her room he said, "Well, don't expect too much, and don't fool yourself. Hattie is on the brink of death, regardless of how she looks or feels or seems to be responding."

This man surprises me sometimes; he seems so sleepy and lackadaisical about things, yet I think he was quite coldly angry that Peterson had wasted even a few days using milder drugs to treat this woman—"sending boys to do a man's work" was the way he put it. He said he thinks she has a malignant, fast-progressing hypertension, and unless she is treated fast and vigorously, Hattie Stevens is just going to shuffle off right under our noses. He wants us to push her blood pressure down to about 150 and keep it there with protoveratrine, one of the violently potent antihypertensives, and if we can't make it with that in a few days, shift to something still more potent. Maybe this will give her a year or two of relatively comfortable life, whereas untreated she wouldn't last another two weeks. We haven't told Mrs. Stevens this, and I doubt she would believe us if we did because she feels so much better. I can't escape the feeling, after what Franklin had to say, that I'm looking at a living corpse every time I see her.

The Barnes boy's liver function tests came back from the lab, and they really gave me a chill. There's no question that that boy has hepatitis, and severe hepatitis at that. He's got enough liver damage from it already that his blood-clotting mechanism is all out of whack, and he has a perfectly terrific jaundice—literally yellow as a pumpkin. He isn't so chipper any more, either; his temp spiked up to 105 degrees the day he was admitted and has been fluctuating between 103 and 105 steadily ever since. I don't know how long the acute phase of this disease lasts, but Pete says it can go on for days or even weeks, killing liver cells all the time. At least, though, he has a good strong body going into it. He was an All-High School center at basketball last year; his team made it to the state tournament. Apparently he's a popular kid, too; we have to turn away whole squadrons of friends who want to come in and see him, and who can't seem to get through their heads that he's got a bad infectious disease.

A really barbarous weekend. From Saturday noon until tonight we had a total of eleven medical admissions, and a number of people in the house who were really sick. We were on the run almost continuously all weekend and on through today as well.

Part of the reason for the rush was that this was the weekend of the Pioneer Days celebration in this city; all the doctors wanted to be free for the fun, I guess, so they kept sending patients into the hospital in order to avoid having to see them personally. But there were some perfectly legitimate admissions, too; it was just that we had a lot of them, and there was a lot of work to be done.

We walked into the weekend with two major problems hanging fire on our service. Old Mr. Mangano was still kicking along not doing particularly well (although he came out of his fog a little bit on Saturday), and he took a nose dive on Sunday. We were sort of expecting him to go out momentarily all day Sunday and Monday, but he just hung on, getting a little bit worse each day.

But the real problem was Rusty Barnes. He couldn't seem to use the urinal and refused to urinate in bed, even though we urged him to, since it was an easy enough matter for the nurses to remake the bed. Maybe he was just irrational from the fever, but he would hold his urine when anybody was around (which was most of the time, with his parents and the nurses in and out all the time), and then he insisted he had to get up to use the urinal, but he couldn't maintain his balance, so he still couldn't urinate, and he wouldn't tell us that, so he would get all agitated and start thrashing around and fighting the oxygen tent until he just exhausted himself. Then he'd finally give in, and if the nurses could get a urinal to him and leave him alone for five or ten minutes, presently he'd be able to empty his bladder. All that fuss every time, six or eight times a day.

Rusty's parents have been no help either. One minute they're wringing their hands saying they know we're doing everything possible, and the next minute they're stirring up a storm with the nurses and doctors about everything imaginable, or fighting with each other, or both. The father in particular is a real chore. From the minute Rusty first came in, the father was questioning every-thing that was done for him. *Nobody* has a whale of a lot to offer in a case like this, let's face it, but the father has been getting in our hair every time we walk by his room, on the basis of no knowledge at all. He wanted to know why the boy's blood hadn't been started yet, or why this didn't happen, or why that didn't happen, and what did this mean or what did that mean, and were we sure that this was the right IV going into the boy, because he'd overheard somebody talking about switching to a different IV, and so on and so on.

By late Saturday night, after we had been called to see the lad a number of times—Pete and I were working pretty much together on this, with a whole lot of other patients taking up our time and attention at the same time—this business with the father began to wear pretty thin. The boy had special nurses on mornings 7:00 A.M. to 3:00 P.M. and at night from 11:00 P.M. to 7:00 A.M., but the father and mother were "substituting" in the afternoon and evening from 3:00 P.M. to 11:00 P.M. because they couldn't get a special for that shift. This seemed to me worse than no nursing at all. The father kept jumping the floor nurse for this and that, and the mother seemed to think it was absolutely necessary to keep the boy awake and responding all the time; she kept trying to rouse him whenever she was in the room, begging him to answer her, just to speak to her, when he needs rest more than anything else. Finally Pete and I talked to Peterson about maybe restricting the parents from the room, but Peterson said, no, let them alone and just try to be kind.

On Saturday the boy's new lab studies came back, and they were certainly gloomy; on admission Tuesday he had practically no liver function at all—the disease had knocked out at least 75 percent—and now these new tests showed no improvement whatever in three days. If anything, they were a little worse. Up to now enough fluids had been gotten into him to maintain a balance, but with all this thrashing around trying to urinate he pulled the plastic needle out of his arm Saturday night, so that had to be restarted; he wasn't able to drink anything, so he had to have constant intravenous feedings, and also a pint of whole blood.

Then just to make everything especially delightful, Pete and I pulled a boner getting that blood started. Mother and Father were both standing around while we worked at it. I got a new plastic needle into a vein while Pete held his arm still, and neither one of us remembered to take the tourniquet off the arm when the blood had started running in. The tourniquet must have been pretty loose because the whole pint of blood went in without extravasating the vein or swelling up the arm, but it must have irritated the boy something awful because he spent the whole evening thrashing around, half-conscious, trying to claw the plastic needle out. He almost succeeded, but not quite.

We came back to check him just as the nurse was removing the blood bottle and adding the next IV, some three hours later, and Pete made the mistake of mumbling to me that the tourniquet was still on the patient's arm. The father picked this up, of course, and immediately became very perturbed. He saw a little of the blood which had escaped onto the bed and seemed to think that his boy was exsanguinating, and wanted to know how much blood he'd lost, and got very excited about it. The man simply wouldn't be reassured, although we could tell fairly accurately from the appearance of the arm that there was no actual harm done. It was still a stupid thing for us to have done; we both should have checked to see that the tourniquet was off, and neither one of us had remembered.

About 11:00 P.M. the boy became really upset, just after the night special nurse came on. He couldn't urinate again even when she sat him up on the edge of the bed. Finally he started fighting like hell, trying to get onto his feet and dragging the IV needle out again. This kid has the strength of a young bull in heat, and it took all of us to keep him from hurling himself onto the floor. Finally we called Jerry, the night orderly, and between us put in a retention catheter. This relieved him of his urge to urinate, but the catheter irritated him enough that he still kept kicking around, trying to pull it out, retention bulb and all. We were really afraid he was going to hurt himself or somebody else unless he settled down, so finally we decided to give him some rectal paraldehyde for sedation. We agreed on a 10-cc dose, and got the parents eased out of the room and finally talked them into going home for the night. Rusty slept like a log.

That was fine for Saturday night, but on Sunday morning the boy was still out like a poleaxed mule long after the sedation should have worn off. We had picked paraldehyde specifically because it was the one sedative we could think of that wouldn't add further strain to the liver, but by noon he was still unresponsive. Woke up enough to mumble and thrash around occasionally, but never really responded. We had to give medications by injection then, and the problem with that was that he would bleed into the site of the injection. More pain and discomfort.

It's really strange how the answers to puzzles seem to turn up all of a sudden, like dawn breaking, and you wonder where you were all this time that you didn't think of them sooner because they were so obvious. I'd been trying to figure out why this boy was so irrational, and worrying that maybe we'd done something dreadful to him with the paraldehyde. I stewed about that all afternoon and evening on Sunday, and about other things, too—the trouble getting in medications, and this irritability he seemed to have that was getting worse even when he was stuporous.

Then Sunday night I had some idiot sedation call about 3:00 A.M. from the night nurses on Second, and I was so annoyed and tense and bone-tired I couldn't get back to sleep, and my mind was on this Barnes kid anyway, trying to figure out what was really happening to him, and suddenly it dawned on me that this boy's liver just wasn't working any more, and that with his prothrombin down to practically nothing his blood-clotting mechanism must be all shot to hell in spite of all the vitamin K we've been dumping into him. Very probably he's been bleeding from his capillaries—into his gut, and into his bladder, and into his brain as well. It seemed to me that there was every likelihood in the world that he'd already had one or more intracranial hemorrhages, and that a lot of his stupor and general irritability could be a result of capillary hemorrhage in his nervous system.

And then it also hit me that this boy was just not going to make it, that even if he did survive the virus that was causing the hepatitis, he just wouldn't have any liver left at all when it was all over.

Well, it seemed to make perfect sense at 3:00 A.M., and when I mentioned it to Pete this morning he agreed that capillary bleeding was almost certainly going on, and that this was probably the reason for much of Rusty's irritability, and also one reason why his prognosis was so very, very poor. He probably will die of intracranial hemorrhage if he doesn't die of utter lack of liver function in the meantime. He did better on Sunday from the standpoint of quietness; we thought he might have exhausted himself Saturday night, but he wasn't responsive Monday either.

This boy gulped up our weekend time, but we had a couple of other problems, too. On Saturday afternoon Dr. Case sent in a gal who had migraine headaches that seemed to be related to muscle tension in her neck, so we put her in cervical traction. I don't know that it helped very much, but that was what Case wanted. This gal had had her migraine headaches for the past seventeen years, so she had to choose a Saturday afternoon to come into the hospital to have something done about them. You figure it out; I can't. It wasn't that she was in any such agony either. When I rushed in to see her, she was lying there in bed grinning at me, all ready to spend the afternoon cheerfully chatting.

Then there was a patient with terminal cancer of the breast; we had to juggle her fluid balance all weekend. And either Pete or I had to be checking on poor old Mr. Mangano about every three hours. He was still just barely limping along, and his family were sort of hovering around his bedside reading off their rosaries. At least on Saturday he was still responsive enough to take fluids by mouth, but Sunday he lost contact and went blah. His veins were so poor I couldn't get an IV started, and the lab girl couldn't even get blood for a prothrombin time, so Pete discontinued the anticoagulants. His chest still sounded pretty clear, but there is just no way to evaluate what the hell is going on with Mr. Mangano.

With these things, and a couple of routine admissions on Saturday evening, and the Barnes boy's problems to contend with, I finally wound things up—more or less—at 11:30 P.M. Saturday and went down to the cafeteria for midnight supper. Schwartz was the only one down there, drinking coffee and looking sour. He'd been dogging a girl with acute belly pain all evening, and then Slater's resident had decided to sit on her for the night instead of opening her up.

"So why complain?" I asked Schwartz. "Maybe you'll get some sleep tonight."

"I know," he said, "but by morning her pain will probably be all gone and they won't operate on her at all."

"So?"

"So last night Herring got to scrub for an emergency gastrectomy, and all I get when I'm on duty is a pain in the ass," Schwartz said. I decided there wasn't any point arguing *that* one. It sounded to me like Schwartz was having all the luck, but I guess I don't have the surgeon's attitude. We chewed the fat a while and decided we had exploded the theory that coffee keeps you awake. Schwartz said it was getting so he couldn't *sleep* without coffee at midnight, and three or four cups at this hour sure haven't bothered me any. When I left him, I went up for quick rounds of the floors to see if I could catch any problems before I turned in, and got in bed at midnight.

Called out again at 1:30 to see a man just admitted on Fifth with hypertension. The night supervisor said he wasn't having any trouble, don't rush up, but five minutes later she called again and said he was having terrible chest pain and would I please hurry. So I got my shoes on and came running up there and really got quite a turn. The guy was out cold in bed and gray as a ghost, and the nurse who was trying to take his blood pressure said he'd just stopped breathing all of a sudden. I tried to get a pulse and shook him a bit, but couldn't get a rise out of him, although he'd been talking to the nurse just five minutes before.

Then pretty soon he took a deep gasp and started breathing again just fine. I couldn't get a history, though; he smelled like a gin factory, and all I could find out was that he had been in some hospital out in the sticks all last week because of chest pain, and his doctor had finally sent him up here for Dr. Fuller to see. Seems he left the hospital there at 10:00 Saturday morning, and was just now arriving at midnight from a trip that should have taken two hours in a slow car.

I went down to get the electrocardiograph machine, and on the way back Jerry, the orderly, presented me with a third-full whiskey bottle he'd found under the guy's pillow. The man came around a little as I was taking the cardiogram and said he was having terrible chest pain, but the cardiogram looked all right. I ordered an oxygen tent, which he thought helped him breathe better, and gave him a sixth of morphine and left him there to sleep off his drunk. There was still no sign of a coronary on another cardiogram in the morning, so I guess he was just having angina (pain in the chest related to heart disease) along with his acute alcoholism. I didn't know how long he would agree to cool his heels in the hospital, and I didn't much care. By the time I got through fooling around it was 3:00 A.M. Sunday.

No more calls then, so I got some sleep, and woke up with a jolt at 9:45 Sunday morning when fifth floor called to remind me of two EKGs that I had to run. Too late for breakfast, so I got up to the floor about 10:15, and from then until midnight I don't think I stopped once to catch my breath. There were a multitude of new admissions and calls all day from second, fourth and fifth floors, all of them insistent, all of them major problems. Pete and I both ran our butts off all day long.

In between working up new patients there were business rounds, and Rusty Barnes to see and catch up on, and EKGs to run, and a variety of minor crises. For instance, one of the nurses on Fifth called me about lunchtime to tell me that some diabetic lady up there, who was getting glucose water by IV with insulin to cover the sugar in it, had been given two separate doses of insulin by two separate nurses, neither of whom realized that the other had given the dose, and what should they do now? I changed the IV solution to 10 percent glucose instead of 5 percent, and the patient seemed all right, but little things like that seemed to plague us all afternoon and evening.

Late in the evening a woman was admitted in severe respiratory distress from asthma. She was just choking something fierce, very apprehensive and fluttery, giving me her history in between gasps as she sat there in bed coughing and wheezing away. I tossed this one over to Pete, who clobbered her with sedation and stuck an IV into her arm with a bronchial-dilating drug in it, and by midnight she was settling down. I turned in about then, but it was a rough night for sleeping—half a dozen calls spaced at hourly intervals, and worrying about some six new admissions I'd barely worked up at all. Later the night nursing supervisor told me that she had carefully defended me against calls from the fifth floor all night long, and maybe she did, but I still only got four and a half hours' sleep before dawn.

Monday was just as bad as Sunday; we never did get rounds made on half the patients already in the house because we were so busy keeping up with the really sick ones. Mr. Mangano was even worse

Monday A.M., unresponsive and breathing poorly. Dr. Gillies saw him and ordered the intern to do tracheal suction. Poor old Mr. Mangano was practically moribund to start with; he didn't understand what we were trying to do with the suction tube, and he struggled and nearly choked on it, and then ripped my jacket arm trying to pull the tube away. And of course whenever you start a dirty job like that, all the nurses on the floor vanish, zip. Pete gave me a hand finally, and we did as well as we could, with the old man's son standing by holding his hands.

By Sunday night Pete and I were both so tired and so rushed that at midnight supper we were just sitting around giggling like schoolgirls. It seems horrible, but you get just so tired and then you get to talking about your patients who are rapidly dying on all sides of you, and then you find things that they say or that you do are hilariously funny all of a sudden, which I suppose is all right as long as the patients or their families don't hear you, but you still feel half-ashamed; yet you just can't control it.

[*Post hoc:* Interestingly enough, this really hits the nail on the head; I've learned since that it's virtually universal for doctors under pressure to find some sort of morbid humor in the most dreadful situations. They will laugh uproariously, in private, about a patient's behavior *in extremis,* caricature the surgeon's efforts to save a hopeless case or make grisly jokes about some really agonizing and frightful problem. The nurses get in on the tag ends of this humor, and the inexperienced ones are horrified to see the men who are supposed to be so dedicated roaring with laughter at some poor patient's expense. An escape valve, I'm sure, pure and simple, that few people outside the profession have any inkling of. A characteristic response to pressure, but, like Shakespeare's "comic relief," the play could get pretty grim without it.]

Ann had a good time Sunday afternoon, at any rate. She was invited to join several of the clinic doctors and their wives over at John Gillies' house for a Pioneer Days cocktail party and dinner. A couple of the docs more or less took her under their wings, including Ned Stern, so she got a chance to meet some of them and they met her. So far I'm not too sure of the social protocol with these men, if there is any, though it would be fun to get better acquainted with some of them personally.

Talked to Schwartz, who is on Dr. Slater's surgical service and wants to be a surgeon anyway, and found out that he is assigned only four months on surgery to my five. It may be that we can finesse a change; I'd far rather have the extra time on medicine.

Wednesday, August 10

Got a little unbroken sleep Monday night at home, and just as well, too, because Tuesday I walked back into two more really barbarous days. We were hoping that on Wednesday things would begin to slacken up a little. Usually Monday is the second heaviest day of the week, Tuesday the heaviest day, and Wednesday comparatively light. But this time Wednesday didn't slacken up in the least. Since Saturday noon this hospital has really been going crazy; all Tuesday and Wednesday we hardly got a chance to sit down and catch our breath. It may sound silly as hell, but Tuesday afternoon I tried three separate times to get into a john long enough to take a crap, and every time I got my belt undone there was that damned page squawking for me with something or other that just couldn't wait. We ended up pretty exhausted by this afternoon.

Well, this is the way it goes. Maybe I'm developing a certain stoicism about it, but I still get a cramping pain in the stomach every time I hear that a new patient is coming in. Once I actually get in to see the patient, I really enjoy seeing what's loose, but I still get tense just seeing more work piling up ahead of me all day long. I suppose I'll always feel that way.

Tuesday afternoon Mr. Mangano died at last. The man's son was hovering over the bedside all morning, as ever, and it was he who finally called the nurse to tell her that he thought the old man had expired. They paged me in the midst of lunch, and I came upstairs. The son didn't say anything, but I'm sure he was very much upset that someone hadn't been at the bedside every moment, and there was no permission granted for a post-mortem examination. Under the circumstances I didn't have the heart to press it at all. We already knew the old man had had a stroke and a coronary back to back, just too many things wrong with him at once, and there was nothing to learn from a post, really. But he was a game old fellow and he really put up a fight while he was conscious. We hated to see him go.

Meanwhile our other major problem was the Barnes boy with the hepatitis and jaundice, up on the fifth floor. Rusty has been going along just about the same as before, which has not been good. He is still not responsive at all, and when I stuck my head under his oxygen tent today, I would have sworn for a minute that I could still smell the paraldehyde we had given him four days ago. Then I realized I was smelling the *fetor hepaticus,* the characteristic sweet-ish breath odor that goes along with liver failure, and not the paraldehyde.

Dr. Smithers has taken over the case while Dr. Peterson is off to a meeting in Chicago, and he was saying this boy is a weird case all the way around. Smithers says he's got a deeper jaundice than he's ever seen before, and also a more potent fetor than he's ever en-countered. We've been keeping him on careful fluid balance, trying to get 3 liters of intravenous fluid into him every day, including some 10 percent glucose solution for calories as well as for the water in it. Also vitamins, cortisone, Aureomycin, etc., but nothing is doing a goddamned thing to reverse things as far as we can see. He's a terrible problem just in terms of maintenance, with his continu-ing stuporous restlessness and churning around in bed.

We also still have the parents to contend with, and in a way it's pathetic. They hang around the floor like lost souls. Every time the mother goes into his room she shouts at him, begging him to speak to her, as if it would solve everything if he'd just once come around enough to say, "Hi, Mom, how are you?" You can hear her clear down the hall, but of course he doesn't respond, just thrashes around all the more.

Then late last night the nurse called me to say he'd finally dis-lodged the plastic needle again. The IV had infiltrated and puffed up his arm pretty badly. This was about midnight, and Pete and I were dead on our feet; I'd actually started down to go to bed when the nurse nailed me, and Pete had turned in a half-hour earlier. I couldn't find another vein that stood a chance of holding a needle, and didn't think it would be right to restrain him. Finally gave up after a couple of tries and called Pete, who had just gotten to sleep. We talked it over on the phone, and I suggested discontinuing the

IV altogether that night and asking a surgical resident in the morning to cut down for a deep vein in his leg. Pete said, well, maybe I could let the stuff drip into a deep thigh muscle by infiltration during the night, so we thought about it a bit and decided to do that.

We didn't think about it hard enough, though. Next morning Dr. Smithers nearly went through the roof, pointing out that 10 percent glucose in that IV was too concentrated to be put in that way. He said that with the poor tissue that Rusty has anyway, we'd be lucky not to have a huge, nasty slough of dead muscle tissue from that leg. Smithers was really disgusted with us, and I can't blame him. This is the second very stupid job of bungling I've been responsible for on this case, the first being the tourniquet we left on the lad's arm.

But in spite of this sort of thing Rusty at least seems to be holding his own. The surgeons did a cutdown on his leg today and ran eight inches of polyethylene tube up a deep leg vein. In the process the boy put up a fight, actually broke the needle off right at the shank with his violent kicking, so they had to patch it together again, and God knows what they're going to do tonight if he tears it loose again.

Rusty's father is still a problem, too. After that second or third night when he was really badgering us, I spoke to Smithers about it, told him I thought the man was hindering the boy's treatment, because we couldn't do *anything* very effectively with the father hanging over our shoulders. Apparently Smithers got next to the father, because on Tuesday morning when Pete and I were down at coffee in the cafeteria the father came in and sat down and had coffee with us, apologized for bothering us while we were trying to relax for a minute, and then tried to apologize for being such a pain in the ass in general.

It sounded pretty convincing at the time, but later Alec Ivy told us the father had tackled him the next night, asking where Dr. Kidder and Dr. Peterson were. Alec told him that Dr. Kidder was on vacation and that Peterson was at a medical conference, and the father had said, "Then there's only Dr. Smithers running the thing here," and Alec had said, yes, but that Dr. Smithers was a pretty good man. And the father said, maybe so, but he was sorry that

there wasn't somebody calling the shots who had the sort of confidence that Dr. Kidder had seemed to have when he first saw the
boy and admitted him to the hospital, that nobody here seemed to
know what they were doing, and nobody seemed to have any hope
for the kid.

This seemed like kind of a low blow to me, and I don't know *how*
we stand with the father now. God knows, Pete and I have been
dogging this case with all we have; it's discouraging to feel that the
boy's parents have utterly no confidence in what we're doing. On
the other hand, I don't really know why they should have, because
we don't have anything really constructive to offer this boy, except
fluids and electrolytes* and hope. We aren't even doing such a good
job of keeping the damned intravenous running, it seems. He does
take up a lot of time; it's embarrassing to me to run into the father
in the hall and have him ask me, "Doctor, has Rusty gotten his
blood yet?" and I haven't seen the boy for three or four hours and
don't even know that more blood has been ordered for him, but I
just can't keep that close track of him, we've had so many other
things to do these last few days.

The alcoholic who came in from down South with the chest pain
turned out to have a full-blown coronary after all, so today he
decided he just had to get out of the hospital to go see his children
or some other damned thing. Franklin said, no dice, he'd never
make it to the parking lot, so the patient tackled me about it on my
rounds this morning. I was dead certain this man was trying for a
bottle, just beginning the old crafty routine to get himself out of
the hospital and find one. Maybe he does have children down where
he came from—who knows? He did very reluctantly give me a name
and number of somebody to call to ask them to see his children and
report back, and when I promised to call he seemed to quiet down a
little. At least this afternoon he wasn't talking about signing himself out of the hospital any more.

Mrs. Hattie Stevens is just getting along. This is the woman Dr.
Franklin is taking care of with the galloping hypertension with
associated heart failure and kidney failure. We got a horrible jolt
when the pharmacy told us that her new blood pressure medicine,

* Ionized chemicals such as sodium, chlorides and potassium dissolved in the
blood stream and necessary for the body's chemical balance.

one of the recent "breakthrough" drugs, is costing her $10 per day; now Franklin is trying to switch her to something that will control her blood pressure as effectively but cost a little less. The woman is not going to survive unless her hypertension gets under control fast and stays there, and she's not going to be able to control it unless she finds some way to support herself and buy the medicine and let her doctor keep tabs on her, too. Just now the pressure is staying between 180 and 200 almost all the time, which Franklin seems to regard as some sort of therapeutic triumph. Of course, it was 280 when she came in, so maybe he's right. She's been fairly comfortable except for some nausea, and she's a chipper, happy little creature. It's too bad that she doesn't understand better how ill she really is. We feel like little gods coming in telling her how sick she is; she looks up at us and says, "But, Doctor, I feel just fine." And she probably does; it's just that she isn't just fine, more's the pity.

Dr. Van Wert finally broke down and brought an interesting patient into the hospital Tuesday. This guy's name is Peter Morley, and he's a thirty-seven-year-old bachelor who was a fairly high executive in the Western branch of IBM until five years ago when he developed rapidly progressing symptoms of myasthenia gravis. First time I've ever actually seen this condition, and it's a dreadful disease: without almost constant medication all the skeletal muscles quit working; the patient gets all flaccid, can't walk or make his extremities operate properly, can't get air in and out of his chest right, can't control his tongue, so that it flops back in his throat and chokes him—a real mess. Then after a dose of Prostigmin, which temporarily corrects the neuromuscular defect that causes the symptoms, everything clears up like magic for a short while. Trouble is, myasthenia is like diabetes: once you've got it, you've got it. It gets worse either slowly or quickly, but it always gets worse, and nobody knows any cure.

This guy Morley's disease has been under some sort of control right along by the use of Prostigmin and atropine, but it's never been under *good* control. He's had to increase his dosage continually under doctor's instructions until now he's been taking enough Prostigmin every day to kill a horse—a whopping dose every two hours during the day and once in the middle of the night. In all, he's taking well above the *maximum* dose recommended by the people who make the drug. He has to take equivalent doses of atropine (or belladonna) at the same time because the Prostigmin makes him salivate all over the place so that he can't swallow it fast enough to keep it from running down his windpipe and choking him or draining out all over his chin. So he's been right on the edge of Prostigmin intoxication for some time just in order to breathe and feed himself. Now Van Wert has brought him into the hospital to try to get him regulated on a fancy new experimental drug, not a Prostigmin-type drug at all, but one with a similar action that's supposed to be more potent and longer-lasting but with a narrower range between the maximum safe dose and the poisonous dose.

This guy is really in tragic shape. He's highly intelligent, and would have a pleasing personality except that he has become so totally preoccupied with this miserable illness, disabled and unable to work and barely able to feed and dress himself, that he can hardly talk or think about anything else. He just lives in deadly fear that he and his medicine will get separated somehow for a few hours and that will be it, for him. He told me that he's almost bankrupt now, thanks to the disease, and unless this new medicine allows him to do some useful work of some sort he just hasn't got any money from now on.

This man came in Tuesday morning. I saw him again last night; he was using the new drug now, and he was scared of what was going to happen during the night. He hasn't gone a night in five years without waking himself up at 2:00 A.M. and again at 6:00 A.M. to take his Prostigmin. He's missed it a couple of times and wakened almost choking to death, unable to breathe and unable to swallow because of the muscular weakness that comes on very rapidly when the Prostigmin is overdue. He didn't sound too confident that the nurses would remember to wake him, so I told him that I'd get up to check him at 2:00. I did, and he had a good night. Also seemed to have a good day today, but went downtown for a walk, on Dr. Van Wert's orders, and nearly exhausted himself.

A funny thing happened with this guy this afternoon, though, just like a shutter clicking open for a moment showing what was back of those eyes in his mind. I'd really empathized with this man from the first time I talked to him on admission. I kept thinking, My God, what a life to have to lead, and I was hoping to build up

some kind of rapport with him, at least to convey that I was interested in him as well as his disease. Seemed to be winning, too; he
seemed to open up to me. Then this afternoon I was in his room
chewing the fat for a moment when Dr. Cornell, the clinic neurologist, walked in, and the guy dropped me like a hot potato and
turned the charm on Cornell as though somebody had thrown a
switch. He just studiously ignored me even when Cornell tried to
include me in the examination, so I quietly trotted out to go on
with my rounds. Pretty obviously this guy's rapport goes to the
fellow who seems most likely to give him some help with his illness
right then. It kind of shocked me; this man clearly recognized that I
was just a slob intern and Cornell was the great neurologist who
was (inarguably) more important to him, but the sudden switch was
illuminating. Quite a blow to my ego, but I guess that's what egos
are for.

Among the three patients admitted at 4:00 this afternoon was a
fourteen-year-old girl named Diane Renton, a case of Dr. Franklin's, and a strange one. A year ago this girl weighed 200 pounds,
and lost weight by diet down to 140 pounds in six months. Then
quite suddenly her blood count began to fall from a normal of 14
grams of hemoglobin clear down to 6 grams in about two months,
and with no history of any kind of hemorrhage. She now has a very
distinct *fetor hepaticus* and has the little capillary "spiders" on her
hands and arms and neck that turn up with liver diseases, but no
jaundice. Her liver and spleen aren't palpable on physical examination, but this girl is in liver failure all the same, maybe in dangerous liver failure.

Franklin suggested that maybe she has cirrhosis of the liver on a
basis of malnutrition from the strict dieting and all, or possibly
Wilson's disease, or possibly viral hepatitis without jaundice. If she
turns out to have hepatitis, it may mean that we're going to have an
epidemic on our hands. County Hospital has a case, too, I've heard.
This is one disease I'd just as soon not see an epidemic of; after
watching Rusty I don't want to get any closer to hepatitis than I
can help. At least Wilson's disease—which is also known as "hepato-
lenticular degeneration," as I learned when I innocently asked
Franklin what Wilson's disease was—isn't infectious. It's one of
those rare diseases that you see once in a lifetime, if you ever see it

at all, Franklin says. The patient's liver just starts rotting away for reasons nobody knows. I suggested that maybe this girl has an acute leukemia with liver and spleen destruction, and Franklin agreed that a bone marrow biopsy is indicated. Meanwhile I will have to stay awake long enough tonight to look up Wilson's disease in my Holt and McIntosh; I never even heard of it before.

Something is going to break loose pretty soon with these nurses on the fourth floor. Last night Andy Case asked me to start an intravenous on a patient of his, an irascible old bitch who needed 2 units of packed red cells in a hurry. Case said she'd had trouble with her IVs before and there had been a big stink about it, so he wanted me to start the blood on her instead of having a nurse do it. That was fine; Mrs. Utley, the head nurse on Fourth, got things ready and I got a needle into the patient's vein on the first try. I told Mrs. Utley to take every precaution to please not let that IV infiltrate, and went down to go to bed. Just got my pants off when Mrs. Utley called me and said, "Doctor, do you know what that stupid IV did? It infiltrated." So I went back up there again and found that not only had the IV infiltrated, but it had run enough packed red cells out into the woman's wrist to raise a lump the size of a goose egg. She was in extreme pain, and the nurse hadn't even taken the needle out of the arm yet; it was still sitting there. It seems that Mrs. Utley had gone back to "check" the IV, and in the process of "checking" it she had given the tube a couple of good sharp whips and the needle came out of the vein.

The old gal would not allow me to do another venipuncture; she was so mad she could hardly talk. So I called Dr. Case at home and told him the news, and he said, "Oh, Christ!" and then he said, "Well, I guess you'd better let it go for tonight." As though I had personally arranged the whole mess. Well, I didn't feel like whining to him that it was all the nurse's fault, but I swear, if there's anything I've developed a vicious hatred for, it's a slovenly nurse. I started disliking them back in medical school, and I've disliked them more and more all the time. A good nurse can help so damned much and make things so easy and save so much time, and a slovenly nurse can kill you by inches. Mrs. Utley is just too busy trying to get her love novel read while she's on duty to bother too much about getting the work done.

Saturday, August 13

We were hoping that Thursday and Friday of this week would slow down to the normal Thursday and Friday pace again, and Thursday morning it looked as though it might. Started off with rounds with Dr. Franklin, who appeared twenty-five minutes late as usual. We made rounds on most of his patients—all of his patients, actually—but spent most of our time talking about Mrs. Hattie Stevens and the alcoholic man with the coronary. Mrs. Stevens' hypertension is cooling off on her new medicine, though for how long nobody can guess, probably not long. The coronary is trying his damnedest to get a bottle into the place, keeps having shifty-eyed visitors with bulging hip pockets trying to see him at visiting hours. Franklin cracked down on that with a "no visitors whatever" order, then grinned at us and said, "I don't know why I should bother, but that's one sure-fire way to get him out of the hospital."

Dr. Franklin is a funny guy, young and hesitant and apparently kind of indifferent about everything. I asked him about some of the exotic new antihypertensive drugs for Mrs. Stevens, since she's going to be dead in three months if her blood pressure isn't held down to normal. Franklin just snorted and said, "Personally, I'm just not strong on pills. I've got maybe ten drugs that make up 95 percent of my prescriptions, and they're the old reliable stand-bys." Went on to say some internists think pills have some kind of magic to them, and therefore stuff every patient they see full of them. "That's one reason the surgeons sneer at us," he went on, "and nine-tenths of the time they're right."

After rounds Thursday morning we looked in on Rusty Barnes. He was still comatose, hadn't shown any signs of coming to, but was still kicking and thrashing around. No sign of improvement there at all. Patients started coming in at 10:30 in the morning Thursday, and by 4:00 P.M. Pete and I had had sixteen new medical admissions, about half of them crocks who didn't know themselves what they were doing in the hospital. By the time Alec Ivy went off at 5:00 I still had nine admissions I hadn't even seen yet, so Pete and I divided them up and planned to churn on into the evening and brief each other about them later.

Then about suppertime the Barnes boy's special nurse called me to tell me that his IV was bleeding. I went up and took a look at it. The surgeons had wrapped it very tightly with Ace bandages, and they were getting soggy with blood from the cutdown incision. Dr. Smithers had been in and decided it was better to sedate the boy heavily than to let him thrash around; he was just exhausting himself. So he'd been slugged down with chloral hydrate and had some more ordered for later.

During the day I'd noticed the boy's mother in there again trying to rouse him, shouting at him, calling to him. I mentioned this to the special nurse as I was sitting at the desk there writing up somebody's history; the specials have been taking quite a beating, too, since they're all personal friends of the family. She said that today was Mrs. Barnes' birthday and that she had confided to the nurse that she just felt sure that Rusty was going to wake up and speak to her on her birthday.

The special also said that Dr. Smithers had pointed out to the parents that even if Rusty did survive the virus, he would have terrific posthepatitis cirrhosis of the liver. He'd be sick for the rest of his life and probably with the brain hemorrhage he'd just be a vegetable as well. The parents just didn't seem to have any understanding or realization at all of what this meant. The mother seemed to think that if he'd only just wake up he'd be well, and that he'd just bounce right out of bed and trot along home with them. The mother gets farther and farther away from the truth all the time, while the father seems to get stronger. Since Smithers spoke to him he's been a lot less obnoxious than before; he smiles at me when I rush past on the floor and has something pleasant to say. He even told me one day that I ought to smile once in a while when I see him; I guess I go around looking gloomy most of the time.

Anyway, it was shortly after this chat with the special—later Thursday evening about 9:30—that Rusty began having a lot of secretions, a lot of gurgling with his breathing. I ordered up the suction machine and listened to his chest. It sounded pretty clear, but I thought I'd better have the suction handy in case we needed it. A while later he was making a lot more noise with his breathing, so I went back in and listened again and cleaned out the back of his throat with the suction—thick, red, bloody mucus, which didn't look good. The more I tried to suck out, the more he seemed to gurgle. I listened to his chest again, and now it wasn't so clear; it was full of gunk. So I stuck the suction catheter down his nostril and into his trachea and sucked out just an awful lot of fresh blood, which cleared him up a bit. I hated to shove that tube down there because it looked as though he was hemorrhaging pretty badly into his lungs, but I knew if I didn't suck the stuff out he'd die of pneumonia or suffocate just as fast as he'd die of anything else. He was almost completely quiet now, hardly even coughed when I put the tube down.

While we were doing this in his room, Mrs. Barnes started going to pieces out in the alcove. The nurses took her and her husband into the little doctor's charting room, got them coffee and got her some Luminal by hypo. The boy was really looking bad by then, gurgling and getting stertorous with his breathing. I was with him perhaps half- or three-quarters of an hour. Pete came in, and just at that moment the boy stopped breathing a couple of times. I suggested using the Bennett valve, the positive-pressure breathing gadget Dr. Kidder thinks is so fine. Pete thought that would be a good idea, and called Dr. Smithers, too, as he went out to order it. Smithers came in, listened to the boy, looked at him. We got the Bennett valve going, finally. By then Rusty was in real respiratory distress. I sucked him out. By 10:30 or 10:45 he was on the Bennett valve, with enough breathing reflex left to trigger the thing himself, but just barely. It only needs a tiny tug from the patient each breath to trigger the valve and force oxygen in under pressure.

Pete and I went down to midnight supper and came back up again. By then the boy wasn't breathing for himself at all; somebody had to trigger the valve for him each breath. The special nurse was going to pieces now, too, saying that Rusty just had to hold on until after midnight so that he wouldn't die on his mother's birthday. Then she got hold of herself, and the boy looked a little better with the air going into him. Pete and I showed her how to work the valve, and I told the father and mother we were going down to try to get some rest but that we'd be quickly available if we were needed. Both of them were pretty much at the end of their ropes, but the father said he was sure everything was going to be all right, that he knew I wouldn't let the boy die.

I went downstairs and got into bed by 11:30; I'd been going

steady since 8:00 in the morning and I was really beat out. Then, in the course of the next half-hour I had three sedation calls that should have been screened by the night nursing supervisor, so I called her up and really reamed her out. I'd just hung up the phone at 12:15 A.M. when they called me from Fifth and told me they thought I'd better get up there and see Rusty. When I got there the special couldn't get any blood pressure reading—it had been dropping steadily for half an hour—and five minutes later there wasn't any pulse any more either, and Rusty was dead.

I knew that Pete wanted to be called. The parents were sitting out in the fifth-floor alcove just outside the room, so I told one of the nurses to go call Dr. Carey, and then after she'd gone I figured, What the hell, I might just as well go out there and tell the family myself as make Carey do it. When I went out to them, the father was praying and the mother was just sitting there looking at nothing. They tell us you're supposed to break bad news a little at a time, but there wasn't any point. I said, "I'm sorry, folks, but it's over." The mother just shook her head. The father put his face down in his hands and wept, and so did I. I left them to themselves then. The nurse had Carey on the phone. I told him that the boy had died and that if he wanted to come up he could, but I didn't see any reason why he should. He said, well, he thought maybe he should anyway, so he came up. The parents went in to see the boy and came out again. The father was taking it very hard. I had the nurse bring some coffee up. The mother didn't want any, but the father said, yes, he'd have a cup of coffee and wanted me to have one, too. He said, "You know, I've been trying to have a cup of coffee with you for a long time."

Pete saved me one thing at least. I didn't feel much like asking for a post on this boy. At best this is one of the really ugly jobs that go along with this work and you have to be cold-blooded about it, I suppose, and I just didn't feel much like being cold-blooded about it right then. When Pete arrived he broached the subject. He was a little bit stuffy and professional about it, but he told them that we would like to have permission. Surprisingly enough (or maybe not so surprisingly), there was no problem. The mother said she felt sure that's what Rusty would have wanted, the father agreed, so the signatures were taken. Then the father got himself together and

asked for a couple of sleeping pills to take home with him because
he was going to have to sleep that night. And finally, he said he
wanted to make sure that everyone involved with Rusty got gamma
globulin shots to protect them from the virus, and we assured him
that we'd see to it that that was taken care of.

This was, I think, the end of the tenth day the boy had been
in the hospital, and one thing the father said really hit me hard.
Apparently when Dr. Kidder had admitted the boy the first day he
hadn't had any more hope than Dr. Peterson or Dr. Smithers had
had, but instead of saying to the parents, "Well, there's not much
we can do; he'll probably die," as Peterson and Smithers had, Kidder had said, "Well, always remember that if we can get him
through the next fourteen days we'll be able to save him." Of course,
we didn't get him through the next fourteen days and Kidder knew
from the start that we wouldn't, but maybe if we could have he
would have survived. At least Fred Kidder hadn't robbed those
people of their hope.

The rest of the night was quiet, thank God. I don't think either
Pete or I had much reserve left; I sure as hell didn't. I don't think I
slept very well either; I sure didn't feel rested when I got up for the
Friday morning conference at 7:45.

After the conference Friday an emergency patient of Franklin's
was admitted, a woman he thought might have polio. History of
headache for two or three days, and now a stiff neck. I did a fairly
thorough neurological examination, did a spinal tap on her and
found the spinal fluid clear, so we were pretty sure that it wasn't
intracranial bleeding, and it didn't look like a bacterial meningitis;
she didn't have any fever. Put her in isolation and watched her
pretty much all day. Fortunately, the stiff neck didn't get any worse
during the day. She had a nasty headache, but this settled down a
little bit with just aspirin, and by Saturday morning it looked as
though she wasn't in too much trouble. I'll have to see what happened over the weekend. Maybe she does have polio. We couldn't
exclude it; we couldn't exclude viral encephalitis (brain fever) either, or a half-dozen other unpleasant things that it might have
been.

Friday evening I spent working up a couple of stragglers, nothing
very exciting. Just finished up about 10:00, ready to go down for

evening supper when Fred Kidder called in (back from vacation) to say he had an old patient coming in with congestive heart failure and long-standing asthma, and he wanted me to evaluate him. So I left word to call me in the cafeteria when he arrived. Pete joined me down there. Pretty soon the call came that the patient was in, an old man named Jerry Dykeman. Floor nurse said he was bubbling and choking and having a great deal of difficulty breathing, and that he looked bad. Pete ordered a small hypo of morphine over the phone, and we hurried on up to see the guy together.

He'd already been given the morphine when we got there; he did indeed look bad, a little, bald, wrinkled-up old man who looked like Gandhi, but the nurse said he was looking worse after the hypo instead of better. He wasn't gasping for air, but you could hear his chest gurgle across the room, and he looked gray. I listened to his chest and thought he had fluid in his lungs; Pete listened and said he wasn't so sure, maybe this was just asthma. And then while we were arguing this fine clinical point there at the bedside, old Mr. Dykeman just quietly quit breathing at all.

He already had an oxygen mask right there ready to go, and he'd take a couple of gasps when we joggled him, but then quit again. Right then we both began to see what we'd done to the old guy: we'd shot morphine into him assuming that he was in heart failure, and his real problem was probably an obstructive bronchitis on top of an asthma, and not heart failure at all, and we'd knocked out whatever the poor man had left of an already very feeble respiratory reflex. Pete started artificial respiration with the oxygen mask on the man's face, and I called Kidder. Kidder seemed to know exactly what had happened before I finished telling him because he said, "Well, Jesus, just keep the old guy breathing until I get over there," and he came right over from home. He didn't exactly chew us out right then for giving the guy the morphine, but he was sarcastic as hell, took one look at the patient and said, "Well, Jesus, we're just going to have to breathe for old Jerry here until that morphine wears off," and went looking for a Bennett valve.

So we got old Jerry's oxygen mask hooked up to the valve, and we breathed for old Jerry—I mean we triggered the valve for every breath, because old Jerry had just quit working altogether; he wouldn't take any breaths at all. So I flipped the valve trigger every four seconds without fail for a solid hour, with Kidder watching me like a hawk, and then he wanted a blood count done on old Jerry, so he took over the valve while I went down to the lab and ran the blood count. Finally, he got a special nurse in to run the valve and let Pete and me go to bed about 1:00 A.M. while he slept on a stretcher in the hall outside the patient's room, and the nurse breathed for old Jerry all night long.

Kidder checked him again at 5:00 A.M. and had the nurse call Pete at 6:00, and Pete called me at 7:00. Kidder took the patient off the valve about 6:30 or so; old Jerry kept turning blue every now and then, but by the time Alec Ivy came on duty for the weekend at 8:00, old Jerry Dykeman seemed to be breathing by himself again, not very vigorously maybe, but breathing. The last thing Fred Kidder had to say before he left, in that sarcastic nasal voice of his, was: "Well, Jesus, boys, don't *ever* give morphine to a patient with old bronchial disease unless you want to breathe for him all night." Actually, if we hadn't gotten the Bennett valve going when we did, old Jerry Dykeman would have just kicked off because we'd given him the worst sort of medicine we could have picked from the whole damned pharmacy. Dr. Kidder pointed out that, sure, this was a common enough error, but it was still an error nobody in his right mind should make. We had just been sloppy.

Saturday morning Dr. Van Wert made rounds with us. His boy Morley with the myasthenia gravis seems to be regulating much better on the new experimental drug, and Van Wert's pretty much pleased with the results. Trouble is, the man wants to get back to absolutely normal, and he probably never will, though he may be going home this weekend.

Got out of there at 10:00 A.M. for a big fat day and a half off. I'm worried about next week because Pete Carey is going to be gone for these next two weeks, getting married yet, honeymoon and all, so I'm going to be working with Milt Musser as my resident for the two weeks. He's been the Chief Medical Resident, mostly covering the service without intern coverage, so I haven't had much to do with him, but he seems to spend a lot of time sitting around making sarcastic remarks to the interns and nurses, or bending the clinic doctors' ears about new drugs. He's a third-year resident, and pharmacology seems to be about all he's interested in. I've been

working very comfortably with Pete and like him a lot, but he's
been doing a lot more of my scut work than he should have to,
especially with a week like this last one. And a lucky thing, too; I
think I'd be stone-dead by now if he hadn't. Whether Musser will
or not I don't know. We'll see how tomorrow goes, or rather Monday.

                                              Thursday, August 18

I think that Monday was probably the gloomiest day I've spent
since I started my internship, not for any particular reason, but just
everything in general. Had a restful weekend off, but I still didn't
get thoroughly rested. Dreaded the idea of going to work Monday
morning, and when I got there I got a bum start. A pretty lousy
day, all day.

Fuller had rounds, with a couple of schlunks from Harvard Medical School in tow, obviously looking the hospital over for internship possibilities. With all the new admissions last week there were
lots of patients I just hadn't seen for three or four days, and Fuller
kept asking me questions about them, naturally. I didn't know
what was happening with them and couldn't help feeling that I
wasn't keeping a grip on my service properly unless I knew what
was going on with my patients. Then halfway through rounds I got
a call that Franklin had an admission, a possible coronary, down on
the second floor, so I had to run down and see what was up.

The patient was there, with severe chest pain. Franklin had seen
him in the Emergency Room, but there was no note, no orders from
him, no nothing, and the man didn't have a clinic work-up either.
So I had to work him up then and there, and wrote orders for some
morphine and an oxygen tent for him. I ordered an EKG and asked
the nurses to have it ready so that Fuller could see it when he came
downstairs. But then when he arrived he went whippety-whip
through and didn't look at the EKG *or* render an opinion about the
patient, just looked at him and walked off muttering things. So I
didn't know what the story was until afternoon when Franklin
made rounds and wrote an order or two on the guy. But that's the
sort of up-in-the-air thing I run into from time to time that always

bothers me, and this Monday morning particularly it annoyed hell out of me, and soured me up for the rest of the day.

Milt Musser is going to be a poor substitute for Pete, I fear. He's a kind of tall, skinny, bulbous-eyed individual with an off-center nose and a kind of slow, drawly way of talking. He's one of these insincere diplomats who will be making sarcastic remarks about one of the outside doctors one minute, and then when the doctor shows up, call him by his first name and really give him the old glad hand. After the good teamwork with Pete it looked on Monday as though I was going to have most of the work strictly to myself. Actually, as the week has gone on, Milt has been doing some of the work, but so far I haven't gotten much help from him, nor even any very sound suggestions about what to do in this case or that. Which is tough because there are now thirty-five patients on the service, and I've only seen about half of them more than once.

Nothing very interesting Monday P.M. until after Alec Ivy checked out to me about 7:30. Then I was busy all evening with just one patient. I'd run over to the library in the clinic to look up something on Wilson's disease, still thinking of little Diane Renton and her unexplained liver failure. There I got a call from Michaelson, the evening nursing supervisor, that there was a patient of old Dr. Homer John's (one of the outside GPs) who was having trouble. This was Mrs. Woodruff, who had had a coronary a week or so ago. Tonight she'd begun complaining of pain in her chest and some trouble breathing. Did I want to come look at her? I knew that the patient had orders covering her for both chest pain and shortness of breath, but I'm still uneasy with coronaries, so I hurried on up there. When I checked her chart I found that Mrs. Woodruff is a Christian Scientist and she had Demerol ordered by mouth for chest pain because the old girl wouldn't take injectable medications. She wouldn't even let them stick a needle into her in order to do lab studies. From the progress notes I gathered this lady was cantankerous and obnoxious and insulting and everything else.

Well, I went back to see her, and she didn't seem so cantankerous. She wouldn't even admit to having any pain, except that it was obvious that she was, and that she was having trouble breathing as well. I ordered up an oxygen tent right away, and then felt her pulse and got a real chill when I found it was just going like crazy. I grabbed a student nurse's watch—according to my timing this woman was running a pulse of 220 per minute.

For a coronary this is no good. I took an EKG while the orderly was getting the oxygen tent set up, to see how it compared with an earlier cardiogram. It looked like she had had a massive coronary, with a whole wedge of her heart muscle knocked out, really a tremendously bad one, and she'd been sick as hell, and this was about her ninth day, which is just about the time the damaged piece of heart wall gets the weakest, and her pulse had been about 76 until just this evening, and now it was over 200. I phoned Milt Musser and told him that this old gal was in trouble.

When he got there, we looked at the cardiogram together; neither of us could figure out whether this fast heart rate came from the irritable damaged ventricle or whether she was just going into massive heart failure. We went down and looked in my Birch and Windsor, and in Stewart's *Cardiac Therapy,* and we still couldn't satisfy ourselves. She obviously needed digitalis, but she'd been getting quinidine for the last few days and Milt was afraid that digitalis on top of it might just stop her clock altogether. I suggested calling Dr. John and asking him what he wanted done, but Milt just sneered and said, "Why bother? He'll just say to do whatever you think is best. That old fart doesn't even know what heart failure is, much less what to do about it."

Finally we went over to the clinic, where Ned Stern was studying for Boards with a couple of bright boys from the university, and we showed them the EKG, but they wouldn't go out on a limb either, so we called Dr. Franklin at home and asked him what to do. First thing he said when he heard that her heart rate was 220 was: "How long since she had the first dose of digitalis?" I said we hadn't given her any yet. So he said go give her half a digitalizing dose intravenously and then call him back; we were lucky she wasn't dead already. I did that, and she didn't object to the needle this time either. Called Franklin back, and he said to check her pulse myself every hour, and then at 2:00 A.M. give her another dose of digitalis, and another at 8:00 in the morning, if she was still around at 8:00 in the morning.

Well, I didn't think she was going to be. Every time I checked her pulse she looked worse. At 2:00 A.M. I came up to give the second dose of digitalis and her pulse was down to 160, but I couldn't get any blood pressure at all. She was white, she wasn't responding very much, and I thought, Oh, brother, this gal is just going out. I thought about calling Dr. John, but Dr. John is such a goddamned boob that I didn't do it; I figured if Milt had wanted to call him, Milt would have called him. So I went back to bed after giving the medicine, telling the nurses to keep the hourly record of her pulse.

Next morning, much to my amazement, the woman was still alive, and she even looked halfway good. Her pulse had converted to a nice, slow, strong 72 since 2:00 A.M. Well, now on Thursday Mrs. Woodruff is still alive and as far as we can see hasn't suffered any extension of her coronary, which is quite a surprise. I think we diddled around a couple of hours too long before starting the digitalis for fear it would do harm and just didn't recognize that she was jolly well going to be dead right soon if we didn't use the medicine. Still, I felt good about the thing in spite of the delay, because at least I had the presence of mind to get an EKG on her right off, and handled my end of the situation about right, or at least as well as the third-year resident did. Maybe the blind were leading the blind, but I was sorry to have to turn the case back to Alec Tuesday morning.

Tuesday we made rounds with Dr. Tuckerman, one of the older clinic docs, who devoted the time to telling us about diagnosing hypothyroidism. About 9:30 we went down for coffee and sat talking some more. Tuckerman is a skinny, sad-faced guy with big pouches under his eyes and a thousand wrinkles in his forehead, and quite a history, too. Seems he had spent a number of years before he went to college working as a coal-heaver on a merchant ship, one of the black gang. He'd been around the world three or four times in all directions, sailed to the Orient, to the Mediterranean, to South America, and then after medical school he was a ship's surgeon for another couple of years. We got to talking about the incidence of syphilis among merchantmen, and about what ship's surgeons do on board ship when somebody gets really sick, and had quite an interesting talk.

One of the admissions Tuesday afternoon was a man complaining of weakness and weight loss, with known heart failure, a patient of Dr. Fuller's. Milt Musser saw the guy first and then told me to take a look at him and see if I thought he had anything wrong besides heart disease. I thought he had cancer written all over him: a thin, sallow little bird who had lost twenty-five pounds in four months and looked sick. I wondered about cancer of the pancreas or stomach, and found a big, hard liver and some swollen lymph nodes, but his lab work showed no loss of liver function, and after two days of rest in bed he was feeling and looking great. Franklin saw him and thought he just had a lousy sick heart and nothing else. He may be right, too, but I thought for sure the man had a malignant disease, and I still think so. We'll wait and see who's right.

Felt like an awful boob on Wednesday when I worked up one of Dr. Harry Smithers' patients, an old man having some pain in the left upper quadrant of his abdomen. The pain was relieved by nitroglycerin, but I couldn't get any history of pain in his *chest* or anything like that, and finally decided he must have an ulcer or something. Harry Smithers came in while I was writing up my exam. He talked to the man for fifteen minutes, and then came back and said, "You know, I think that man's got angina pectoris from his heart, and nothing in his belly at all." Damned if he wasn't right, too—and Thursday afternoon the patient proved it. Just before I was going off Thursday Milt stopped me and said, "Hey, that old guy with abdominal angina had a coronary today!" Sure enough, there were changes in his cardiogram between 8:00 Thursday morning and 3:00 Thursday afternoon, and he's started having some real chest pain now. So that was one I missed completely.

Wednesday afternoon we got in a real doll. I heard her coming in—I mean literally; I was down in the doctors' lounge looking at my mail when I heard her clear down the hall at the admitting desk screaming something about a goddamned son of a bitch, and the hospital couldn't keep her in, and a whole lot of foul stuff at the top of her lungs.

I kind of hid there, hoping she was on somebody else's service, but no such luck. Five minutes later the nurse on Fourth was calling me to see a wild patient of Dr. Franklin's who had just come in. I went up and there she was, throwing herself around in the bed, jiggling and jumping and screaming intermittently with bursts of tears thrown in, complaining how her husband beat her and how everything was so terrible, etc. She was about fifty or fifty-five years old and reeked of garlic. I didn't know any history, or what she had been drinking, or what the hell was going on, but the nurses sure wanted me to do something to quiet her down.

I gave up trying to get a coherent story, just did a very inadequate physical examination to make sure that she wasn't going to die on me. Her referring doctor was old Dr. Donald MacDuff, one of these doddering eighty-year-old herb-and-root specialists who are still practicing medicine on a license granted fifty years ago and haven't read a medical journal since. He came tottering in presently and told me a bizarre tale of how this woman had been calling him at all hours of the day and night about pain in her belly. She was always drunk when he saw her. After he'd made a couple of night house calls she, according to aged Dr. MacDuff, had asked him to go to bed with her. When he refused, she tried to extort $10,000 from him for coming to visit, complaining of attempted criminal assault, and then tried to blackmail some judge when he threw the case out.

After putting all this together, I just ordered 15 cc's of paraldehyde for sedation, and she went out like a light, slept right on through until Thursday morning. When I saw her then, she was much more coherent, and gave a pretty clear history of a gastric ulcer the year before, so maybe we're dealing with a gastric ulcer now instead of old knobby-liver cirrhosis; I don't know for sure. If nothing else, she added to my growing regard for paraldehyde as a sedative. It really does a very smooth job, even if it does stink up the whole wing of the hospital, and for a person with even a little bit of liver trouble it can do a lot.

Got quite a big kick Wednesday evening when I ran into Cora Baker in the hall. This was the lady with sprue who had been at death's doorstep during my first weeks of internship. She's been home for about a month now, and she looks like a completely different woman, has gained thirty pounds, looks strong and healthy and says she feels great. She still looked like a skeleton when she left the hospital; now she's rounding out a bit and looks good. She was going around the hospital shaking everybody's hand; apparently she'd been over to check with Dr. Peterson and came back to see all her old friends here, too.

By Wednesday night we had nearly caught up with ourselves. I was on for the night, and cleaned things up by 9:30 and then turned in, hoping for a quiet night. It was quiet, too, except for one really weird thing that happened after I'd gone to bed. This one really shook me up; it's funny now, but it wasn't funny then. I'd just crawled into the sack when I got this call from the nurse on the second floor telling me that some patient Alec Ivy had worked up was having trouble; his blood pressure had suddenly dropped from 160 to 90 in the course of the last two hours. The nurse said he was looking a little shocky, and would I come and see him.

Well, I got my pants on fast. They told me the man had a couple of pints of blood ordered on stand-by, and I thought, My God, this guy is hemorrhaging into his bowel or something. Ran up to Second, and the nurse handed me his chart. His name was Mr. Muller, and apparently he was under observation for possible chronic leukemia. He'd been having blood showing up in his stools and had a hemoglobin of 8.7 grams, and they had him lined up for a bone marrow biopsy the next day, and now the bottom was dropping out of his blood pressure. I took his blood pressure myself, and, sure as hell, it was 90 over 40, and he was just about breathing, just barely responding, and looked pretty bleak. He had an intravenous running, glucose and water, with a 21 gauge needle in his arm.

I went back to the nurses' station and looked at his chart again, and I just couldn't decide what to do. I thought, Jesus Christ, if his pressure is dropping like this and he has blood on stand-by, I'd better start pouring it into him. On the other hand, if I give him the blood, sure as hell I'll botch up the bone marrow biopsy they want to do tomorrow and this will delay his diagnosis and everybody will hate me.

Then the more I looked at that chart, the more things didn't quite jell. First, I couldn't find any blood pressure record. Then I couldn't find any IV ordered on the man, but I'd just seen one running into his arm a few minutes before. There were two pints of blood ordered for stand-by, all right, but no IV. The nurse couldn't figure that out either. I must have sat there pondering this for ten minutes, trying to grope my way out of the fog, and worrying myself sick. Then Musser came by, and I said, "Milt, what the hell should we do with this guy?" He looked at the chart with me, and then we saw that Alec's work-up described this man as a bald, short, stocky, sixty-eight-year-old man, and the man I'd seen in bed was a regular skeleton with hair falling down over his ears. So Milt said, "Let's go see this Mr. Muller," and, sure as hell, when he snapped on the light, the name on the bed was Kasnowsky or something. The nurse had been taking the blood pressure on the patient in Bed 4 instead of Bed 3, and when we looked around the curtain at the patient in Bed 3, there was short, stocky Mr. Muller snoring like an elephant. His blood pressure was 150 over 80, he didn't look the least bit shocky, and he was very much annoyed at being disturbed at 1:00 A.M. by two doctors and a very red-faced nurse. He didn't have any IV going either. On the other hand, Mr. Kasnowsky's blood pressure was at an all-time high at 90 systolic and he'd been looking shocky for the last two weeks, without any change.

So this is an illustrative example of how dull nurses can be sometimes, and also how dull you can be when you're ten feet under your first hour of sleep and you get hauled awake to see a patient you never heard of before.

Thursday was a very uncomplicated day. I was called at 6:30 A.M. to pronounce one of Alec's patients who had just died. In the afternoon I was called to pronounce one of Dr. Van Wert's patients who had just died. Mrs. Blomberg, the woman with carcinoma of the rectum, is just about terminal now, too, and as pitiable a soul as you ever saw. Last night when I checked her chart, the nurse told me that Dr. Slater had ordered that she was to have no more IVs. He didn't want the order written on the chart, but he wanted it passed along to us on the house staff. So I don't know. Dr. Fuller had come in afterward and written an IV order, so she got that IV. I don't know what the story is supposed to be for sure, but I have a good suspicion of what the story is supposed to be and I don't know if I like it or not, but I almost think I do, for Mrs. Blomberg.

Friday, August 19

After teaching rounds I went up to check a couple of new patients who had come in. One was interesting, a boy who had been brought in from the country in a sort of semicoma. His doctors here suspected a brain tumor; he'd been very active up until four

weeks ago and then began having nausea and vomiting and acting
very strangely. Both Randy Brock and Alec Ivy saw the guy (he had
come in on a night I was off), and both of them listed catatonic
schizophrenia as their working diagnoses. I had to do a spinal tap
on the lad, and he sure acted like a schizophrenic: he just lay there
in bed, didn't look at you, and when you talked to him you got
back a kind of vacant stare and nothing else. When he answered at
all, it would be in monosyllables. Spinal fluid pressures were normal, so I guess maybe schizophrenia *is* this boy's trouble and not
brain tumor, although you have to rule it out before you shoot him
over to the mental hospital. After seeing his mother, it made sense
that he might be a schiz. He also has a couple of screwy brothers
and sisters; one sister in the family withdrew some years ago by
going into a nunnery. I guess this mother must be real fierce.

Got around to see some older patients during the afternoon.
Hattie Stevens is probably going home tomorrow; her blood pressure is under control, for the present at least. Her kidney function is
still lousy, but she's not feeling bad and she's evidently not in frank
renal failure, so Franklin is going to let her go home and check with
her twice a week in the clinic.

Spent the last hour of the afternoon marking time, hoping no
patients would come in, and fortunately none did. At 5:00 I went
down to quarters and showered, and Ann picked me up at 6:00 for
our first dinner date in a month.

Monday, August 22

Milt Musser said this was the quietest weekend he'd worked in
years. Certainly it was a lot quieter than the last weekend I worked,
but I wouldn't say it was exactly quiet. It was busy but not rushed,
which is a very pleasant way to have a duty weekend be.

Saturday morning I made early rounds by myself on some of my
own patients. Milt drifted in about 8:45, and we talked over a
couple of problem patients while we drank morning coffee. Randy
Brock briefed us on the sick ones on his service that he was leaving
in our hands. Milt was taking most of the responsibility for keeping
track of them, so all I had to worry about were a few very sick ones
on my own service.

There are some subtle little problems that turn up from a call system like this, things you wouldn't ordinarily think of. I don't usually see any patients on the opposite medical service except on call nights when I am covering for Alec. The nurses know this and take advantage of it to try to get me to change orders that they don't like, or to get things ordered for their convenience which the other house doctors either won't or haven't ordered. For instance, they called me at midnight Saturday for permission to put a retention catheter in some old bird who had had a stroke and kept urinating in bed. It just happened that they'd called me four days ago about the same patient and I'd told them to check with the people who were taking care of him and see if they wanted a catheter installed in his bladder or not. They hadn't bothered, and now the poor old guy was still urinating in bed. So I told them to go ahead, put a catheter in. I also blew up in their faces and told them what a slovenly crowd I thought they were up there. That fat slob of a blonde that works on Second was highly incensed by this, but I suppose she'll survive it, and just go eat another five pounds of candy to make up for it.

Saturday evening was filled with piddly little things, three or four purely annoyance admissions. Some of these doctors use this place as a dodge to avoid being bothered by patients on weekends. If somebody calls them about something, they shoot him into the hospital where there's a nice handy intern and resident staff waiting to take care of him, so the attending doctor doesn't have to move his butt until Monday morning unless he feels like it.

They do this especially at night, naturally. Saturday night, for instance (really Sunday morning at 2:00 A.M.), Dr. Isaacs sent in a little girl with a supposedly injured shoulder. The nurses on Second called me out of bed to see her, but Isaacs had ordered ¾-grain of Nembutal to be given when the girl was admitted, so by the time I got to the floor the kid was sound asleep and snoring. So I said, the hell with this; if she was so sick that she was sound asleep, she could wait until morning to be seen. And next morning here was this bright-eyed little girl who didn't have anything more wrong with her than I did. Seems she had awakened during the night crying, and her parents had gotten all excited and called Dr. Isaacs, so he said, "Take her to the hospital," and then rolled over and went back to sleep. I was glad I'd gone back to sleep, too. On the chart I wrote my diagnosis as "Normal child, no disease." I hope Isaacs sees it when he comes in, but I don't suppose it will bother him very much.

About 11:00 Sunday morning a whole string of outpatients started coming in to the Emergency Room, and that kept me hopping. There was a lady with a broken wrist, a real "silver fork" deformity. The films showed that she'd broken the head of the radius clean off and displaced it backward. She was a patient of one of the outside doctors; when I called he said, "Well, go ahead and take care of it, if you want to, or if you think it's really bad, get one of the clinic orthopedic men to look at it." I called George Garvin, who was the surgical resident on Orthopedics. We took her up to the operating room and called Anesthesia, and I got to set my first wrist fracture, with Garvin nursing me along.

Also on Sunday afternoon a young colored woman came in, accompanied by her slightly drunken boyfriend, with a big gash in her scalp which she said she got when she fell down. While I was fixing her up, the boyfriend went to sleep in his chair. The woman then whispered that she hadn't fallen down at all, the boyfriend had let her have it with the butt of a gun. I asked if she wanted to report it, and she said yes, so I took her down to X-ray to get skull films and let her notify the cops from the switchboard phone on the way down. The cops were delighted; the boyfriend had a police record ten yards long, including assault and battery, robbery, narcotics peddling and addiction. They came to scoop him up, still sleeping in his chair, and I sent the girl on home after her head was sewed up again.

Wrapped Sunday up with a real shocker. A patient of Dr. Peterson's came in about 8:00 in the evening, a pleasant man of forty-seven named Jack Kelley. Admitting diagnosis was a possible coronary; he'd been having pain in his chest after meals off and on for a month, and then Sunday he'd had two quite severe attacks. I debated waiting until morning for an electrocardiogram, but finally decided not to wait. I couldn't see much abnormal on the EKG tracing, but he did have a few premature heartbeats now and then and complained that his heart felt like it was jumping around a little bit. I decided to assume that he'd had a coronary, and gave him some morphine and put him to bed in an oxygen tent. Dr. Peterson asked me to have Dr. Franklin see the man, so I called Dr. Franklin, told him the problem, and he came in about 10:00 to talk to the guy. He agreed we couldn't tell for sure whether Mr. Kelley had had a coronary or not just yet, but it certainly was not a typical history for a coronary. I asked about ordering stomach X-rays for Monday morning, but Franklin said, "Well, let's pretend he's had a coronary and get another tracing on him Monday and see what it looks like before we move him around too much." Meanwhile his pain had gone away on the morphine, and he seemed to be doing okay.

I figured the man would hold for the night and went down to the cafeteria to meet Ann, who had driven over to have supper with me at 10:30. We chewed up old sandwiches left from lunch—boy, I'm getting sick of sandwiches. Ann went on home about 11:00, and I went down to go to bed. An hour later the phone rang. Mr. Jack Kelley had just expired, and Dr. Musser was on the floor and had pronounced him. I rushed upstairs and asked what had happened. Nothing had happened, really. They had come in to change Mr. Kelley's oxygen tank and found him dead; an hour before he'd been happy as a clam and wondering why he was there. We got permission for a post, so the pathology resident got called out to do that, and I asked him to give me a buzz when he got the heart out. He called me about 2:15 A.M., and I walked down to the morgue. Mr. Kelley hadn't had a good coronary artery left in his heart; you could feel them like little calcified pipestems even before the heart was opened. Gave me a funny feeling, though; six hours before I'd even been debating whether to do a cardiogram on this patient or not, and now I was holding the pathology right there in my hands, the heart was still warm. It just goes to show that you don't have to have a typical picture of a coronary to have a patient just up and crap out on you. This man was one of the 3.5 percent of all coronaries who die with their first attack, that was all.

Wednesday, August 24

I think I neglected to mention that Mrs. Blomberg died on Sunday morning, about 7:30 A.M. The nurses saw Dr. Slater's name on the chart, and Schwartz was on the floor at the time, so they asked him to pronounce her. It was a relief for everyone, a long, hard struggle over and done with; Mrs. Blomberg was as classic an example of the grisly fashion in which terminal cancer patients die as you could ever find. And after watching it once I think I'm beginning to understand why doctors hate this disease more than anything else there is.

This poor woman was only forty-seven years old, and she had a cancer of the rectum which Dr. Slater tried to remove just eight or nine months ago, and found an inoperable tumor down there. He closed her up without doing anything but relieving some bowel obstruction. She was readmitted about a month and a half ago with jaundice from involvement of her liver and with intractable pain in her rectum. When huge doses of morphine wouldn't hold the pain any longer, Dr. Cornell finally cut the pain-carrying nerves in the lower spine, a sort of permanent spinal anesthesia. The operation relieved her pain, all right, but then other unpleasant things began turning up.

First, she began having nausea and vomiting that was almost intractable—not enough to throw her electrolytes completely off nor enough that she couldn't eat, but she couldn't enjoy her food. We couldn't relieve the nausea, and she became very weak, couldn't move around, could barely sit up. For a while the nurses would get her up and sit her in a chair, but pretty soon even this was too exhausting for her.

I missed seeing her for about a week at this time, and when I did see her I was really staggered at the change. The woman was slowly starving to death. Pretty soon she began developing diarrhea, first four or five times a day and then up to fifteen times a day. We tried to stop it with paregoric, and when this didn't work we tried just plain tincture of opium. This didn't stop it either, and she got more nauseated because the medicine smelled so terrible and she could taste it all the time.

As if the poor woman wasn't miserable enough with all this, about that time the skin on her back began to break down. I spotted it before there was any actual bedsore, and the nurses tried to get her to roll over on her side to relieve pressure and expose her back to air. We tried a rubber doughnut under her sacrum also, but good preventive care was almost impossible with all that diarrhea, and within a few days Mrs. Blomberg had a large, dirty, festering bedsore. She had to have intravenous fluids all the time; her jaundice was becoming more and more marked; her prothrombin time dropped down very low; and she had practically no liver function at all. We were doing no more than sustaining her, and yet she hung on and on.

Finally, things fell apart all at once. She was getting weaker and weaker, and she went into coma from liver failure. Now she was living on intravenous fluids alone—sugar water and saline. When Dr. Slater gave verbal orders to stop her IVs, that was that; she expired in coma two days later. There's no telling how long she might have lasted if the fluids had been continued, maybe another week, maybe another two or three, but it was a pretty frightful thing to watch even as it was. I know I was upset by Dr. Slater's order at the time and I know they say that a doctor can't play God and a doctor just must never allow himself to quit and toss in the sponge. But I think maybe the ones who insist that there can never be any justification for mercy killing should be given the joy of special-nursing a Mrs. Blomberg or two and then see how they can justify keeping alive for an extra day or week a woman who is already nothing but a living, breathing, suffering corpse. I don't know whether Dr. Slater was playing God or just doing a little bit of God's dirty work for Him, on orders.

At least there was one blessing with Mrs. Blomberg: after the nerve-cutting surgery she didn't have pain. Mrs. Hathaway, who came to the hospital on Tuesday afternoon, is an example of a terminal cancer patient who does have pain. She's had separate primary cancers in each breast and another primary cancer of one ovary, all three of them removed surgically, and she now has recurrent cancer which has just about destroyed the whole of one vertebra in her mid-back, as well as invading several other bones. This woman has been having constant, unremitting pain in her back because of the collapsed vertebra. X-ray therapy has slowed the process, and so has hormone therapy, but now she just lives with pain. She had a coronary last February, just to help things along, but naturally she had to recover from that. Question now is whether to do a cordotomy (a nerve-cutting operation to control pain) or not; she's addicted to Demerol; we've tried everything else we could think of including cobra venom, of all things, to control her pain, and she still has it. The pain comes in swift, stabbing spasms whenever she moves just a little bit wrong, and this poor woman, who has always been game before, just lies there and screams with it whenever it comes.

The pain has begun to break her spirit now; she's gotten to the point where she's so afraid of the pain that she just loses control of herself in the face of anything she thinks might start it.

Again, I can't for the life of me see why Cornell should hesitate about doing a cordotomy. Here is a case of a woman who has been a real fighter, who has had a terrible disease for a long time, and only just now is her personality beginning to break down. This is the thing that one of my old professors at Hopkins told us was so often the case with people who know they have cancer. He said that the most terrible thing in the world is to see a strong personality just disintegrate before your eyes when the final limit of tolerance has been reached. Once we get Mrs. Hathaway out of pain for a little while, she bounces right back, a cheerful and very charming lady, but I don't think she has much reserve left. In fact, she looks us in the eye and tells us point-blank that she can't take very much more of it, and I don't see why she should have to go on with it if a cordotomy can help.

I was worried about narcotic addiction in regard to this woman, and got into an interesting discussion with Dr. Tuckerman and Milt Musser about it. Tuckerman pointed out that there was a curious difference between pain-addicts and pleasure-addicts. When you have an individual who has pain and becomes addicted to the use of morphine for relief, his requirement for morphine may increase tremendously—he may need a grain or a grain and a half at a time to control the pain and become a confirmed pain-addict—but in cases where the pain is removed, either by cordotomy, which relieves the pain, or by removing whatever lesion is causing the pain, these people (according to Tuckerman) almost invariably stop the morphine completely and without any trouble. They simply stop taking it and suffer no withdrawal symptoms whatever.

On the other hand, the pleasure-addicts who take narcotics for the kicks they get out of them go into the most terrific physiological withdrawal symptoms when their stuff is withdrawn. Time apparently isn't a factor in this, because these people, the pain-addicts, sometimes will be carried for months and months on morphine and still have no withdrawal trouble nor any inclination to stay on the stuff when the pain is relieved. It makes you wonder exactly what addiction is and what part is psychogenic and what part is actually physiological. Certainly Mrs. Blomberg went off opiates after her pain was relieved by her cordotomy, and that was all there was to it; she didn't have any withdrawal problem.

[*Post hoc:* I know that seemed true at the time, but I wonder about it now. She didn't have any of the *psychological* dithers of narcotics withdrawal perhaps, but maybe a lot of her nausea and vomiting and diarrhea was a direct physiological response to withdrawal.]

To get back to Tuesday morning: We made rounds with Dr. Smithers. We got back the new liver function tests on little Diane Renton and found that there was no significant change since the eleventh of August—her liver function was still lousy. She still has the jaundice, and although she seems to be getting along all right and seems to feel better, her liver disease, whatever it is, has not improved a bit. Smithers says it isn't going to either, that it's just going to get worse until she goes the way the Barnes boy went, only maybe less swiftly and dramatically.

Looking at this girl, it seems incredible that she is really on her way out, but I admit that the prospects seem gloomy. She's been on absolute bed rest here for seventeen days now. If her trouble were just a recurrence of a chronic hepatitis, you would expect to see *some* reversal of this thing by now. If it's cirrhosis and scarring of her liver that's doing it, then she's going to be on the brink of complete liver failure for as long as she can limp along that way. Then the next time she gets an infection or anything else to knock her resistance down and put a strain on her liver, she's going to be dead, just like that. Probably we're going to send her home, because there's nothing we can do here at this point that can't be done just as well at home, but it's going to be awfully hard to explain to her mother how the child can be so severely and critically ill and not look it. It's hard for me to believe.

Oh, yes . . . little Sharon Bibble, Andy Case's four-year-old leukemic girl, has gone along home, for the time being. Case stuffed her like a sausage with packed red cells and cortisone and sent her along. Such a solemn child! I don't think she smiled once all the time she was here, even though she seemed to like me. I asked Case how long he thought it would be before she was back, and he shrugged and said, "One month, two, six . . . who knows?" and then gave me that tight little ironic smile. "No doctor is going to decide, my friend. She's God's little girl now; He'll do the deciding."

After rounds with Smithers we went over to his office in the clinic to do proctoscopies with him; he has a flock of them scheduled every Tuesday morning. This is one of these ludicrous situations we run into every now and then: most of the people in for proctos have been referred by other clinic doctors and have never even met Smithers before. The proctoscopy is the most utterly undignified of all physical examinations, barring none. The object is to examine the lower twelve inches of the bowel for bleeding sites, ulcerations, polyps or cancer by means of a long metal tube containing a light, which is inserted in the rectum and then threaded up to the hilt. The patient stands at the end of an L-shaped table and bends over it, puts his arms down, removes his trousers (the ladies simply hike up their skirts), and a nurse drapes them with a sheet with a six-inch hole in it centered like a target. Then the doctor steps on a foot pedal and the table tilts forward so that the patient's head drops down with his legs pointing straight out and his anus pointing upward. The position alone is uncomfortable, and people hate it. But there's an aspect of low comedy, too. These people come into the office and Dr. Smithers says, "Hello, there, glad to meet you," and without further preamble tips the table down and proceeds to thread a twelve-inch rod up their rectums. Then after they are all over with it, sweating and panting and smarting, too, they stand up and Dr. Smithers says, "Well, splendid, we'll send a report to your doctor today," and the patient almost invariably says, "Thank you, Doctor, glad to have met you," and goes out.

Anyway, today the script was a little different since we were to accompany Dr. Smithers. The first patient was a crusty little old lady who was draped and ready for the tilt when Smithers trooped into the examining room with Milt Musser and me on his heels. This old girl looked us over and said, "Well, what's the parade here, anyway?" So Smithers said, "Oh, these doctors are rectal specialists who are going to help me," with a perfectly straight face. This she accepted, warily, so Smithers put on a glove and did a digital rectal exam first and then turned to me and said, "Now, Doctor, I'd like you to give me your opinion of the sphincter tone there and feel that stricture we find up about two and a half inches." So I put on a rectal glove and rendered my "opinion," namely, that I agreed that it was there, and then Dr. Musser rendered his opinion, too.

Thus we all three finessed a rectal examination on the lady, and then Smithers said, "Now, Mrs. Gotz [or whatever her name was], I'm going to dilate your rectum again for a moment," and he nodded to Milt. So Mrs. Gotz thought Dr. Smithers was inserting the proctoscope, but he wasn't because Milt was, and all of us got a look at the inside of her bowel. A small polyp was sitting there six inches in. With successive patients each of us got to do a procto, and the patients all went away flushed with the knowledge that not one but three rectal specialists were interested in their problems.

The proctos took until 10:30; then we met Dr. Peterson for coffee and discussed a couple of patients. After that I made rounds on some of my other patients. The service is down remarkably now, only about twenty-two patients, which is a number that I can keep track of with some degree of facility, and until Tuesday afternoon I didn't really have any sick ones.

Then a patient came in and gave me a little lesson on how things can go sour in a hurry. This gentleman, Mr. Siding, was in the late stages of hypertensive disease, with both his heart and his kidneys already pounded to a pulp by his long-standing high blood pressure. He was in frank kidney failure and had been for some time, with a severe anemia as a result. Dr. Van Wert saw him on admission and pointed out that there were only two things to do for the man, who was about fifty-eight years old: first, treat the anemia so that we had some hope of treating the high blood pressure; and, second, try to knock his blood pressure down before his kidney function went out altogether. His kidney function tests were dreadful—he was in severe uremia—but at least he wasn't in heart failure and he didn't look too bad, so Van Wert ordered some saline intravenously to be followed by a whole blood transfusion to bring up his hemoglobin, and then went home to dinner.

I ordered the unit of blood to be given pretty fast, thinking the sooner the better for the poor man, and then, when about a third of a pint had gone into him, the man suddenly went into heart failure. I mean the bottom dropped out: all of a sudden his heart was fluttering at 120 per minute and he was gasping for air and his lungs were filling up with fluid and he was in real trouble. I tried to organize in my mind the steps you are supposed to take when this kind of thing happens: give oxygen, morphine, get tourniquets on the legs and arms to reduce the load on the heart, give Aminophyllin to help clear fluid from the lungs and open up the air passages. But I'd heard Van Wert say that the man had old bronchial obstructive disease and so no oxygen because it might depress his respirations, and I kept thinking of old Jerry Dykeman and the morphine, so I just put tourniquets on and gave the man Aminophyllin, and he just steadily got worse. I didn't even discontinue the unit of blood; I didn't recognize that it was the blood going in too fast that had dumped him into heart failure in the first place.

Well, I fiddled around, with the nurse who was there getting all excited about how bad he was looking, and listened to his chest and tried to look as if I knew what I was doing, and the man was turning gray and gasping for air, so I finally told the nurse to call Milt. He came up and took one look and said, "Oh, for Christ's sake!" and the first thing he did was to stop the blood from running in, and the second thing was to order a sixth-grain of morphine, and the third thing was to slap an oxygen mask over the man's face, and then he said, "What are you trying to do, kill this guy?" and stomped down the hall to call Van Wert.

All this happened fast—maybe twenty minutes from the time the failure started until Milt arrived. I didn't know heart failure could move that fast; I guess the man was just on the brink of failure, and the extra load of the whole blood going in too fast was all it took. Randy Brock smelled trouble and turned up on the floor and seemed to think my predicament was somehow amusing. Milt was just four-plus disgusted. "At least you gave him some Aminophyllin," he said, "which is certainly one of the first three things to think of. But the morphine should have been first before anything."

I told him I'd thought of morphine but I was afraid of it; we'd thought old Jerry Dykeman had been in heart failure and we'd given him morphine and he'd just stopped breathing altogether. And Randy, who was listening, said, "Yes, but old Jerry *wasn't* in heart failure," and I said, "Yes, I know, but we thought he was," and they both agreed that therein lay the rub. Pete and I had misdiagnosed old Jerry from the start, whereas with this guy there wasn't too much doubt about the diagnosis.

Well, anyway, by the time Van Wert arrived a half-hour later the man's breathing was better and he was beginning to rally, plenty sick but doing better than he was. Van Wert took one look at him and ordered more morphine, then wrote for another sixth-grain to be given in two hours and another sixth four hours later. He listened to my sad tale and shook his head and said, "When a patient in this shape goes into heart failure, Aminophyllin is a stick in the wind. There's only one weapon we have against heart failure in this man, and that is morphine sulphate; you have to give him enough morphine so that he's effectively treated with it, and if it stops his breathing, you get a Bennett valve and you breathe for him until he either dies or rallies, because he will surely die without the morphine."

So by midnight we were able to take the tourniquets off the man's legs and much to my amazement he survived the night; he looked lousy, but he was still with us. And I, by God, won't mistreat another case of congestive heart failure. I learned for one thing that you don't give blood rapidly to a patient who is in danger of heart failure, and that when you face a situation like this there are certain things you do first, quickly, and worry about the consequences later, if you don't want to be worrying over a dead patient.

Today—Wednesday—Van Wert ordered more blood for Mr. Siding. We gave it extremely slowly, and when I went off duty at 5:00 he had about half of it into him and was doing all right. So perhaps we're out of the woods with him for a while. Van Wert says that with this man every day we can gain is a great achievement, considering his over-all condition. Who knows, we might have a chance to bail him out for a couple more years of useful life if we work at it.

Up on the fourth floor I was amazed to find that the little girl who came in Saturday night with the "sore shoulder" was still there, still with no sign of any disease. She's a cute little kiddie, a blond, blue-eyed girl with pink cheeks, cheerful and friendly as can be. I got a little more inside dope on her. It seems that when the parents brought her in Saturday night they were both drunk. They dumped her here, and until Tuesday evening they hadn't even called the hospital to see how she was, much less come to see her. Then late Tuesday night they called and wanted to bring her home right then. The nurse had told them they'd have to talk to Dr. Isaacs to see if the child could be released. So the father said he would call Dr. Isaacs, and that was the last that was heard of it. Apparently he didn't call Ike, and the girl still hasn't gone home. Seems to me this is just criminal; if she weren't such a cute little kid, if she were a horrible mess with a big rachitic skull and bulbous eyes or something, you could maybe at least *understand* parents doing something like this, right or wrong, but she's just a sweet two-year-old little girl. She's having a glorious time here, everybody on the floor babies her, but it's kind of a revolting way for parents to treat a child, it seems to me. At first I was disgusted with Isaacs for admitting her to the hospital at all, but maybe old Ike was just being kindhearted to the kid. They say the worst of parents are better than the best of institutions, but you sure wonder sometimes.

Tuckerman and Gillies didn't have any patients in, so we didn't have teaching rounds this morning. Nothing went on until 1:30 when I was called to see Mr. Perez on Second, who was having one of his "attacks." This is a gentleman who flew up from Mexico yesterday for diagnosis of his episodes of very rapid heartbeat that make him break out in a sweat and leave him with pounding headaches afterward. He said these attacks last for a half-hour or so, and he's been having them two or three times a week, with increasing frequency. He's also been having some heart pain with them recently. He's a thirty-three-year-old man, very obese, and a real pill. He sits there feeling sorry for himself and looking suspiciously at everyone who goes by. He wasn't having any trouble when I admitted him, but I'd ordered that if he had an attack they should get an emergency EKG on him while it was going on, and call me.

So now I hurried upstairs. The attack was over before they could get the EKG, but the nurse said his heart rate had been over 200 per minute while it lasted, and that his blood pressure had been way up to 170 at the same time.

That should have been a tip-off, but the significance didn't dawn on me until Milt Musser suggested that an active adrenal gland tumor could account for attacks like these. I should have thought of it; this is one of these rare and exotic diseases you learn about in detail in medical school and then never see. I didn't even think of it, so I may have missed my chance to make a real diagnostic coup. We scheduled a histamine test tomorrow morning; if that kicks off an attack right on cue, it will clinch the diagnosis.

Very slow the rest of the day. I keep wondering when the boom is going to fall; this service has been pretty quiet for almost two weeks now, which probably means that all hell is going to break loose. Tuckerman and Gillies are both back from vacation; I suppose they will start hauling them in off the streets any day. Alec Ivy, on the other medical service, has been working like crazy. He had eight admissions on Monday, seven of them patients of Dr. Isaacs.

Ike is one of the old-time GPs in the city with such a mammoth practice that he has four offices and hires two bright young boys to help him run it. The clinic doctors don't like him a bit, partly because he's just a crafty old GP and not a specialist, and partly because he's such a slob, with a stinky old cigar in his mouth all the time (they say they have to restrain him from wandering into the operating room with that cigar). He's an altogether too successful Jew to suit their fancy, and he's got too damned many patients who think he's God and won't give the clinic doctors a tumble. I hear the clinic puts the heat on the hospital periodically to rescind Ike's privileges, and some of his practices could surely be criticized from the medical viewpoint, but the hospital leaves him alone because he brings in so much business. The residents and interns love him because he lets them do his surgery and deliver his OBs and set his patients' fractures and all that.

Anyway, there's a running joke that every now and then Ike goes

berserk and tries to admit the entire city to Graystone Memorial
Hospital by quadrants; last Monday he was chiseling away at Desertview Heights, and Alec was stuck.

Schwartz and his family are making plans to go up to the mountains with us this coming weekend for a little fishing and camping.
Schwartz and I are both off. I'm getting a little better acquainted
with him now and like him a little better than I did. He seems to be
a good-natured guy, in spite of his beefing. He still complains about
everything in sight, and I hear he doesn't knock himself out to work
very hard. But at least with him I don't have to worry about cheap
little tricks the way I do with Alec. I guess Schwartz really wants to
be a surgeon, which puts him at the other end of the pole from me
as far as medicine is concerned, but we might get to like each other,
who knows?

[*Post hoc:* As a matter of fact, Schwartz and I became close
friends during the latter part of internship and later when he
stayed on for surgical residency at Graystone while I went into
practice. We became hunting and fishing partners and had many
good days together. Later he became Slater's Fellow in surgery
(fourth year of residency) and then went East for special training in
pediatric surgery. Today he is establishing himself as one of the leading pediatric surgeons on the West Coast.]

I'm a little more happy about Milt Musser's coverage and help as
my resident as we go along. He has really been helping on some of
the cases, and functioning most times almost as well as Pete did,
although I don't like him as well. But, God, he sure is a vague
individual, one of these guys with this infuriating habit of sitting
and looking at you while you are telling him something and simply not hearing you. Sometimes he just stands up and walks away
while you're still talking; other times he'll say, "Yeah, sure," and go
right on writing or whatever he's doing at the moment, and when
you get through telling him something that's critically important,
he'll start off talking about something completely different.

On the other hand, sometimes Milt makes the effort to pay attention and tries to be helpful, and on those occasions he's splendid.
He is sharp as can be, and he can teach, when he feels like it. This
afternoon we had a little time, so we sat down in the pharmacy and
had a Coke, and he went through a brief but very good review of

the things one should always look for in screening an EKG tracing. I've read books and heard a dozen doctors try to teach me how to read EKGs, and it has never made any sense to me before. And here, in fifteen minutes, it all began to be clear for the first time. He said, "Forget all the fancy details and just memorize these few things to always look for, and you'll be able to tell what you have to know right then from any EKG. Then go back and learn the fancy details, or just get an expert to give you a detailed reading. You'll still be able to use the EKG effectively as a diagnostic and therapeutic weapon." It made sense, and I wondered why some of these medical school whiz-kids never put it that way. And why Milt couldn't break down and teach like that a little more often.

I've also gotten better acquainted with Lou Franklin these last couple of weeks. I have the impression that he likes me and thinks I've been doing a pretty good job on his patients. He's been more friendly than at first, takes more time to talk about patients, and has started to ask my opinion occasionally, or throw out little diagnostic questions just to see what I will say. I used to think he was kind of a sloppy physician; he never wanted to say anything definite about anything and you got the impression he didn't give a damn whether the patients lived or died. I don't think this is true now; he just has a peculiar attitude of diffidence that you have to get used to.

Harry Smithers is friendly, too. I've pulled some awful boners with patients of his, and I don't know why he seems to like me. He's one of these moody, sit-and-think-about-it types, and he'll go ahead and do things without giving the intern any indication of why he's doing them unless the intern asks him. I get the feeling that he doesn't really want to share the treatment of the patient with the intern, or with anyone else in particular. On the other hand, he will ask my opinion of things. He has a cute habit of asking the intern an obviously trick question all of a sudden, and then sitting back and grinning at him while he tries to struggle up with an answer. But this I can put up with because he isn't malicious the way Dr. Van Wert or Dr. Kidder can be, and I think the guy is teaching me something.

Of all the docs in the clinic, probably Orville Peterson is the sweetest guy of them all. He isn't so old—maybe forty-five or fifty— but he is a gentleman of the old school, with a courtesy and diplomacy that seem natural and not put on. He has the smoothest way with patients that I've ever seen, but he also approaches the interns with the attitude of a kindly and interested teacher.

I've noticed an interesting thing: the older docs in the clinic maintain a distinct distance between themselves and the house staff. Tuckerman and Peterson and Fuller invariably address me as "Dr. ————," and there is a certain aloofness that the younger men don't have. Dr. Fuller has warmed up a little bit recently; he jokes with me now and we get along pretty well. And this morning Tuckerman opened up again, over coffee in the cafeteria, and started talking about his fishing experiences, and we had a good chat. But this little barrier of names remains. With Smithers and Franklin and most of the younger men we have been encouraged to put things on a first-name basis, and there is more of a feeling of equality and maybe even camaraderie there.

Dr. Fred Kidder is the puzzler of the group, as far as I'm concerned. I don't know whether I like Fred or not. He uses my first name and I call him Fred and we get along well enough, but he uses sarcasm both for criticism and humor and you seldom know whether he's pleased with what you're doing or not. He will never criticize openly; instead, he will work in a sort of underhanded jab, loaded with sarcasm, and then laugh it off as though he's (ha, ha) really joking. Like this business with Jerry Dykeman; he said, "Jesus Christ, boys, we're going to have to breathe for old Jerry," and then treated us like simpletons, handed us a solid hour of sarcastic remarks while we ran the Bennett valve. We'd have felt better if he'd reamed us up one side and down the other, but not Fred.

I've heard that he is a brilliant clinician, some say the most brilliant man in the clinic, where there are quite a few sharp boys to be found. He's short and dark and wiry, with a nasal voice and a kind of a sly weasel face. Of all the men in the clinic I think he's the one I would go to last and trust the least, even if it meant picking an inferior doctor. When I get onto his service next spring I have a feeling it's going to be a matter of checking every single detail right down the line with Fred Kidder before we do anything. As it is, no matter how carefully and thoroughly you have managed a patient's care, Fred will always—repeat, *always*—find something else you should have done. As far as I can recall, he's never missed once in this respect. Hell of it is, the things he lights on are almost always things you should have thought of yourself already and haven't. This bugs Milt Musser more than me; he will get through a session in which Fred in five minutes has just nailed him to the cross by picking up six significant omissions in a patient's work-up, with Milt looking green and saying, "Well, I guess you're right, Fred; I'll do that right away, Fred," and then when Fred leaves, Milt will shake his head and say to me, "I swear, it's just uncanny," and stomp off down the hall.

[*Post hoc:* For what it is worth, after knowing Fred Kidder for years now, and dealing with him repeatedly on both a professional and social level, I find these journal observations still express my feelings about him perfectly. But I think I understand the reason now better than I did then. Fred Kidder is one of these compulsive perfectionists you run across in medicine from time to time, and a brilliant and opinionated perfectionist at that. And as such, he's practically intolerable to be around. I don't like him for beans, and neither do half his clinic associates; he delights in making them feel inferior. But when I have a patient with a rough chest problem, I'll send him to Fred every time rather than to any other chest man in the region. He's insufferable, but he's also one of the five top men in his field in the country.]

Well, I've digressed, but I've been wanting to get down something about these men I see every day. We sort of live in each other's hip pockets around here; the personal and professional relationship with these doctors is often very close and very intense, and, like them or not, you can't just walk away and leave them. I will say that not one of the staff men I've worked with so far has let his personal liking or disliking for me color his treatment of me as an intern, as far as I can see: no vindictiveness, no feuds, no dirty infighting. You get a strong feeling that they just naturally regard this as a team project and it never even enters their minds to start digging at a team member who is a little slow and dense.

In general, I'm feeling 100 percent more at ease now, more confident of myself in what I'm doing. The only time I really shrink from seeing new patients now is when I'm very tired, or when it's a quarter of five and I'm hoping to get off duty. Of course, there are

ups and downs; periodically I feel awfully damned stupid and awfully insecure, particularly when I've missed some perfectly obvious
diagnosis, or when I have gotten some poor patient into the soup. I
get especially depressed when these are things I could have avoided
if I'd just thought a little faster. I seem to go in cycles, from periods
when I get sloppy and slovenly in the way I work up patients and
follow them up to the opposite extreme, really going whole-hog,
keeping tight control of rounds, writing orders and seeing patients
in close follow-up and patting their tummies and doing this and
that. Every now and then when I get a really good medical work-up
done it's discouraging when somebody comes along and points out
some obvious things that I've missed. God only knows what I miss
when I'm in a hurry or sloppy.

In general I feel a little more sense of being a part of an organization now; I am actually fulfilling a need. The medical men are
beginning to develop some confidence and letting me do more, and I
can tell pretty well which orders I can just go ahead and write and
which I'd better check with the attending doctor first. And with
most of the men except Fred Kidder and perhaps Ted Van Wert I
feel pretty much at ease now.

Saturday, August 27

Two things of interest on Thursday and Friday of this week. Mr.
Siding is one. He continued to limp along with his high blood
pressure and his kidney failure no better, thanks to the heart failure
episode, but no worse. Then sometime Thursday evening Mr. Siding began losing his wits. The nurses called and said he was tearing
up his oxygen tent; wasn't there something I could do? This is the
sort of call that's always a great joy to receive because there is
seldom anything very effective that you *can* do, and with Mr. Siding
I was afraid even to try much. Most of the sedatives offer one
potential danger or another. Finally, I ordered paraldehyde to be
given rectally. This is not a very pleasant medicine to use because it
stinks up the room something fierce, but Mr. Siding was sedated
pretty well with it. We kept him on fluids, and much to everyone's
surprise he survived Thursday and Friday and through Saturday
morning, going along without much difficulty. But he was hard to

handle, pulling out his IVs and ripping up the sheets. There isn't much hope for Mr. Siding; if anything, we're amazed that he has hung on as long as he has, but by rounds time today he was still pooping along.

The other patient of interest on Friday was a forty-five-year-old lady who came in with congestive heart failure. This poor soul had rheumatic fever when she was eleven years old, with heart valve damage. No symptoms or recurrence of the rheumatic fever until she started getting into heart failure five years ago because of the scarred, stenotic valves. Today she was in trouble, had to sit bolt upright in order to breathe, and her legs were swollen up like balloons from the edema fluid. She looked like the Wicked Witch of the West, but turned out to be a very pleasant lady. Very meek and mild as I took her history; when I asked one of the routine questions, whether she'd ever blacked out or passed out on any occasion, she gave me a sheepish grin and said, "Well, only at fraternity parties in college." Started treating her heart failure, mostly trying to get the fluid out of her legs, but she was still looking about the same by this morning, and Milt was worrying that maybe she had kidney failure and couldn't pass enough urine to get the water off. This case I sort of left dangling when I went off duty this morning at 10:00 for the weekend. We are heading off for the mountains with the Schwartzes, and with two comparatively light weeks behind me I may be able to do something besides sleep. Certainly not as beat out as on my last off-duty weekend, at any rate.

Tuesday, August 30

Had a good and thoroughly pleasant weekend. We took off for the mountains around noon, with Floyd and Marilyn Schwartz and their son Karl following behind in their car. Glorious weather, bright blue skies, fine open pine forest, some lovely streams. We found a good campground, fooled around, fished a little. Sunday morning we walked up to one of the higher lakes near our campground and I caught a nice, fat, fourteen-inch golden trout; then nothing. We could see them follow the flies, but they wouldn't strike.

Did have a better chance to get acquainted with Marilyn, who is pregnant again, and to do something with Floyd away from the hospital. This was our first real outing since we came to this country two months ago, certainly the first where I've had a chance to do any fishing.

Back to work Monday at 8:00 A.M. Things started off with a bang. Pete Carey was late for rounds because his train back to the city with his new wife was late. Milt Musser and I made rounds with Dr. Fuller, then met Pete coming in and went down and had coffee with him and briefed him on the new patients. This is really a pretty terrific load to dump on somebody who is just back from a two-week honeymoon; to all intents and purposes Pete is just walking into a brand-new hospital service, and has to learn thirty-five new patients. There were only one or two left that were here when he left two weeks ago; as Milt put it, "We either kill them or we cure them around here," and nobody laughed.

Then the new admissions started to roll in; we had a total of ten medical admissions by midnight. A couple of these patients had been pretty well worked up in the clinic, but most of them were new patients and they flooded in thick and fast all afternoon and evening, and I was just running to keep up.

On rounds I learned that Mr. Siding had survived until 4:30 A.M. on Monday and then quietly died. A post was done on him, and among other things he had kidneys shrunken down to the size of acorns, and a pericarditis. Certainly the cause of death was no mystery to anyone. The man died in the end stages of a malignant hypertension with both heart and kidney failure. Probably the hypertension was the primary disease and the others were secondary to it. At any rate, nobody was too surprised that we failed to cure Mr. Siding. Even starting earlier in the game you don't *cure* this disease; Hattie Stevens will sooner or later be another Mr. Siding if she doesn't get hit by a truck or something first. We're hoping that by controlling her blood pressure at this stage we can put off the reckoning a while and give her a few more years of comfortable and fruitful life.

The lady with the rheumatic heart disease and heart failure was very bad Monday morning. She had had a kidney shutdown, so the fluid that's choking her to death can't be gotten off very well. On rounds she looked pale, and was running a fever, sweating, just looking bad. By noontime we didn't think she'd survive until night. She might have SBE (subacute bacterial endocarditis, a bacterial infection of the inner lining of the heart valves). More likely, though, she will just go ahead and die in heart failure if it can't be turned. Later in the afternoon we put her in an oxygen tent, and she seemed to straighten out pretty well for the moment. Fuller was not very cheerful about it; he's had lots and lots of experience with this sort of thing, and after he saw her on rounds he just shook his head and said, "Well, boys, this is a matter of hours, not days." Still we keep our fingers crossed in hopes we can bail her out this time, and have a chance for establishing a little longer-term control. Trouble is, this looks like the kind of heart failure that may be awfully hard to bail her out of.

Started off the evening with seven things hammering on me at once. There was a call to see a man in the Emergency Room at 5:30 P.M., a taxi driver who had been in an auto wreck. He had a lacerated hand and took a blow to the chest from the steering wheel. Took me an hour to evaluate what was going on and what wasn't. I decided I needed chest and rib X-rays to rule out fractures there. The X-ray technician was all poised to go home and was pissed off that I made her stay, so she took a set of rib X-rays that God himself couldn't have read. You couldn't see a damned thing on them. I was so mad I almost made her stay and take another set, but finally decided, what the hell, life was too short. I don't know what the radiologists will think when they see those rib films in the morning—I hope they don't think *I* took them. I've been getting some pretty good films of extremities when I've been taking them.

Anyway, I patched the man's hand up and sent him home. In the middle of that I got a call that there was a little eight-year-old boy being admitted on Fifth in diabetic coma. He was Dr. Stern's patient, and Stern happened to be in the house, so he and Carey were right on the spot. This little boy had gone into coma in the morning. Never known to be diabetic before, but he had been eating like a hog, drinking water like mad and urinating almost continuously for two weeks prior to this, and had lost ten pounds in the course of this time. Looked like a severe juvenile-type diabetic. I'm sorry that I won't be following him—he's on Alec's service—because a juvenile diabetic in coma is one of the true crash medical emergencies. If these kids reach a certain depth of acidosis, they will just plain go ahead and die then and there, no matter what you do.

This lad was beginning to look better about 11:00 P.M., after three hours of touch-and-go, but Pete had to be with him—right there and no place else—all night long. Which meant that he couldn't give me any help with the other patients who were turning up in a steady stream, and also meant that I couldn't find time to look in and follow what was happening with the diabetic kid. But I guess I'll see plenty of these when I'm on the other medical service next spring.

On top of this there was a boy with a minor fracture of his foot. I took him up to the OR and put a cast on it. Then there were another six or seven patients who had come in that I hadn't seen yet, so I was running up, down and crosswise trying to get my new admissions settled for the night. About 11:00 Pete and I took ten minutes' break to have a bite to eat. I still had four patients to work up. Pete told me that the diabetic boy was at least responding from his coma now, and Stern had gone home, but it looked like an all-night stand for him. I said, "Well, all I'm going to do is kill somebody if I keep rolling much longer. Can't I let some of these work-ups go until morning?" And he said, sure, go to bed, maybe he could at least get a note in a chart or two since he had to be around anyway. So I closed up shop and went down to quarters, feeling guilty as hell and depressed, too.

In the sack by midnight, out at 1:45 A.M. to see somebody in the Emergency Room who had dropped a keg of beer on his toe. Great. No fracture, not even much pain, but it just couldn't wait until morning to be seen. Just as I was writing up the Emergency Room note, Miss Foulkes, the night supervisor, came by and said a patient of Dr. John's who had had a coronary had started up a fast pulse rate—almost 180 per minute. I thought, Oh, my God, not Mrs. Woodruff again. It wasn't, but it might as well have been: same problem, except that the EKG was easier to read and I was pretty sure that digitalis was the answer this time. I called Pete just to let him know the patient was in trouble and he said go ahead and start the digitalis. She converted to a normal rhythm and a rate of 76 per minute right on the spot with the first dose.

Got back to bed again at 3:00 A.M.; at 5:30 I got the happy news that Mrs. Hammerman was back in again—comatose, not responding, but breathing pretty well. By this time I was ready to tell them to put her in bed and take her pulse and blood pressure every half-hour and call me if she came to, and just not go up to see the old bitch. She's a woman with hypertension who periodically drinks herself into a stupor and has to be brought in to be nursed along until she wakes up. I decided that Mrs. Hammerman could just drop dead as far as I was concerned, and I stuck to my guns for a while, but after blinking at the ceiling for a half-hour and getting myself so mad I couldn't sleep, I tossed in the towel and went up to see the woman. I remembered quite clearly that the last time she came in like this she was fine while she was sleeping or comatose, but as soon as she woke up she couldn't breathe and she wouldn't lie still and started screaming and gasping and having a horrible time. So this time I took pains not to rouse her, just did a quick physical examination on this inert, snoring lump in the bed and left orders to let me know if she came to.

Got back to bed again at 6:15 A.M. Up at 7:00 to go down to Stern's office at the clinic for a glucose tolerance test, part of a study on a new insulin that he has roped the interns into. It was an intravenous sugar injection followed by three or four blood samples, and with the great big hoses I have for veins the girl couldn't seem to hit them without two or three stabs each time. So it took three times longer than planned, and the test wasn't done until ten minutes after the cafeteria closed for breakfast, and there wasn't any food left. So my breakfast consisted of 25 grams of IV glucose and a large old cup of coffee.

Rounds with Smithers were almost over when I finally caught up, but I got there in time to see the last patient or two. On the floors I had a spinal tap to do and a bunch of other scut work which kept me busy until lunchtime.

I was glad that admissions today were slow so I could see a few of the other patients. A day like yesterday is really rough; you feel like you're in a squirrel cage, and then you don't remember anything about anybody you saw.

Wednesday, August 31

A fairly quiet day today after a busy Monday and Tuesday. Made rounds with Tuckerman and Gillies on some of the more recent patients of theirs who have come in, including a discussion of a woman who had a brain hemorrhage and is now being considered for surgery. The neurosurgeon wants to go into the neck and clamp off the common carotid artery on the side of the hemorrhage. Seems a little like cutting off the leg at the hip to get rid of a bunion, but Tuckerman says that otherwise this woman is going to have another hemorrhage sure as snowflakes melt and you have a damned poor choice. She can either die in her bed for sure or die on the operating table maybe. It's the maybe *not* part you have to gamble on.

Finished off the last call night on the service with about two hours' sleep, not because anything was happening, but because of six or seven sedation calls that the night supervisor, Miss Wood, allowed the floor nurses to buzz me about. It seems like there's about one night a month that this babe just tosses in the sponge and lets every damned thing imaginable come through. Milt Musser claims that it's just that time of month for Miss Wood. I don't know; all I know is that I had a pill call from somebody every hour on the hour all night long.

At 6:00 in the morning they called me to see one of the nurses' aides who apparently had had a *grand mal* seizure in the elevator and sliced her eyebrow open on the rail as she fell. Great big fat slob of a woman who had blood all over everything—face, dress, elevator, the works. All from just a small laceration, too. I had to practically physically restrain her from going on down to work. Apparently she was afraid the word would get out that she was epileptic and had had a seizure. I don't know if she was out of control with her Dilantin or what, but she was thoroughly confused, wanted to go on down to hand out breakfast trays on Second with this blood-spattered white dress on.

Got back to my room about 6:45, too late to go back to bed and too early to get up. Felt I hadn't slept all night because of the calls; each one would make me sore, and I'd lie awake for half an hour just trying to get back to sleep again with all that adrenalin pounding through my system. Finally gave up and went over for breakfast before going up to the OB floor.

It's hard to believe this medical service is over, and now I'll only catch medical patients when I'm on duty nights or weekends covering for Alec. OB will be a complete and abrupt change, which seems peculiar to contemplate; seems like I've been on this medical service for about five years now, and it will go right on rolling when I change because there's no beginning to it and no end.

II

Obstetrics and Gynecology

The obstetrical service at Graystone Memorial Hospital was a bad service for interns at the time of my training there. I had expected it to be, and I can see from the journal for that period that it was—perhaps the worst service of my internship year.

I can understand better now than I could then just *why* it was such a bad service, but that, obviously, did not help much at the time.

In obstetrics, as in any other area of medicine, you learn by doing. There are textbooks to read, of course, and lectures in medical school, and charts and demonstrations with models and dummies, even the student's clinical observation on the labor floors, but in the end a doctor learns to deliver babies by delivering babies. He learns to deal with the crises and emergencies of the labor and delivery room, which can arise with such appalling swiftness, by facing them under the gun and dealing with them then and there. There is no other way to learn.

In the charity hospitals, where the patients have no private physician and pay no hospital fees, it is easy. These "house patients" become the responsibility of the interns and residents, with experienced obstetricians looking over their shoulders. But Graystone had no charity beds in those days.

In the time when general anesthesia was used for deliveries, with the patient put to sleep at the critical moment and her husband hustled away to a waiting room somewhere, it was also easy. Then even the most private of private patients could be delivered by the intern, with the private doctor in attendance, and with no one the

116

wiser but the intern. But general anesthesia had its flaws: it produced sleepy babies as well as sleepy mothers. Good obstetricians were embracing the saddle block and the caudal and other "wide-awake" anesthesias; "natural childbirth" was in vogue, and husbands were welcomed into the delivery rooms. Patients could no longer be fooled about who was doing what. Not only was the intern cheated of his vital training; the obstetrician learned to enjoy the spotlight, introducing an element of carnival showmanship into the white hospital rooms with the glaring overhead lights. Once it had been enough that he emerge bloody but unbowed with a good mother and a good baby. Now, at last, he could dramatize, detail by enthralling detail, exactly *how* he managed this.

The mothers loved it. The obstetricians loved it. And if the interns hated it, that was too bad.

Of course, there is a difference between obstetrical practice and any other field of medicine. There always has been. There is no need to wander here into the psychiatric crossfire regarding the relation between a pregnant woman and her doctor. Suffice it to say that the doctor-patient relationship here is indeed different from all others—more sharply defined, more deeply important to patient *and* doctor, more inviolable, than any other. There was no place for an outsider in the delivery room, and the intern at Graystone was an outsider.

But he had to learn, all the same, and so he learned—one way or another. As these pages show so clearly.

THE JOURNAL, SEPTEMBER

Thursday, September 1

One thing is sure, there is no fanfare about changing services around this place. You'd think that everybody would go out and have a party—after all, each of us has one major service behind us now, and that must be some kind of a milestone. At the very least it would have been nice to go home and have an unbroken night's sleep in order to start off the new service fresh . . . bright eyes and twinkling smile and all that. But no such luck.

I found Alec Ivy and Luke Hamilton in the cafeteria munching rolls and looking sour, and I'd been up all night finishing off Medicine I and hardly felt like rushing up to greet the morning on the labor floor. Pretty soon Schwartz and Garvin, the resident on orthopedic surgery now, came hustling in for a cup of coffee before their first scrub, and we grunted at them and they grunted back at us, and that was the extent of *that* scintillating breakfast conversation. Alec said, "So you're on OB now, huh?" and I said, "It looks like it." He gave me his special you-poor-bastard grin and said, "Well, if you find out anything about how to deliver babies while you're up there, let me know. I hear you'll be lucky to learn anything at all."

So I finished my 29-cent special a little before 8:00 and then wandered up to the nurses' station on the labor floor on Seventh, and there was Miss Hardy, big as life, leafing through a *Time* magazine. She said, "What, are you up here now?" without any sign of enthusiasm, and I said, "I sure am. Put me to work." She said, "Great," and flipped a page, and then said, "Well, you might as well have a cup of coffee. There's nothing going on around here right now."

An hour later there was still nothing going on that I could see, and I couldn't even enjoy it. I hadn't sat around on my can for a straight hour on a weekday morning since I'd come into this place, and it just made me nervous.

About 9:00 Dr. Goodfellow walked in and gave me a hearty smile and a hearty handshake and said the other men on the service had asked him to give me the word about what would be expected of me on the OB service, so we walked down to the doctors' room and chewed the fat a while. Part of the word consisted of telling me how he wanted me to call him "Horace," and how everybody on the OB staff got along fine with everybody else on a first-name basis, and how the men expected the interns to toe the line and be on their toes, but how the men in turn felt that the intern should learn some obstetrics and have at least twenty or thirty deliveries during their month of service, and how the OB men were a generous and outgoing lot, but the doctor-patient relationship was a little different in obstetrics than in other areas of medicine, and the intern would really have to win the OB man's confidence if he expected to be given much to do, and so on and so on. . . .

This was all very smooth and man-to-man and confidential and sincere. The only thing was, I'd already heard from Pete about what a crowd of conceited, self-centered bastards these OB men were, and what a lousy intern service they ran, and how the intern could run his ass off doing their scut work for them, but when it came down to delivering babies, the OB men always seemed to feel that the intern hadn't "won their confidence" quite enough yet.

And as for Goodfellow, I'd already heard him using the same silky-smooth tone of voice to convince a patient that black was really white if you looked at it closely enough, and leaving the patient nodding and saying, "Yes . . . yes . . . black really *is* white, isn't it?" So I don't know. Pete says I'll be lucky to get ten deliveries during the whole month on OB and that I'll have to fight to get those. Goodfellow's little spiel sounded more promising than that, but somehow he didn't quite convince me.

At least I had a chance to look at the man for a few minutes. I've heard that Goodfellow and his partner Ben Boggs have between 60 and 80 percent of the deliveries in this hospital; if so, they should be able to determine whether an intern learns anything or not on this service. And I also gather that Goodfellow is the boss and Boggs the flunky in this particular partnership. Goodfellow certainly looks the part of the dignified, high-toned specialist: about fifty years old, pure white hair, handsome, gentlemanly, prosperous-looking, soft-spoken. I think it was Ted Van Wert who remarked one day that Goodfellow's patients thought he was God incarnate, and that old Horace wasn't so sure but what they were right. To me he seems a little *too* smooth; his face is a little too florid—three highballs every night before dinner, I bet, and stiff ones at that—and you have the feeling he'd never permit a dirty word to pass his lips no matter what he was thinking. Van Wert is a pompous ass, too, but at least he'll say "shit" once in a while if that's what he really means.

Talking to Goodfellow did give me a picture of the OB setup, quite different in many ways from Medicine I. For one thing, there's not much diagnosis involved. Most of the girls admitted on this service display a pretty obvious diagnosis. Most of them are also healthy as horses except for their term pregnancies. The intern's job is to be on hand during labors and to assist at deliveries, and to cover in a pinch until the OB man gets there. I will sleep in the doctors' room on the OB floor now on duty nights instead of down in the interns' quarters. Most of the patients are either waiting for delivery or already delivered, and according to Miss Hardy it's usually a matter of feast or famine. They have some 120 deliveries a month, but you can sit around all day with an empty floor, waiting for something to happen, and then admit eight patients in fifteen minutes, all trying to deliver at the same time. Technically, the service includes female surgery, too, but since the intern has to be on tap in the delivery room, one of the surgical interns scrubs on all major gynecological cases except Caesarean sections.

As for coverage, the schedule has me opposite Luke Hamilton now—he's on Medicine II—so he covers the OB floor on my off-duty nights and I cover his medical service when he's off. But OB is my first responsibility, so the medical resident on duty is supposed to cover the medical emergencies when I'm tied up in the delivery room.

In the midst of this briefing Miss Hardy stuck her head in the doctors' room door and told Dr. Goodfellow that a patient of his was in and would he please check her before he left. We went down to one of the labor rooms and talked to the woman. She was a primip* in very early labor, but he decided to keep her in the house. Later two more women came in, one for Goodfellow and one for Dr. Arnold Prince; both delivered during the afternoon, but by the time I left at 5:00 the primip still hadn't budged.

I hope when I get rested up I'll be able to give more detail about the physical setup on the labor floor, and the patients and doctors and procedures there. Right now I don't remember anything about these three except that they were there. I don't know whether this will be such a hot service or not; we'll see. At least things may not be in such an ungodly rush all the time. Pete says I'll have a lot of free time.

---

* Pronounced "prime-ip"; lazy and inaccurate medical slang used to denote a woman who is in her first labor. Technically, she is *primagravida* (first pregnancy) until she delivers, whereupon she becomes *primapara* (once-delivered). The term is significant because the obstetrician is always more nervous about a primip: he anticipates a longer, more difficult labor than usual, and the woman is "untried" in that she hasn't yet *proven* that she can have a normal uncomplicated delivery.

Friday, September 2

After a light first day I thought Friday and the weekend might be man-killers, but they turned out light enough so that I could keep up with both the OB activity and the medical call on Medicine II (Case's and Kidder's service). Remembering the fearful load during the first month, I was expecting the worst, I guess.

Partly, I think, it must be me: I seem to handle things now with less fuss, take care of more things by telephone when I'm tied up with something else, and get my work-ups done more quickly. And just as well, too; when a woman has finally decided (after fiddling around all night thinking about it) that the time has, by God, come to have her baby, you can't just rush downstairs to see a medical patient right then. You grab a telephone and tell some nurse on the medical floor how to stick her finger in the dike until you can get there.

But it sure would be fine to have some kind of crystal ball to tell when an emergency is really an emergency. Saturday evening I had three panic calls from the third floor to rush down and see some old man who was allegedly in heart failure and dying on the spot, and I was standing by with a girl who was doing her damnedest to have her baby on a cart in the hall before we could even get her into a delivery room, and the nurse on Third couldn't find Carey anywhere, and they just *had* to have an intern, and Schwartz was in surgery, and "Oh, Doctor, what are we going to do?" When I finally got down there, I found an old man who *had* been in heart failure two weeks before, but now was chiefly complaining that he hadn't had a bowel movement in two days.

The trouble is that another time, same situation, same story from the nurse, the old goat could have been stone-dead by the time I got there, and everybody would blame me for not believing the nurse and dropping everything to rush down. So how can you win?

Anyway, there were enough uncomplicated deliveries for me to see how the OB setup works here, and it doesn't look too cheering. From what I see so far, these OB men do their own deliveries, period. The intern is expected to do a perfunctory admission work-up when the patient comes in, and keep tabs on the progress of her labor, and I suppose it's always possible that he might pick up some unsuspected complication—an undiagnosed breech or some such thing—but otherwise the whole rigamarole seems a little superfluous. The attending men like to have the intern scrub in with them to assist at deliveries, but "assisting" so far seems to mean standing around watching how they deliver babies. Goodfellow insists that I will get some solo deliveries and also have a chance to apply forceps, repair episiotomies (the incision that is made just before the baby is born to prevent stretching and tearing of the vaginal outlet; after delivery it is surgically closed), do some curettements and so forth. Well, we'll see. I think I will start complaining to him daily if all this doesn't seem to be coming about pretty soon.

At least I met several of the OB men over the weekend. Dr. Arnold Prince was in and out several times, and so were Dr. Howard Bensen and several other men. Prince is one of the most popular of the OB men among the doctors, not an unmixed blessing, I guess, because they say he has so many doctors' wives on his OB list that he has trouble paying his office rent. Goodfellow wasn't around much, but his partner Boggs was, and Boggs I didn't like anything about.

This is a very odd team: it seemed to me that Boggs is about as coarse as Goodfellow is smooth, a sort of Basic Boor who knows it and tries to hide it but can't quite manage. I don't think I'd care to have him near my wife with a ten-foot pole. He's a short, stocky, hawk-nosed man with very broad cheekbones and sandy brown hair. Friday morning he delivered the primip who had come in on Thursday, and he was doing his damnedest to use the same slick delivery-room spiel that Goodfellow manages so smoothly, except that he didn't quite enunciate the words, saying "dese here" and "dose dere" and "Dis is da placenta." Outside the delivery room he seems to have a pretty sleazy, coarse attitude toward his patients, which he can't quite completely conceal in their presence. I guess he probably sounds the way Goodfellow would like him to sound most of the time, but at 2:00 A.M. when he's been called away from some party for a delivery the veneer gets thin and the slob shows through.

Then there was Dr. Harold Jason, who is even more of a puzzle. I've run across him once or twice before and thought there was something odd about him; everybody seems to sort of snigger whenever his name comes up. He's an older guy, about fifty-five, with too-long graying hair combed too prettily, an obstetrician from out in the hinterland somewhere who brings his own scrub nurse with him to the hospital for his deliveries and surgery. I'm not sure why he makes me so uneasy. Milt Musser once said something about Jason liking to take out uteruses whether they needed to come out or not, but then Milt sneers at anybody who isn't upper-echelon Graystone Clinic, so I didn't pay much attention. Anyway, I assisted Jason at a Caesarean section on Saturday, and he was pleasant enough to me, told me point-blank that he'd see that I got some deliveries if I took good care of his patients for him, without making a sneaky little threat out of it the way Goodfellow did.

The labor floor is in the north wing of the seventh floor of the hospital, with two big delivery rooms separated by a scrub room at the end of the wing. Back along the corridor there is a large nurses' station from which the nurses keep tabs on the three labor rooms directly across the hall. Tucked away in a corner is the doctors' room, with showers, toilets and shelves for scrub suits, and a room at the back with a double bunk, two cots and a telephone, the inevitable telephone. The intern on call sleeps up here, along with the anesthesiologist on call and any stray OB men who happen to be hanging around sweating out their patients.

The idea is good enough, but in practice it gets ridiculous; the doctors' room has more traffic going through it than Grand Central Station, and when the nurses want somebody at 2:00 A.M., they bang on the door with a sledge hammer a couple of times and then stick their heads in and shriek his name at the top of their lungs along with some tidbit of disastrous news designed to rout him out if he's in there. Whether you're the one they're after or not, you by God wake up, bolt upright and blinking, and with this going on every half-hour all night long, you've got to be pretty damned exhausted to get any sleep at all.

As for deliveries, Room I is used unless somebody is already in there. Normally Room II is reserved for such "obstetrical" surgery as curettements and tubal ligations and such. Caesarean sections go down to the main OR. But I guess when the heat is on they deliver in both delivery rooms, in the labor rooms or even on carts in the hall if they have to. Things get that tight sometimes, I hear.

Friday was relatively quiet—a couple of women in labor when I

came on in the morning, but neither of them doing anything exciting. A third woman, a patient of Dr. Jason's, was scheduled for a
Caesarean at 10:00 A.M., and Jason wanted me to scrub on it with
him. This gal came into the hospital with a "NO INFORMATION"
sticker on her chart; that means no publication is to be made to the
papers of the birth, or even of the fact that she is in the hospital.
Usually these are illegitimate pregnancies in which the baby is going to be given up, but this girl, it seems, was going to keep her
baby, and her husband was in the room with her, which seemed
even more odd; usually there's no husband in evidence. Later I
found out that all the hush-hush had nothing to do with marital
status at all, it was just that this gal has an embarrassing anatomical
curiosity: a double vagina, double cervix and double uterus, and
that Jason was going to section her because he wasn't sure she could
manage a vaginal delivery with this sort of setup. He kept her on
"NO INFORMATION" mostly so she wouldn't have half the medical
fraternity of the city trooping through her room to examine her on
one pretense or another.

The section went along fine; the baby was a big one, born howling, and we got a good look at the inside of the uterus, which had a
septum dividing it into two at the bottom but was completely open
at the top. Unfortunately, there wasn't any need to examine the
cervix or vagina during the operation, and I couldn't think of any
graceful way to ask, so I don't know what sort of arrangement she
has down there. This section was bloody, as they all are, but Jason
had the baby out within five minutes of his first incision. Then it
took an hour and a half getting everything gathered back together
again and sewed up. This is what I hate about surgery: it takes so
wretched long to get an individual sewed back up again once you
get them cut open.

After that Ben Boggs had a D & C (dilation of the mouth of the
womb and curettement) to do up in Room II, a woman who had
miscarried but was still bleeding. After he finished his curettement
he handed me a blunt curette, one without any cutting edge on it,
and told me to get the feel of the inside of the uterus with it. Later
in the afternoon Goodfellow turned up for another D & C and let
me handle the sharp curette after he had finished using it. So maybe
these boys will let me do a D & C or two before we get through. I

hope so. It's a procedure that needs to be done often enough, either to clean up a uterus after a miscarriage or for diagnosis of abnormal bleeding, and it's really so simple to do that it's ridiculous.

[*Post hoc:* Simple, that is, so long as everything goes right. But when it goes wrong, you have one bloody mess on your hands, and I had no notion at that time just how easily it could go wrong. I still think those OB men could have taken more pains to teach the interns such techniques as D & Cs, but at least I can sympathize a little now; they just didn't want to have to spend the rest of the day packing a uterus to stop it from bleeding just because some eager-beaver intern took too vigorous a swipe at the interior with a sharp curette and pushed it right through into the abdomen.]

Friday there were a couple of deliveries, too, but nothing very remarkable. Got home at 5:00 for a good night's sleep before the duty weekend.

Monday, September 5

A very dull weekend, at least to start with. When I came on duty at 8:00 A.M., there was nothing happening on the labor floor—just no patients in labor.

Saturday night was a bit different, though. About midnight two women came in back to back, both in active labor. The first was moving right along, so I asked the nurse to call Anesthesia first and then notify her doctor she was in. The second was in labor, all right, but the baby's head was still high. By the time I had her checked the first one was ready to go, and Boggs appeared for the delivery, about 1:30. At 3:00 A.M. Mrs. Webber called me out to help Dr. Carl Sand deliver the second woman. This annoyed me because he had the woman half-delivered by the time I got called—seems both of them had just overlooked the fact that I was around. By the time I got scrubbed and gowned the show was over, so I went back to bed.

Then an hour later I got a taste of one of the really nasty ones that turn up now and then on this service without warning. You get to thinking that OB is just orderly, dull routine, and then when you're not looking you get hit in the guts with a real screamer. I was just getting nicely to sleep, about 4:30 A.M., when this Webber creature, who is night OB nurse, banged on the door and stuck her head in and screeched, "Dr. ———, there's a woman delivering down in the lobby!" By the time I got piled out of bed and found my pants in the dark, she was back to say that they were bringing the woman up in the elevator and I'd better get scrubbed. I told her fine, to take the woman right into Room 1 and then see if she could get an emergency pack open at least.

I was out scrubbing my hands when a nurse and an orderly trundled the woman into the delivery room on a cart, street clothes and all, moaning and groaning. I asked if anybody had called her doctor, and Webber said, yes, it was Dr. Flagg, but he lived clear across town and wanted me to watch the patient until he got there. From the fuss going on in the delivery room while I scrubbed, it didn't sound as though I was going to have to watch anything very long, but then Miss Tuttle, the quiet little night nurse, stuck her head in the door and said, "You know, this woman has been in before, and she's a placenta previa, and she's really bleeding."

Well, I stopped scrubbing right then and got into the delivery room. Bleeding she was, all over her dress, the cart, the floor, everything. The nurse was trying to get her undressed on the delivery table, and her dress was just saturated with blood, great clots of blood all over the place. The woman had stopped moaning now; she just lay there panting, and she looked gray. Webber was trying to get her blood pressure, and could only get a level of about 50, and I thought, My God, this woman is going out on us right here and now. I was still confused; I couldn't see how she could be delivering if she was a previa. Tuttle said, "You won't want to examine her, will you?" and I said, "No. I sure won't. Let's get shock blocks under her feet, and get an IV set and cross-match tubes."

By the time her clothes were off it was obvious that she wasn't delivering, just bleeding a steady stream. I got blood drawn for a cross-match, but the vein collapsed before I could get the IV going, and then I couldn't find another vein to save my soul. I told the girls to get the blood over to the bank for an emergency cross-match, 2 units, and have somebody wait and bring it back—the bank can get you blood in about ten minutes flat if somebody sits on their neck—and then while I was digging away for a vein to start the IV, somebody was arguing with me about the emergency cross-match, saying the OB men didn't like them, and the blood bank didn't like them, and I'd have to take responsibility, and I told them, okay, fine, just go get that blood fast, and then we'd all sit down and argue about it later.

By now the woman was unconscious, and Webber couldn't get any blood pressure at all, and I couldn't get into a vein, and then Pat Gallo, an anesthesia resident, turned up—I guess somebody had called him, thinking we would have an instant delivery—and he started to make some wisecrack and then got a look at the woman's face and said, "Well, let's get a needle into this woman!" and pitched the 20-gauge needle I was using onto the floor and grabbed a syringe with a big plastic needle on it, telling me to monitor her blood pressure, and, snicker-snack, he had the needle in and the sugar water IV running in about fifteen seconds flat. As soon as the fluid started into her, her pressure picked up a little, and we got a unit of plasma going, and she started to respond by the time the orderly turned up with the blood from the bank.

The bleeding had slowed up some, too. I made some remark about thanking God for small favors, and Gallo said, "Yes, if she's a previa and bleeding, shock can sometimes be your best friend." Then he looked at me and said, "Say, you didn't shove your finger in there and poke around, did you?" and I told him, no, thank you, I hadn't. Lord knows I'd heard enough horror stories in medical school about placenta previas; normally the placenta implants high on the inside wall of the uterus, but occasionally it implants at the bottom and covers the outlet so that the baby can't be expelled at term. Then when term comes and the cervix starts to dilate, the placenta starts bleeding, and an incautious intern can stick an examining finger right through it and have the patient exsanguinate in front of him in about five minutes with no way on God's earth to stop the bleeding in time to do any good. So that was one lesson at least that I had remembered.

With the transfusion going in and the bleeding slowed down, the woman began to look a lot better. About then Dr. Flagg turned up, took one look at the pools of blood lying around and told Gallo to get the OR crew ready for a section. We trundled her up to the OR, and Flagg surely didn't fool around—we had her on the table with

baby and placenta both out about fifteen minutes after he had
arrived. The baby was only about three and half pounds, but it was
alive, and the woman was doing okay, too, and after a while I quit
shaking enough to hold onto the idiot sticks (retractors) and get a
look at what was going on. So it came out all right, and I guess I
did the right things at the right time, but I still wonder just what
the hell I should have done if Flagg had had a flat tire on the way
in, and I decided I just plain didn't know what I should have done.
As it was, I was plenty glad Gallo turned up when he did.

We were finishing up about 6:30 A.M. when Arnold Prince stuck
his head in the OR and said he had a section coming up as soon as
we were through, a primip girl with a breech baby (one that enters
the birth canal bottom side down instead of head down as is usual)
that he was afraid to try to deliver from below because she was so
tiny. So after Flagg was finished I ducked down to get an early
Sunday morning breakfast, and then went up to help Prince with
his section.

Prince was a much slower operator than Flagg, so it was almost
11:00 before we were finished with his girl. Again a good baby, and
a girl with such a narrow pelvis that she'd have had trouble with a
normal delivery from below, to say nothing of a breech.

By this time there were half a dozen calls for me on the medical
floors that kept me busy through lunch and all Sunday afternoon.
After supper two more women were admitted in labor. According to
the OB nurses, this is Standard Operating Procedure: the women
come in with contractions around 9:00 or 10:00 in the evening and
deliver about 4:00 A.M. Sure enough, one of these girls delivered at
3:00 A.M. and the other at 4:30. I was called out to "assist" with both
deliveries, and again got to watch, but had no chance to do anything else. So even though the weekend wasn't frantically rushed, I
was feeling rum-dum by this morning.

All in all there have been about fifteen deliveries on the service
since I came on (not counting the sections), and I haven't gotten my
hands on one baby yet. I get to do the circumcisions—no glory in
that—but not the deliveries. With the patient lying on her back on
the delivery table with her eyes wide-open watching him, the
obstetrician wants the whole show to himself, and some of these
guys should be on the stage. They have not only the patient and her

husband watching their performance, but the intern as well, and it really brings out the ham in them.

But it also adds up to no deliveries for the intern. I've been thinking of ways I might beat out this business, and I have an idea that might corral me a few deliveries one way or the other. I may suggest it to Goodfellow next time I see him and see what he says. The trouble is, these OB men don't really need an intern at all. At worst he's in their way; at best he's a very minor convenience to them, strictly expendable. Of course, a weak OB service can make it hard for the whole hospital to get interns, but I suppose the OB men couldn't care less whether the rest of the hospital has interns or not. Still, there must be some way to make things a little more satisfactory.

Today—Monday—was a nice, long restful day of doing nothing much but looking at my feet. Only one patient in all day, a woman of Dr. Howard Bensen's, who delivered her fifteenth-odd baby after about three more or less indifferent contractions, and then wondered why she couldn't pack up her things, baby and all, and go right home again. I slept half the afternoon, and had three cups of coffee with the nurses, and it was 5:00. Home in time for early dinner, and then Ann and I went to a movie.

Wednesday, September 7

Found just one patient in labor when I got to the hospital this morning, and she wasn't doing anything spectacular at the moment. One nice thing about this service is that there is rarely anything urgent going on the moment you walk in the place. You have time to sit down, drink some coffee, check out the floor with the nurses and generally collect yourself before you plunge in. If somebody is already in the delivery room when you arrive, the guy who is covering for you goes ahead and follows through so that there isn't a parade of people going in and out in the midst of a delivery.

This morning the only woman on the floor was a patient of Dr. Jason's, who was taking her own sweet time getting ready to deliver after coming in at 5:00 A.M. in a panic rush. Dr. Jason was sitting around waiting to do the honors. His scrub nurse, Harrison, was there, too, gossiping with the floor nurses. Jason asked me if I had

ever heard of the "flat table technique" for deliveries, claimed that
this was the greatest technique in the world. You put the woman
out flat on the table for the delivery instead of putting her legs up
in stirrups and pushing her down until her behind hangs off in mid-
air, which is the usual way. I couldn't quite see how the doctor
could get close enough this way to get his hands on the baby, so Dr.
Jason promised to demonstrate when this woman was ready to go.
Meanwhile we sat around and chatted for half an hour.

Seems Jason is a horse enthusiast, owns about twenty-five horses,
and he launched into a long, sad tale about his experiences as a race
horse owner and breeder. Next he started telling me the "facts of
life" about the economics of general medical practice, including his
own particular problems. He has two offices—one downtown, the
other in Desertview Heights near his home—and now he needs a
pediatrician to work with him and take care of all the babies he
delivers. Pretty soon he was wondering if I happened to be interested in pediatrics, by any chance. I just told him no, as politely as
possible. Dr. Jason is probably a very rich man, but somehow I
don't think he is exactly the sort of guy I'd feel like joining up with
in practice.

Presently we went in to deliver this patient of his by the "flat-
table technique," putting the woman's heels together with her
knees bent and delivering the baby from the side. It seemed
massively clumsy to me. This one went all right, because the woman
had had several previous babies and didn't need either episiotomy
or forceps, but I sure don't see how you would go about applying
forceps with a setup like that. Maybe Jason just doesn't believe in
using forceps. I didn't ask him.

After that I made rounds on some of the post partum patients,
including the three sections done over the weekend. They were all
doing fine. (There aren't any formal rounds on this service, since
the OB men drop by to see their patients any time of the day or
night that they get to the hospital.) The only complaint I heard was
from one girl who was beefing because her stitches hurt. This was a
girl Goodfellow had delivered Friday, a funny little creature with
pigtails and immense breasts who had wanted to go Read* for her

* Grantley Dick Read's celebrated method of "natural childbirth," emphasiz-
ing prolonged prenatal acquaintance with the mechanics of childbearing, physi-

delivery and then decided after about two good walloping hard labor pains that she didn't want to go Read after all, so that Goodfellow had to call in the anesthetist to give her a caudal block.

I've been very much interested to see the use of the Read method up here. Apparently quite a few girls are all enthusiastic about it, at least until they get to the hospital. I don't think any of the doctors really care for it or advocate it very much, except Dr. Baldwin, who seems to think it's great and talks it up to all his patients. But most of the doctors will go along with a girl if that's what she really wants. The trouble is that, with all the publicity about the Read method, there is more involved than just a supposedly satisfying and fulfilling way of having a baby; with a lot of these women it seems to become a matter of pride—of succeeding or failing. And the deck is loaded against them because if they've never had babies without anesthesia before, they don't have any idea what the hell they're bargaining for when they decide to go Read, and then when they get into it and find out that it isn't as gloriously delightful as they imagined it would be, they're trapped, they feel then that they're quitting if they ask for help.

Part of the Read idea is for the mother to be awake during delivery, with both mother and father participating, and you can't argue with that. But at this hospital, where most of the doctors use "wide-awake" anesthesias—saddle blocks, for instance, or caudals— instead of gas anesthesia, it's hard to see exactly what is gained by doing without. With caudals the anesthetist injects procaine a little at a time into the caudal canal of the sacrum, well below the level of the spinal cord, which deadens the pain nerves to the uterus, vagina and rectum as well as the motor nerves to the muscles of the wall of the birth canal, but not the motor nerves to the uterus itself. If the caudal is started at the right time, uterine contractions keep rolling right along, you get splendid relaxation of the birth canal muscles so that the baby doesn't have to fight tense muscles all the way down, and the mother is wide-awake and able to help by bear-

---

cal exercises and breathing control to make labor and delivery possible and painless without use of drugs or anesthetics. In the years since this was written Read's method has been modified and expanded considerably, especially by Lamaze. Its popularity waxes and wanes; "going Read" was quite the thing in the Southwest several years ago, until caudal anesthesia became popular, and again today interest in "natural childbirth" methods is on the increase.

ing down and what not without any pain at all, and can watch her own baby being born in a big overhead mirror above the obstetrician, with her husband on hand and a relatively painless childbirth to remember.

Of course, there are some drawbacks: if the caudal is given a little too early, it may slow down or even stop the labor for a while, so you have to wait until the cervix is dilated about halfway before you give it. This means that the patient has a certain amount of labor pain, sometimes quite a bit, before she reaches the right stage for the caudal. But this is nothing compared to the pain of the actual delivery.

All in all it seems to me that a caudal anesthetic offers all the advantages of the Read method without the pain, so I am at a loss to see what going Read has to offer, other than some kind of masochistic satisfaction. I guess in theory there isn't supposed to be any pain with the Read method, and the doctor is supposed to provide "verbal anesthesia" to cover the little discomfort there may be. But there seems to be quite a long gap between theory and practice. One night over the weekend I was assisting Boggs at a delivery with caudal anesthesia while Dr. Baldwin was delivering a Read girl in Room II, and she was screaming bloody murder over there. His girls get a little Demerol and a sedative and nothing else, I am told.

Just out of curiosity I asked Miss Tuttle how many of the girls who came in wanting to go Read actually succeed in sticking it out to the end. She said maybe one out of three; the rest of them get into it and decide they want an anesthetic after all. She also said they had lots of post partum problems, too: painful episiotomies, trouble getting their babies to nurse and so on. Worst of all, the ones who don't make it feel so guilty and depressed afterward that they can hardly live with themselves. Seems to me that this is a lot like deciding arbitrarily that you are going to stick a needle through your lip every day for twenty days in a row and then feel guilty because you decide to stop it after the fifth day. It just doesn't make too much sense to me. Maybe some of the girls do feel some tremendous emotional uplift if they succeed, but what about the psychological damage if they flunk out? All I can say is, uplift be damned; I'd never encourage my wife to try it without some very concrete evidence that it really had something magnificent to offer.

So far I've seen three girls who *have* succeeded in going through it. One was another gal of Goodfellow's who delivered on Tuesday, and she was a strange one: a kind of squat, Slavic type, arrogant as hell, didn't want to give me any history, objected even to a superficial heart and lung check, taking this "Just who in the hell do you think *you* are, Jack?" attitude, as if she owned the world. By morning she was well along in labor, and I got a look at her husband, a withered little creature who was hovering around her as if he were scared silly of her, sort of a "Yes, Tilly . . . no, Tilly . . . please don't strike me, Tilly" type. She had her baby Read, and she didn't let out one squeak all the way through, not one sound from beginning to end. She just gritted her teeth with the contractions and pushed and panted and had a terrible time of it, and glared at the doctor and shoved the nurse's hands away—the most malevolent-looking woman I ever saw. Everything about her was saying, "By God, I'm going to do it this way or else!" She had said she wanted a girl, and when the baby finally arrived and turned out to be female, she acted as if she had personally dictated to God the sex of the baby. And all through it (about two hours of rough stuff) poor hubby was sitting there palpitating, as if he were afraid that any minute she was going to turn around and clout him one. She was a good-looking girl, too, about twenty-three or twenty-four years old, but, God, what an unyielding type! I never saw such. She succeeded in going Read, all right, and it's probably just as well that she did. I think she'd have been a sorry mess if she hadn't made it.

Another girl who did pretty well was a kind of a goon-girl who acted half-stupefied all through her labor. Her husband was there to pat her face with a wet washcloth when the going got rough, and she kept thrashing around and groaning and howling with her pains and then insisting that the doctor not give her anything when the contractions relaxed, as if she were afraid he'd sneak up on her with something when she wasn't watching. The baby finally came, to everyone's relief. At least this girl seemed to have a healthy attitude toward the Read method and toward the baby, her husband and everyone else. I got the strong impression that her husband was merely humoring her in not insisting on an anesthetic, but was really a little embarrassed by it all and would have liked her to have some help.

Then the third one had a Read baby this afternoon. She was a cute little girl whose husband was one of those superintelligent lads with thick glasses who kept asking prying questions all the way through the delivery. This girl did pretty well, the best of the three by far. Why the difference I don't know, except this girl didn't seem to be scared of the whole business. She had some painful contractions, all right, but she wasn't *afraid* of them. Maybe this is a silly distinction, but it seemed to me that she was just saying, "Okay, so it hurts—so what? Pretty soon it will be over and I'll have my baby, so why fret?" and it seemed to me that this covered a lot of ground.

[*Post hoc:* A whole lot more ground than I realized at the time. I'm now certain that in normal, uncomplicated labors and deliveries a whole whale of a lot more depends on what is going on above the patient's ears than down in her pelvis. I've observed a lot of deliveries and delivered a lot of babies myself since this was written, and I'm convinced that fear is the single biggest factor there is in difficult labors. The frightened woman is going to have trouble every time no matter what anesthetic you use; the woman who comes to labor without fear will go through it in a breeze, anesthetic or no anesthetic. Maybe it's fear—or lack of it—that determines whether a woman can succeed in any kind of "natural childbirth," but I think most women are going to be afraid of pain unless they know their doctors will do something to help them when the time comes. The ones who want to tie their doctors' hands ahead of time had better know their own natures pretty well.]

Anyway, I'll have a chance to observe the outcome of the Read method as I go along, especially to see how Dr. Baldwin manages with it, since he is the one who seems to advocate it around here. Maybe I'll have a chance to talk to some of these girls and find out just what in the hell they think they are doing, and why they want to do it.

Finally, at last, yesterday evening I got my first delivery on this service. Goodfellow told me about noon that a Mrs. Carter who was then in labor was going to have a gas anesthesia and be asleep at the time of delivery, so I could deliver her. Either her husband was away or she was divorced or something, but she didn't want to be awake during labor or delivery either one, so Goodfellow had agreed to use "twilight sleep," which simply means giving enough Demerol and scopolamine and Seconal that the patient is out in left field through the whole affair. Scopolamine is a sneaky medicine, an amnesic, Goodfellow says, rather than a narcotic. It doesn't do a thing for pain, but after the baby is born and the drug wears off the woman just doesn't remember any of it and thinks she had a nice, quiet, sleepy labor and delivery. The nurses don't like it because the patients have a tendency to start climbing the walls, so somebody has to sit with them practically from beginning to end, listening to a lot of irrational babbling throughout, but there's that old amnesia afterward.

Goodfellow promised I could deliver this woman, and he made such an issue of it that it was ridiculous, as if he were offering me some kind of a real plum, conspiring to give me a real delivery, and one of his very own patients, too. Well, I wasn't about to argue the niceties of it. Goodfellow was on hand to officiate and supervise, but he kept his hands off, let me apply the forceps, deliver the baby and repair the episiotomy incision, confining himself to helpful comments and suggestions here and there. He is a *good teacher*; I'm sure I learned more from actually doing this one delivery with his supervision than from watching him do a dozen himself. I was all thumbs repairing the episiotomy, but I got the woman back together in a more or less straight line. A little more actual *practice* and I wouldn't have any trouble at all. Incidentally, we got a very sleepy baby, but it started breathing immediately. Then when the mother was coming out of the anesthesia, I asked her how she felt, and she said, fine, fine, but she was afraid that the grapefruits were spoiled, so God knows what she was dreaming about during the delivery.

After that I had a busy evening. Goodfellow had two patients in for induction of labor in the morning, but one of them was already in active labor and about half-dilated. She just went ahead and had her baby around midnight, induction be damned. There were three other deliveries before she was ready to go. About 12:30 I made a stab at going to bed, but got called out again at 3:00 A.M. for another delivery, and again at 4:00 to go down to Fifth and pronounce some patient on the medical service who had just died. This was a man I had never seen before. Apparently his wife had had to go down and tell the nurse that he'd stopped breathing, but I didn't know that. I went in and listened for heart sounds, with the wife watching me all the while, and finally I looked up and said that I was afraid he was gone, and she said, "Well, of course he's gone. He stopped breathing fifteen minutes ago." So I went back up to bed, feeling like an ass.

Breakfast with Andy at 7:00 this morning. Since these are supposed to be gripe sessions, I sounded off loud and clear about this OB service. Case asked what was wrong, didn't we have rounds? So I said what was wrong was that we didn't have any deliveries; the OB men wouldn't let the intern do anything. Ted Van Wert, who was also present, nodded and said something about "the same old story again" and remarked that he had understood that the OB men were going to try to improve the service for interns this year. I asked Case if anything could be done, but he hedged, just suggested that maybe things would improve when I'd been on the service a little longer. So I promised to make a progress report at the meeting next week.

Friday, September 9

The place was like a tomb Thursday morning—nobody in labor, not even any deliveries during the night. About midmorning two patients of Goodfellow's came in and delivered within ten minutes of each other. Goodfellow trotted up from surgery about 11:00 A.M. when the first one was already prepped and draped on the delivery table in Room I; he delivered her, then trotted across to Room II to deliver the second; dusted off his hands and trotted back downstairs again by 11:30. Instant childbirth, so to speak. I wonder how he does it.

After lunch a patient of Dr. Tony Marin's came in who decided she wanted gas instead of a caudal, so Marin asked me if I wanted to deliver her. I said yes, and had my second delivery on the service. Nothing very exciting, though; this babe had seven previous children and a vagina big enough to admit a Mack truck. She dilated, crowned and delivered all in about five minutes. At least I got to control the baby's head. Big thrill.

No calls all Thursday night. I would have slept fine except that I kept dreaming that I was being called. Early Friday morning a patient of Dr. Stanley Plotzman's came in, a mother of five in precipitous labor, and nobody could get hold of Dr. Plotzman. I got scrubbed in time to catch the baby right in the labor room, with the mother still in her street clothes. Miss Hardy got all excited because the cord was wrapped around the baby's neck, and I finally had to take the scissors away from her before she stuck them in the baby's jugular trying to get the cord cut.

Later Ben Boggs had a D & C that I watched. The patient allegedly had miscarried, but Boggs couldn't seem to find any tissue with the curette, and I really think he was worried. After five minutes of futile scraping he said, "You know—ha, ha—these are the kind of D & Cs that OB men find embarrassing to explain," and kept on scraping around until finally he got some necrotic-looking tissue out. Thus relieving his embarrassment, I guess, because he grinned at me and said, "Well, I guess that'll keep the pathologist happy." I don't know who the OB men have to answer to around here when they get back suspicious pathology reports, but I do know that they actually want to *see* some expelled tissue before they will go near a pregnant woman with a curette. Even then they like to have some other OB man write a consultation note on the chart before they go ahead with a D & C, so somebody must be watching them.

[*Post hoc:* Somebody was, of course, namely, the hospital's Tissue Committee, a group of doctors who review all pathology reports returned on D & Cs done in the hospital. One funny pathology report and the Chief of Obstetrics collars the doctor privately and suggests that there hadn't better be any more; on the second the doctor gets censured by name at the monthly hospital staff meeting; a third time and he gets booted off the hospital staff for good. As Ben Boggs once put it so delicately, "That lets a guy take care of his daughter and his girl friend before he gets kicked out." Of course, no criminal prosecution is involved in all of this, but a doctor who needs to use the hospital doesn't play around with criminal abortions. He might get conned into a bad D & C once, in honest error, but he's got to be an awful fool to get caught a second time.]

It was quiet after lunch Friday, but about 4:30 P.M. four patients trooped in, all rolling right along. One was bleeding heavily; Boggs scheduled her for a Caesarean at 6:00. The woman was scared but otherwise okay. Alec Ivy was supposed to relieve me for a three-day weekend to make up for the one I gave him, so he turned up at 5:30 in time to scrub for the section and I headed home. I suppose I should have stayed, but I just wasn't too interested right then.

Tuesday, September 13

Had the usual Monday morning griping pain when I came back to work this morning after a long weekend of rest. I haven't been getting as tired on this service as I did on the medical service; I have a lot more free time during the day, although it turns up very erratically and is extremely difficult to use to any advantage. Women only have babies so fast; there's nothing to do but sit around and wait until they're ready, which may mean two or three hours at a stretch with no particularly demanding duties. I try to cat nap during the day since the nighttimes are almost always busy. On call nights I'm also vulnerable to medical calls, but there have been very few—seems as though the medical service and Emergency Room have been very slow lately.

I find on this service that I'm not paying much attention to the patients' names. We have such a rapid turnover, see patients so briefly and have so little to do with them after delivery that I rarely learn their names at all, just refer to them as "Dr. Sand's patient" or "Dr. Bensen's patient." I've also puzzled at some little mysteries on this service that nobody seems to be able to explain. One is the disproportion of night deliveries. There are about three deliveries between midnight and 7:00 A.M. to every one during the day. Another mystery is this business of simultaneous deliveries: two women will come in three or four hours apart in the morning, both in indifferent labor, and lie around all day with a contraction every now and then until about 10:00 at night. Then both of them will suddenly take off and be ready for delivery within five minutes of each other, so I can assist at only one. This is no coincidence; it's happened half a dozen times this past week, and it drives you crazy. I don't know whether there are sympathetic vibrations going back and forth between these ladies or just what, but the timing is uncanny.

Things were hopping when I came back to work Monday morn-

ing: four or five patients in active labor who delivered in rapid
succession between 10:00 A.M. and lunchtime. One girl was slower—
a patient of Dr. Flagg's who had come in just as I came on duty.
This gal was only fifteen years old, and her husband looked about
twelve. I guess this was a shotgun wedding, because the gal got
pregnant in December and they were married in May. She was one
frightened girl. As her labor went on she behaved just the way
you'd expect a fifteen-year-old girl to behave under the circumstances. I was a little at a loss; you can usually assume that a girl in
labor is a reasonably mature woman until she demonstrates otherwise. At least you can assume that she has some idea of what's going
on. Not this little girl. Her husband was wandering around like a
lost soul. He spent most of the day with her in the labor room; at
first there was much hand-holding and giggling, until the labor
began to get to her, and then he just looked helpless and sick.

Then about noon the nurse made a really bad mistake: she let
the girl's mother in to see her. It was supposed to be for just a few
minutes, but once Mother got in there she wouldn't leave until I
practically threw her out bodily an hour later. It really made me
sore; under the best of circumstances there is no place for a mother
in the labor room with her daughter if the husband can possibly be
there, and certainly no place if the husband *is* there. Mothers tend
to revert to the primitive, pouring on the sympathy with each labor
pain and taking delight in reminding their little darlings that it's
all hubby's fault that they're suffering so—and treating the husband like some sort of unnatural monster, if he's around. It may
sound unlikely, but that's exactly what they do, and it seems to me
that this is about as wrong as it can be. It's the antithesis of the
whole idea of husbands staying with their wives during labor. After
all, having a baby is something quite strictly between husband and
wife. There's an opportunity there to cement a love and a marriage
in a way that's impossible any other way.

Take this particular case, for example: a couple of children who
already have practically no chance at all for a happy marriage. First
nailed with an unwanted pregnancy, then a wedding forced down
their throats on top of it. They didn't even know what pregnancy is.
With a baby on their hands they're going to have to grow up in a
rush; what better way of driving home the responsibility of parent-

hood than to let the husband sweat with his wife through her labor, just the two of them, so they get some idea of what that roll in the hay signifies now, nine months later?

Well, the mother was much incensed that I threw her out, and so was the nurse when I crawled down her throat about it, but after Mamma left, daughter quieted down and went on through her delivery just hanging onto her husband's hand for dear life. And I had to hand it to the kid; he was white as a snowbank, but he just kept telling the girl to take it easy, that he was going to stay right there with her, and he hung onto her as hard as she hung onto him, and he didn't get sick all over the delivery room floor the way I've seen some thirty-year-old longshoremen do either. I know I've thought sometimes that the way husbands and wives act together in the delivery room is very amusing, but it really isn't anything of the sort. I'd never before thought of the process of delivering a baby as an act of love, but I'd swear that was what it was with these two kids.

She delivered about 7:00, still scared silly. She had a good caudal, so she wasn't really having any pain then, but Dr. Flagg, who is not the gentlest of humans, dealt with her in the same rough-and-tumble fashion he deals with all his girls, which was too bad. He didn't pause to explain that the forceps wouldn't hurt before he applied them, and she got one look at those big curved blades and just about crawled off the table. I suppose it seemed like just her and her man against the world, and then it was all over and the baby was squalling and Dr. Flagg was strutting around as if he'd accomplished some kind of miracle. He hadn't. It was the kids who had accomplished the miracle that day in spite of everything.

I got called to admit another woman about 2:00 in the morning, a really sad one. This girl was about twenty years old, and had had severe diabetes since she was seven. Two previous pregnancies both miscarried in the first couple of months. Now she was six or seven months pregnant, starting in premature labor. She was a walking pathology book: diabetic cataracts, high blood pressure, albumen in her urine, a history of a diabetes so hard to control that she had had about three episodes of diabetic coma a year since she was fifteen. Now she hadn't felt any movement from the baby for a week, and was starting in precipitous premature labor. Goodfellow came in and shook his head and went down to the doctors' room to wait her out; he didn't even have anything very reassuring to say to her. The baby was born dead, of course, with half a dozen anomalies: a huge cyst at the base of the spine, two thumbs on one hand, a fibrous constriction ring around one leg. A misshapen little brute with a big head and no feet to speak of, so it's lucky it didn't live.

Later Goodfellow and Ned Stern were talking about the case in the doctors' room. Seems the mother had been advised not to become pregnant, and then when she conceived Goodfellow had urged her to let him interrupt the pregnancy, or at least tie her tubes, but she refused both. He said she'd probably keep getting pregnant until she either had a good baby or died, whichever came first, and Stern said not to worry about it too much, that with this much diabetic pathology she should have been dead two or three years ago and the chances are that she won't survive another pregnancy.

That shocked me a little, coming from Stern, who is one of the experts on diabetes around here, so I asked him why she couldn't make it if she had ideal control of her diabetes. He just said, "Look—that girl is dead right now. She's got no kidneys left, she's got no blood vessels left. This pregnancy was just whipping a tired horse. She's still breathing, but she's dead just the same."

On top of the OB work a distressing thing happened on the medical service Monday night, one of these things that you can find all sorts of rational excuses for, but still leave you sick and disgusted with yourself. Around 10:30 P.M. the nurse on the fifth floor called to tell me that old Mr. Dorcas in 513 was having trouble with his breathing again. Mr. Dorcas was a patient of Stern's and Compton's, a diabetic of long standing who also had some heart trouble. I'd never seen Mr. Dorcas, but I had sure heard about him from the interns and residents and even Dr. Compton himself. Apparently Mr. Dorcas was regarded by general acclamation as the biggest pain in the ass in the whole hospital.

Every now and then a patient turns up that nobody can stand, not even his own attending physician; these are the ones that the profession speaks of as the "crocks"—usually old, cantankerous, complaining, uncooperative people who seem to go out of their way to make themselves especially repulsive to everybody. Mr. Dorcas had won the title of "The Patient We'd Most Like To See Go Home," as Ned Stern remarked sourly one evening. His diabetes had gotten out of control, mostly because he had decided unilaterally that he didn't care to take his insulin any more; he got hauled to the hospital in acidosis at 3:00 one morning. Once he was out of immediate danger, he started a campaign to fight his doctors and the nurses and the house staff and everybody else who was trying to help. He would refuse to take his insulin unless Compton himself came in and coaxed him to take it, and then would dump his breakfast tray upside down on the floor on grounds that since he hadn't had any insulin he couldn't eat anything. Then when his blood sugar got up to 500 or so and he started feeling bad, he'd accept the insulin but stuff his dinner into his pillow case, telling the nurses he had eaten it, and then go into insulin shock at 4:00 in the morning and stir half the house staff out of bed to get him bailed out of it.

When I first heard about this nonsense from Hamilton, I thought the old guy must be off his rocker, but Hamilton said, no, he was lucid as could be, just doing his damnedest to annoy everybody he could annoy. He had long-standing bronchitis, and brought his own oxygen equipment to the hospital with him, but he wouldn't use it when the intern ordered it, and then would run the nurses and interns ragged all night because he couldn't breathe.

Well, just when everybody already had a gutful of Mr. Dorcas, one of the X-ray boys thought he spotted a lesion in the old man's lung on a chest plate, and, sure as hell, more films showed that Mr. Dorcas had a tumor in his lung. Dr. Richards had the joy of opening his chest a week ago to try to remove whatever it was, and now Mr. Dorcas was postoperative as well as an uncontrolled diabetic, and now he *really* had episodes of shortness of breath, which he rode to the ground, complaining constantly.

I noticed on his chart that he had had the intern out twice or three times per night every night all week. Hamilton had seen him the night before and left a sort of frustrated, disgusted 3:00-in-the-morning note in the chart to the effect that if Mr. Dorcas would only just leave the oxygen valve in his tent alone he might have less trouble breathing and be able to sleep.

I went down to see the guy, a little beady-eyed, bald-headed gnome who greeted me at the door with "Well, do something! I can't breathe!" He didn't look very good, but his cheeks were pink enough, and when I listened to his chest in front (he wouldn't sit up for me to listen in back), I could hear air moving on both sides. The nurse was saying that he'd been ringing his call bell constantly since she'd called me, saying he couldn't breathe, he couldn't get comfortable, he wanted to vomit, and so on. Earlier in the evening he had gotten a little shocky from his insulin, and she had finally talked him into eating a little sugar after he refused to drink any of the orange juice they keep on hand for such occasions.

Well, I couldn't see any immediate reason for him to be short of breath, and I could just see spending the rest of the night up and down trying to humor this old fart. I reassured him that he was going to be all right, and ordered the oxygen to be left on all night so he could get some sleep. Ordered a capsule of Seconal for him, and then went down for midnight supper. Found Milt Musser there and thought he might have some ideas, but all he said was: "Oh, Christ! I don't know why Stern doesn't just give that bastard about 5 grains of morphine all at once and cure his breathing troubles for good."

So I went up to the OB floor and turned in for sleep about midnight. At 12:30 the night nurse on Fifth called to tell me that Mr. Dorcas was just having a terrible time, he was all upset and couldn't breathe, and wasn't there something I could do? I was afraid to order any more sedative, so I asked if he was still getting the oxygen. "Oh, no, he turned that off himself an hour ago!" So I told her, for Christ's sake go turn it on again, and maybe try to get him to eat a little more sugar in case he was still shocky. She asked if I didn't want to come down and see him, and I told her I'd just seen him an hour or so ago and that she'd better just try to manage the situation by herself.

Well, that was fine until 2:30 A.M. when she called again and this time *she* was practically hysterical. Said Mr. Dorcas wasn't breathing right, he was ringing his buzzer every two minutes and just having a terrible time, and couldn't I please do something? She woke me out of a dead sleep to tell me this. By now I was so pissed off at Mr. Dorcas *and* the nurse that I was damned if I was going to crawl out of bed and go down and see him. I told her to go ahead and give him another Seconal, and she said he'd refused to take the first one I had ordered because he was afraid he might go to sleep. Well, that blew it. I told her for my money I was afraid he might not, and for her to go down and give him two grains of Luminal by hypo whether he happened to like the idea or not, and then to quit bothering me. If she couldn't get the old goat to quiet down, she would just have to put up with him, that was all, because I wasn't coming down there just to humor her *or* Mr. Dorcas.

I slammed the receiver down, and then lay blinking at the ceiling and getting madder by the minute; I kept thinking, Jesus, maybe I'd better go down and see what's going on, and then I'd think, the hell with it, all I'd find was what I found when I saw him earlier, namely, nothing. So I just lay there wide-awake, cursing Mr. Dorcas up, down and sideways and generally feeling very bitter about it all.

I guess I succeeded in intimidating the nurse because there weren't any more calls from the fifth floor until 6:15 when Miss Wood called with her chipper, cheerful, early-morning voice and told me she thought I'd better come down to 513, it looked as if Mr. Dorcas had just expired. . . .

I got my clothes on in a cold sweat and got down there, and, sure as hell, Mr. Dorcas had "ceased respirations." He was very dead indeed. The night nurse just glared at me and stomped off without a word, and I sat there at the desk looking at his chart and trying to figure out just what the hell to write in it about the evening's events. I could just hear the nurse telling all the girls how she had begged me to come see this poor dying man and all I had done was swear at her. To top it off, when I called Ned Stern to tell him Mr. Dorcas had died, he said, *"Died! What happened?"* which made me feel even more delightful, and then I had the joy of calling Mr. Dorcas' sister to tell her he had died. All in all, I was feeling like a first-class shit about the whole thing.

I saw on the chart that the nurse had called Pete Carey about 3:30, in desperation, I guess, and Pete had ordered some Demerol for the man but had also refused to come over and see him. Dr. Richards said later that at surgery he had found Mr. Dorcas had an extensive lung cancer all over the inside of his chest and extending up the esophagus and down into the abdomen, totally inoperable, and that all he had had ahead of him was three or four bad months anyway. Which was comforting to know, in a way, but doesn't really excuse my own negligence. Maybe I couldn't have done much. You could argue that the man had just called wolf once too often; certainly you could argue that it was just an error in judgment on my part, assuming that all the hullabaloo was just a matter of Mr. Dorcas' crock-ism when he was, in fact, choking to death. Still, my job here is to be on call and see people when they need attention whether I'm annoyed at them or not, or tired or not, or inconvenienced or not. Strip it down to the bone and the fact was that I was just too lazy and irritated and stubborn to drag my fat ass out of bed and walk down two flights of stairs to see the man. I depended, instead, on a snap judgment that just happened to be wrong. I feel lousy about it, and so does Pete, but there you are. Maybe I've learned something.

[*Post hoc:* Now, some years later, I can still remember this episode in sharpest detail: the look of the little man in bed, my own anger at patient and nurse, the sound of Ned Stern's voice on the telephone (I learned later that he had just come back from vacation and hadn't heard about Mr. Dorcas' chest trouble at all). I also remember that there was not one single voice raised suggesting negligence, which I think bothered me more than anything else. I think now I know why nothing was said. There is no good solution to this kind of problem; you only learn by having it happen to you, and every doctor has his own "episodes" sharply etched in his mind. And if there is a single dread that haunts doctors even after years of practice, it is the dread of misjudging a situation because of anger, irritation, laziness or selfishness. You can judge correctly a hundred times and be furious at having to make needless night calls, extra trips to the hospital or precautionary phone calls, just to be on the safe side, but there's always that sleeper waiting for you, the one patient that may *really* need to be seen, even though you doubt it. If it is a lesson you have to learn by getting nailed, at the cost of a death you might have prevented, it is also a lesson you don't forget. And when you see a colleague get nailed, I don't think there are many doctors who feel very much like casting the first stone.]

Thursday, September 15

Wednesday would have been a dull day, except that I finally talked to Goodfellow and Arnold Prince about my bright idea to get around this business of the intern getting no work on this OB service. This idea turned up one night when one of the men—Baldwin, I think—was eager to get back home after a late delivery, and handed me the needle holder with instructions to "finish up those last few stitches" when he hadn't even started the episiotomy repair. It annoyed me at the time; if it was okay at 2:00 in the morning when the bastard just wanted to get back into his warm bed, why wasn't it okay at high noon? But it got me to thinking all the same.

Basically, the problem has been that I've spent two weeks of my month on the OB service, where I'm supposed to be getting experience doing routine deliveries, and so far I've had just two. And it dawned on me, finally, that it isn't a matter of the OB men's confidence in the intern, or worry about the intern fouling things up, or even really worry about the patient not getting first-class care. These are facile excuses and nothing more; delivering a baby just isn't that tough. These obstetricians could go stand at the end of the table with a bucket to keep the baby from bouncing on the floor and they'd end up with good babies and good mothers 99 percent of the time. Of course, complications do turn up. When the ax drops in obstetrics, it drops hard and fast; somebody has to know *exactly* what to do *right then* and have skill enough and guts enough to do it, or you have a disaster on your hands. But I've noticed that these men, even including Goodfellow, aren't too worried about having the intern deliver their patients when the patient is out cold with a general anesthetic and hubby off down in the waiting room. It's only when the patient is awake in the delivery room, and with hubby right there holding her hand, that the delivery becomes something that only the OB man can handle and the intern is just a slob who can mop up the blood maybe, but nothing else.

Well, maybe that's unfair, but it has seemed to me that what these guys are *really* afraid of is having the intern stealing their thunder while the patient is watching and/or of having the patient raise hell because she sees that somebody else is delivering her, when it's the obstetrician who is getting paid the fee. Basically, it's the use of caudal anesthesia that is scotching the intern's chances of doing anything on this service, and this is going to continue to crowd the intern out unless some way is found to get around it. The frustrating part of it is that caudal anesthesia is about the best there is for most deliveries, from the standpoint of safety and comfort for the patient. Goodfellow and Boggs introduced the technique here about two years ago, and also started letting husbands into the delivery room, since they could watch the delivery without having to see their wives in agony. It was just a short step to this hammy delivery room performance they put on. It's a hell of a dramatic show as long as you aren't preoccupied with how much it's hurting, and the doctor is the star. He can explain what he's doing, step by step, and laugh and joke with the patient in the process, and make himself out to be a very slick operator indeed. If he's as good a native-born showman as Horace Goodfellow, he can really wow them. Most of them aren't that good, which may be why Goodfellow seems to shine so much around here, but they try, they really try.

A few of the doctors don't use caudals, but very few. Old Barton Howard doesn't, specifically because he wants the interns to have his deliveries with him supervising, but he's about eighty years old now and couldn't care less if the patients get indignant. Dr. Plotzman also uses general anesthesia, but he is a kind of a backwoods type who seldom makes it to the hospital for his deliveries anyway. All his patients keep coming back to him, even though he's been known to miss five deliveries out of six with one patient! The city boys just aren't all that blasé about holding onto their OB patients, I guess.

I complained again to Andy Case at breakfast Wednesday, and he still had no suggestions. But I got to thinking that most patients and their husbands don't know a damned thing about who is supposed to do what in the delivery room; if their doctor is there and holds up a good, squalling baby for them to see, they aren't going to know or care who exactly did what in order to obtain it. The patient will consider important whatever her obstetrician emphasizes is important and ignore everything else. What they really want is to have the doctor they trust there with them, and to get a good baby; if they have those things, they won't have a complaint in the world.

[*Post hoc:* Years later I was very much upset because a patient in my care had had a long, difficult labor and an extremely tough and traumatic delivery. I mentioned my discouragement over the case to an older and wiser doctor. He just sighed and said, "Well, sure, you'd like to have made it easier, but you got a good baby and a good mother out of it. And that's all that really counts."]

Anyway, yesterday I presented Dr. Arnold Prince with my Bright Idea. I told him I realized that with the patient wide-awake the OB man might feel that he couldn't just stand there and let the intern do everything, but that he could let the intern handle one step in the process at one delivery and another step in another. At one delivery he might say, "Doctor, would you apply the forceps, please?" as if that were the way it was always done. At another delivery he could ask the intern to deliver the placenta, in another to repair the episiotomy and so forth. The intern might not get many *full* deliveries from beginning to end that way, but by splitting up the procedures he would end up with the equivalent of fifty or sixty deliveries during his time on service without stealing the OB man's thunder at a single one, and without the patients even knowing that he was around.

Prince listened, and sucked on his pipe for a while, and then said, "Jesus, I don't see any reason why it wouldn't work. Let me think about it." The whole idea seemed to startle him a little, but at least he went off scratching his head over it. Later I cornered Goodfellow in the doctors' room and went over the scheme with him. He had a couple of minor objections; he pointed out that even under the best of conditions lots of patients with healing episiotomies have a certain amount of pain during intercourse after having a baby, nothing too dreadful but something for them to complain about. This is perfectly normal, but some of the doctors might feel that it would be hard for them to explain if somebody else had repaired the episiotomy. I told him that sounded to me like a rather petty objection, and he kind of grinned and agreed that it was.

The upshot of our talk was that he suggested I come to the OB staff meeting on Monday evening, and he would introduce the idea to the other obstetricians and I could be on hand to answer any questions they might have. Meantime we might try it a few times to see how it goes. Twice Wednesday evening at deliveries Goodfellow handed me the forceps and said, "Now, Doctor, you apply the forceps, please." No trouble, and nobody blinked an eye; the patients accepted it as though deliveries were always managed exactly that way. I don't know if Goodfellow thought the sky would fall or not; he just seemed a little nonplused that it didn't, and afterward said, "You know, that worked, didn't it? I wonder why nobody ever thought of it before."

Well, I think the reason that nobody had thought of it before was because none of these obstetricians had bothered to think very hard about how they could arrange to give the intern more work. During the night there were two more deliveries, this time with Boggs; I applied the forceps on one and repaired the episiotomy on the other while Boggs took the placenta up to wave it under the patient's nose.

On Thursday the scheme got lost a little because for some damn reason the floodgates opened and we were suddenly up to our knees in patients. I never saw so many pregnant women in my life. Goodfellow had admitted two patients Wednesday night for induction in the morning. At 4:00 A.M. I got called to assist Dr. Bensen at a delivery and discovered that two more patients had turned up, both of them pooping right along. I worked them up and went back to bed about 5:00. At 6:00 Miss Tuttle banged on the door and said, "Doctor, I think maybe you'd better get up, we've just admitted seven more patients in the last hour." I roared out of bed, and, sure as hell, there were seven of them scattered around the place, three of them practically precipitating on the floor. So I was working at a dead run from then until 2:00 in the afternoon; seemed like a new one came in the door every time one was delivered, and we had them delivering in the labor rooms, on carts in the hall, everywhere. A total of eleven deliveries between 6:00 A.M. and 2:00 P.M.

In spite of the rush Goodfellow stuck to the system. With the first he asked me to deliver the placenta, with the second to repair the episiotomy. Part of the patter came in handy here. For some reason this guy is convinced that his patients want to have a look at the placenta, so he invariably trots it up to the head of the table. He'll pick it out of the basin and hold it up by the cord, dripping blood all over the floor, or else slop it over his hands and shove it under the patient's nose, saying, "Now, this is the placenta that fed the baby," and blah, blah, blah. I've seen patients—and especially their husbands—turn white and look like they are about to vomit on the floor during this little display, but Goodfellow keeps on doing it. Anyway, in this case he handed me the needle holders and said, "Now, Doctor, would you mind finishing that episiotomy repair for me? I'd like to show the mother the placenta." So he took the placenta up for the mother to see, and the nurse brought the baby up so that mother and father were occupied. The placenta was dangling around in mid-air for a while, and little me was sitting all unnoticed at the end of the table repairing the episiotomy like mad before somebody came and took it away from me.

Later this afternoon I ran into Goodfellow in the hall and thanked him for the greater participation. He really seemed surprised at how well the scheme had worked, and said, "This might just work out very nicely. Of course a lot depends on whether the patients complain, but this might just be the solution to our problem. Now it would be nice if we could run up a small series of cases here under actual conditions between now and Monday, so that Monday night we could tell the other men that we'd actually been putting the system into operation and that it works."

I told him I thought that would be great, and to myself I said, Dr. Goodfellow, you crafty old son of a bitch, you'd just like to be the one to "introduce" a good solution to this problem at the staff meeting, and get the drop on the rest of the staff men, wouldn't you? Well, more power to him if he makes points out of it. Between now and Monday I have the weekend on duty, and we should have another half-dozen deliveries. Could have a tidy little series to present, and time to find out if there are any awkward wrinkles in the scheme as well.

One interesting sidelight turned up this afternoon, though, when a patient of Dr. Howard McClintock's came in for delivery just before I went off duty. McClintock is a fairly young GP with a surprisingly good reputation around the hospital. This woman had a caudal ordered, and then brought the baby down fast after the caudal was given. The nurses paged Dr. McClintock and called his office but couldn't locate him. While they were trying, I checked this patient again, and thought she wasn't going to wait for anybody very long. It was either move her into the delivery room then and there or deliver her in bed. I told the girls to move her in, and scrubbed and gowned in a hurry, and then McClintock turned up.

He waved to the patient and said, "My golly, you that far along already?" and proceeded to scrub and gown, carrying on a running chat with the patient and me. When he got his gloves on, he checked her, and then to my amazement said, "Why don't you go ahead?" and handed me the forceps. I placed the forceps, and he said, "Now, we'll have to get you a stool," and pulled the stool up for me with his toe. I proceeded with the whole delivery from beginning to end while he stood by chewing the fat with the patient and assisting me with the episiotomy repair. Everything went fine, and the woman was happy as a clam about the whole thing.

I was really amazed; this was the first time that a man has allowed me to do a complete delivery, supervised, with the patient wide-awake and looking at me, and this man hadn't even met me before, just knew I was the OB intern. After the delivery I thanked him, and remarked that most of the men had been reluctant to let me deliver their caudal patients. McClintock said, "Yes, I know, and that's all a lot of bullshit, too. This old business about the patients and their husbands objecting is all in their minds. These people don't know who's doing what as long as their doctor is around to keep them happy. Tell you what: you go down and talk to this woman tomorrow. I'll bet you ten dollars she won't know who delivered her, or care. These guys are all scared silly over nothing, that's the truth of it."

So at least there's one man around here on the interns' side. Old Dr. Barton Howard is another. He came in this afternoon and asked me if I would be on the service another week or so. I said, yes, until October 1st. "Morning, noon and night?" he asked. I said yes, except for my evenings off.

The old boy shook his head. "No, that's no good. I've got a couple of women who will be ready to deliver in a week or so, and I want to know whether you're going to be here to deliver them or not. Yes or no?"

So I said, "Don't worry, I'll have the nurses call me when they come in whether I'm on duty or not." Dr. Howard nodded and said,

"Okay, they're yours," and stalked out. I put a note up on the bulletin board for the girls to call me any time one of Dr. Howard's patients came in. Pat Gallo saw it and thought it was very funny, but pickings are just slim enough around here that I'm not going to hand Hamilton any deliveries on a platter just because I'm off duty.

Friday, September 16

A short but lively day. Mrs. Morehouse, wife of one of the clinic doctors, came into the hospital to have her baby. Don Morehouse is in command of the clinic anesthesia department. His wife came in about 8:30 in the morning in early labor; seems this was her third baby, and both previous labors had been precipitous.

I didn't see much of her all morning because her husband was around, and all the other clinic doctors were coming by to say hello to her. Then about noon she started having very active labor and dilating fast; Morehouse called the anesthesia resident to put in the caudal. She kept right on rolling, and of all things the caudal didn't take too well. In about twenty minutes she was practically ready to deliver, and the nurses were trying frantically to locate her doctor. They finally reached him—clear across town. He said he'd come right over, but when Morehouse heard where he was coming from, he said, "Come on, let's get her set up. She's not going to wait that long."

I proceeded to scrub and glove and gown, not knowing whether Morehouse himself was planning to deliver her or what. But he didn't make any move to scrub, so I just went ahead as though this were the thing I always did. By the time they got her up on the table and draped, you could see the baby's hair, so I proceeded to deliver her. No time for forceps, not even time to cut an episiotomy, although I controlled the delivery enough that there was no laceration. Her doctor arrived panting just as I was clamping and cutting the cord. He seemed to approve of what had been done, and Mrs. Morehouse seemed to approve heartily, and so did Don, apparently. I got ribbed all day about being the new staff man on the OB floor, but there were no beefs from anybody. I learned later that with her last delivery she had gone just as fast, and Morehouse and the

anesthesia resident had stood there arguing about who should deliver her until the baby almost delivered itself.

I left Hamilton with a full house when I signed out at five. He
was unhappy about it, but I was glad to get out of there for a while,
with the weekend call coming up.

Monday, September 19

Saturday was surprisingly quiet. I sat around the doctors' room
most of the day reading a murder mystery, and even that was boring. About 11:00 in the morning a patient of Dr. Jason's came in
with a threatened abortion, and a while later she passed the fetus, a
little malformed thing about two and a half months along. I called
Jason, and he told me to try and hold up her lunch if I could, but
she had already eaten, so we set her up for a D & C at 6:00 P.M.

When the time came I went in with him to scrub, and he asked
me if I wanted to do the D & C. I said of course I did, and went
ahead with it; Jason stood by but didn't even scrub. It was the first
D & C I'd done by myself. No trouble with it, but doing one is sure
different from watching one being done. I was so nervous I could
hardly hold my hands still.

The rest of the evening was relatively quiet, only a couple of calls
and one or two medical admissions. I got to bed about 11:00, then
got called out again at midnight because Dr. Sand had a patient in
ready to deliver. I might just as well not have put on gloves. All I
did was watch. Back in the doctors' room afterward he made some
sort of stupid remark about not knowing if that had been too
instructive or not, with that wise-guy grin on his face, and it was the
last straw, I guess. I turned around and said, no, it sure hadn't been
very goddamned instructive, and I couldn't see why he had to drag
a man out of bed at midnight for a performance like that. He just
looked at me and walked out.

I suppose I should have kept my trap shut, but with Dr. Sand it's
100 percent take and no give. I went to bed good and sore, then, for
insult added to injury, got called out again at 2:00 to see a new
admission that Dr. Silver had just sent in with a penicillin reaction.
Found out that Silver hadn't seen him at all, just told him to go on
into the hospital. All the patient had was a few small hives, and I

was furious. There was no reason whatever to call Silver, but I called him anyway about 3:00 A.M., merely told him his patient was doing just fine and hung up on him. So I guess I made enemies all over the place, or maybe I was especially irritable for some reason, but this sort of thing just gets tiresome.

I was on my way back to bed after working up Silver's patient when a very strange thing happened on the OB floor, something that gave me a little more insight into Dr. Henry Baldwin's enthusiasm for Read deliveries, and soured me once and for all, I think, on the whole idea of "natural childbirth." The way it happened, I almost felt like a Peeping Tom: Baldwin had had this Read patient in the delivery room when I went downstairs, and I hadn't been called to assist him. But when I came back upstairs I heard this piercing shriek from the delivery room, and then another that ended up in a wail, and I rushed down there to see what the hell was going on.

Well, it was quite a sight. I'd seen Dr. Baldwin before—a young, soft-spoken man with curly blond hair and a most engaging smile, the sort of guy you couldn't help liking. But this was a slightly different Dr. Baldwin. He was gowned and gloved at the end of the delivery table, wearing cap and mask so all I could see was his eyes, and he didn't even know I'd stuck my head in the room. He was too wrapped up in his patient. The woman was on the table with her legs up in stirrups, shrieking and writhing and twisting with every contraction, trying to push that baby's head out, and begging Baldwin over and over to do something, make it stop hurting, and he was pouring sweat and his eyes were bright with excitement and he was just saying, "That's all right, Mary, take a deep breath, it doesn't really hurt, does it?" in that silky voice of his, and then saying, "Bear down with it! *Bear down!*" when the next contraction came.

Then suddenly the woman gasped and screamed, "Oh, God . . . *help me!*" and pushed the baby's head out, and the nurse said, "Doctor!" and Baldwin gave a start and stepped forward to deliver the baby's shoulders and go on through the routine of slapping the baby and clamping the cord, while the mother lay there sobbing and panting, and all the time Baldwin was saying, "Oh, that was *fine!* That was *wonderful!* It didn't really hurt a bit, did it?" and grinning at her. The nurse looked gray; she could hardly hold her hands still to take the baby, and the mother stuck her knuckles in her mouth and turned her face to the wall.

I got out of there fast and just about made it to the doctors' john before I threw up. And then I couldn't get to sleep; I just kept thinking over and over, So *that's* why Baldwin likes Read deliveries so much. . . .

Somebody must have passed the word on Sunday that Emergency Room business was slow, because I had a steady stream of out-patients to see all day Sunday. In the midst of this Dr. Flagg admitted an OB in labor who was to have a general anesthetic, and told me I could deliver her when she got ready, although he wanted to be there. So all afternoon I kept getting calls from the OB nurses that this woman was getting more and more ready to deliver, and I was trying to avoid being tied up sewing up somebody's leg just at the critical moment.

As a final blow Dr. Tony Marin admitted an OB about 6:00 whose baby was lying transverse with no presenting part. He was afraid the cord would prolapse out and decided to section her then and there. It looked as though Flagg's patient would deliver right in the middle of the section, so I begged off scrubbing and took Flagg's patient into the delivery room instead and delivered the baby with him watching.

Monday morning started off with a bang. At 5:30 A.M. Miss Wood woke me up with the news that somebody had just hurled himself out of a fifth-floor window and they wanted me down on Second immediately. Got my shoes on and rushed down to Second, trying all the way to get a cigarette lit. There wasn't a soul in the second-floor corridor when I got there, and when I got to the nurses' station I saw why: everybody was staring out the window that opens onto a section of the first-floor roof. An old man was lying out there, pajamas and all, crumpled up like a rag doll. The orderly was out there with him but scared to touch him. I crawled out through the window, sure at first that the guy must be dead. He wasn't. He was just barely breathing, hemorrhaging from his right ear. He had a Levin tube in his nostril; blood was pouring out around it, and he was sort of gargling with every breath. Then I got a closer look; one leg was twisted and cocked at an off angle and the right side of his skull was crushed in. A three-story fall, and he must have lit right on his head.

Well, the nurses for once didn't seem to have anything at all to say, not one thing, and the orderly was sort of wringing his hands, and all I could think was, Good Christ, what am I going to do with *this* mess? Somehow the orderly and I and an engineer who was standing gawking got the man onto a stretcher and hoisted him through a window into the nurses' station. He was an old patient of Ted Van Wert's in for treatment of his high blood pressure. Apparently he had been very depressed. I tried to suck the blood out of his airway and then called Van Wert to tell him what had happened.

There was a long, long pause, and then Ted said, *"God damn it to hell!* Three times this has happened to me in the last seven years! Why can't they pick somebody else?"* He said to try to keep the guy alive and he'd be right over. I didn't think he'd have time to make it, but when he arrived the man was still gargling, you could at least barely feel a pulse, and his blood pressure was still measurable. Van Wert thought he had a fractured neck as well as skull, and called the neurosurgeon. I had to go back up to the OB floor to get ready to scrub on the two Monday morning sections that were scheduled. It was an exciting thing, in a way, but it was also sickening. Van Wert was just coldly furious. I asked him if he thought the neurosurgeon would try to do anything, and he said, "Sure, I suppose so; he'll probably spend all day up there picking pieces of bone out of that guy's brain, and I'll be damned if I know why we've got to bother."

At the OB staff meeting this evening Goodfellow brought up the notion of having the intern split deliveries with the OB men. No great ground swell of enthusiasm for the idea, even though both Goodfellow and Arnold Prince urged them to give it a try. So I don't know what's going to happen to it, probably nothing. I got the impression that these obstetricians were nothing but a bunch of petty little merchants sitting around jealously guarding their patients from each other, and that the last thing any of them gave a damn for was trying to teach anybody anything about anything.

Wednesday, September 21

Yesterday morning when I came on duty I heard that the old guy who flung himself out the window Monday morning died about midnight without ever regaining consciousness.

The neurosurgeon didn't touch him; he thought the insult of anesthesia and surgery would just bump him over the edge for sure. So he went on out without anybody nudging him along.

For some reason Tuesday was a particularly miserable day. I was depressed about the Monday night meeting, and everything Tuesday went wrong. There were two Caesareans scheduled, one for 8:00 and one to follow. The first wouldn't have been so bad except that Goodfellow had a visiting fireman there to watch, some Italian doctor visiting the States, so he had to put on his "Great American Doctor" act, which was so damned patronizing that I was just embarrassed.

The second section was a mess. The girl was twenty-one and had had three previous sections. Just as they were wheeling her up for anesthesia, Dr. Plotzman began wondering if maybe she was premature, so she was sent down to X-ray to see if the baby looked full term or not on a film. Brought her back up, then took her back down because the first picture didn't show them what they wanted to see. So it was 11:00 before they finally got around to starting the section. Then the spinal anesthesia they wanted to use didn't work; the girl was still sensitive three fingers above the pubis when they were all set to go, and naturally they just couldn't wait for it to take a little better, nothing would do but they go right ahead.

So after pinching her with the tweezers four or five times to see if she still said ouch—and she still did—they tried to get away with local novocaine in the skin for the incision, but she was so uncomfortable and tight they couldn't get into her belly, so they had to give up and give her a gas anesthesia. That meant they really had to hurry to get the baby out, so it wouldn't be slugged too far down with the gas, and then when they got inside they found that whoever had done the previous sections had succeeded in leaving her with a belly full of adhesions. The lower part of the uterus was stuck tight to the abdominal wall, and the bladder was hung up four inches higher than it was supposed to be so they couldn't open the uterus where they wanted, and so on and so on all the way through. All told it was a sloppy, bloody mess, even though they did get a good baby and a good mother. I was depressed enough before I even went in there, so I was really depressed by the time I got out.

Then Tuesday afternoon I had a big squabble with the anesthesia people, who gave a caudal to a patient in labor and then disappeared, so that we had to give the final dose ourselves just before the patient delivered, and then the anesthetist tried to tell me he'd been in the doctors' room all along when I knew damned well he hadn't. I blew up at the guy and then had Don Morehouse on my neck—this anesthesia department just can't seem to stand admitting that they are ever in error in any way. So that just added one more gloomy note to the day.

At least there was one bright spot: a twenty-year-old girl, a patient of Dr. Dick Rivers who had been in two weeks before for diagnosis and then discharged. She'd been having afternoon fevers and swollen lymph glands in her neck and armpits and groin. No diagnosis; she said they'd biopsied the glands without any answer. Now she was back in the house with an FUO (fever of unknown origin), a temp of 104, chills and a dry cough, and was just feeling miserable. I could see nothing exciting until I listened to her heart and found she had a gallop rhythm that was very distinct and a very fast heart rate. At first I thought, My God, she's got rheumatic fever and she's in heart failure; but other things didn't fit that.

Then something caught in my mind about gallop rhythms and young girls, and I asked her if she had ever had a rash on her face. She said, yes, she'd broken out all over her cheeks and across the bridge of her nose when she first got sick. I asked about joint pains, and she said her fingers hurt now, she could hardly bend them, and before her knees had been painful, too. And I thought, Hoodly-doo, you've diagnosed a case of lupus erythematosus that everybody else has missed, a notoriously tough diagnosis to make because the disease has so many really obscure symptoms. I wrote it down on her chart, and ordered some lab work for morning. Then later I saw Pete Carey and told him of my diagnostic coup and found out that lupus had been considered by almost everyone who had seen her. It was Rivers' admitting diagnosis, which just hadn't gotten down on her chart.

So I wasn't all that smart, but still I felt very good that I'd picked it up. Sometimes it seems to me that diagnosis is about half pure chance and half magic. You take a history and do a physical examination with your eyes and ears constantly open for the red flags. So a red flag drops somewhere in the history, something that kicks off a signal, and you start poking around in that direction; or maybe the flag drops because something in the physical exam doesn't seem just right, and all through you are thinking of possibilities and discarding them a mile a minute. I tried later to remember the different things I had thought of while I was working up this case and it was just fantastic. I'd bet I sifted through forty different diagnoses in ten minutes and had at least one solid reason for discarding every one of them. And some of these guys just seem to pick the right answer out of the air every time. How they do it I don't know.

Today wasn't quite as bad a day as Tuesday. Dr. Marin admitted a girl with a threatened abortion, and she started hemorrhaging while she was getting undressed, all over her coat and the floor and the bed and everything. She was so scared she nearly passed out, but we got her clothes off and got her up on the table in Room II and got her quieted down. Found the fetus half in and half out of the cervix when I went to examine her, so as soon as Marin got there we did the D & C—he did half the curettement and let me do the other half. Later this twenty-nine-year-old girl told me that she'd been married five times, had four pregnancies, lost two of them by miscarriage and delivered two term babies. One of them had been adopted out and she had the other at home with her. I wonder what kind of a little wreck he is.

Made rounds on the post partum patients before I went off duty and found one girl with a very sore, red, swollen leg—an acute phlebitis, one of the nastier postdelivery complications you run into. I tried to call her doctor, but couldn't reach him, so I started treatment with hot packs and elevation of the leg and got some lab work ordered for her, in case the doctor wanted to start anticoagulants on her. Later when I reached him, he just said, "Fine, go ahead with what you've started," so I guess I judged right for once.

I was glad for the night off, even if it does mean sitting and coughing all this up before I get to bed.

Saturday, September 24

First a couple of quick follow-ups, since I seem to leave a lot of things hanging in these entries, and then never get back to them. Carey saw me Thursday night and told me that the diagnosis on the girl with the fevers had been established beyond doubt now. Her blood studies for lupus had come back positive this time, and a bone marrow exam had also shown the funny cells that appear in cases of lupus. This is one of the connective tissue diseases in the same family as rheumatic fever and rheumatoid arthritis, only a meaner one; before we had cortisone it was usually rapidly fatal, but now we can control it to some degree at least for a while. The disease I guess gets its name (which means "disease of the red wolf") from the masklike red rash that shows up across the cheekbones and nose of some of the victims. Or maybe it has something to do with lycanthropy; I'm not sure. Anyway, this was one of these cases in which you feel good about making the diagnosis, but you hate yourself for feeling good because it's such a miserable thing to have to diagnose on a nice kid.

Carey also agreed with my diagnosis of the woman with phlebitis. I guess it was caught early, because it got much better just with the hot soaks and elevation, but I'm glad I saw it and got to work on it fast.

Wednesday night Dr. Marin brought in a patient who has turned into a real puzzler. This is Mrs. Wallace, a thirty-one-year-old woman who came in in labor with her first baby. Apparently she pooped along most of the night without making too much progress, then after six or seven hours of labor, just up and stopped. Her membranes had ruptured at home when she started labor, so Marin wanted her to keep on going; he let her rest a while and then started her up again with shots of Pitocin, which is the stuff these guys use pretty routinely for inducing labor. She was on Pit most of the day and still was having an extremely long, unproductive labor. Finally, late Thursday afternoon Marin started giving her Pit by IV drip because her uterus had just pooped out in spite of the shots.

This seemed to me kind of whipping a tired horse, but she started up again and finally dilated and brought the baby down enough for delivery. By then, though, she was chilling and got a little shocky during the delivery, and lost a little more blood than she should have. She had stopped flowing pretty much by the time we got her sewed up and back to her room, but Marin asked me to keep an eye on her and call him if she had any trouble.

She delivered around 5:00 P.M.; at 10:00 the floor nurse on Seventh called me and said Mrs. Wallace wasn't doing too well. She didn't feel particularly bad, but she didn't look good. Blood pressure was a little too low, flowing a little too much, and while I was examining her, she had a chill. I kept thinking about shock from too much bleeding or from the long labor, but that didn't seem to fit. I called Marin, and he ordered some Ergotrate to tighten up her uterus and told me to be sure one of the nurses massaged her belly every fifteen minutes so as to keep the uterus down tight; also told me to get some blood cross-matched and on hand in case we needed it.

Well, the nurse on that floor never was dynamite in a crisis, and I ended up having to do everything myself: get a blood sample for the cross-match, start the IV, the works. When the blood finally came back from the bank, Mrs. Wallace still looked lousy. I started the blood transfusion and then called Wood, the night supervisor, to be sure somebody stood by in the room. Somehow the woman got through the night, but she didn't get any sleep, and she looked like hell in the morning—all upset, exhausted and worried. Marin seemed to think her problem was mainly just exhaustion from the long labor, and pooh-poohed anything else.

All the same, something didn't smell right to me. I looked in a couple of times during the day Friday; by midnight I thought she was doing better.

Then at 5:00 A.M. Saturday they called me that Mrs. Wallace had just awakened from her sleep and had a temperature of 104. I said "You mean a hundred and four-tenths, don't you?" and the nurse said, no, she meant 104. I hurried down there, and the woman said she was feeling pretty good, but she was flushed and *hot*. We sponged her down, and the night nurse started giving me a lot of lip about how she couldn't spend the whole night again with one patient. So I blew my stack and called Wood again and said, "Look, damn it, we've got a sick patient up here on Seventh, and I need a nurse who will pay some attention to me." So Wood came rushing up herself, and we had a real stew about it, but I got Mrs. Wallace's fever broken one way or another.

Marin was upset about the fever. We talked it over on the phone and decided to draw a blood culture and then start penicillin. An hour later he turned up to check her himself and ordered more penicillin, and before I went off for the weekend I briefed Hamilton to watch this woman like a hawk. Old-fashioned childbed fever is a dirty word around a place like this, but I'm afraid that's what Mrs. Wallace has got. What I had thought was shock was really just plain blood poisoning and uterine infection; I'll bet her blood culture is just loaded with streptococcus or staphylococcus. And certainly this girl had the classical setup for childbed fever: early rupture of membranes, a long and exhaustive labor with plenty of semisterile examinations along the way, then the uterine inertia, followed by an exhausted uterus after delivery, compounded by blood loss and shock. I felt bad that it took me so long to get onto this, and Marin should never have missed it. I just hope things go okay over the weekend. Her temp was still 103 when I went off at 11:00 Saturday morning.

I sure was mad at those nurses, though. They get all wound up in their routine idiot work—morning care, baths, meals, charting little things on the charts—and then they resent an emergency as an intrusion and go right on washing people's mouths out and giving back rubs while some patient is dying off in the next bed. They can't seem to understand that the emergency has to come first and morning care be damned. So you scream at them and they hate you and there you are.

Starting Monday, I'll have only one more week of OB service, and I can't say I'm sorry. There is an occasional Mrs. Wallace to keep you on your toes, but so much of the work here is just routine, and sort of a petty routine at that. I was talking to Ted Van Wert over coffee the other morning and said I couldn't see how OB men could stand spending their lives doing this, I just couldn't see where the challenge was. And he agreed, said he'd never understood why doctors would want to spend their lives being "midwives," as he calls them with such magnificent scorn. I'm not exactly looking forward to four or five straight months on surgery either, but it will be pleasant to be relieved of OB.

Tuesday, September 27

Yesterday morning when I came in everybody was running around in circles. Dr. Jason had a patient who had precipitated about ten minutes before, Goodfellow was delivering another patient, and there were two others waiting who weren't ready for delivery yet and wouldn't be for a couple of hours. So I changed into my whites and went on down to the conference. The floor nurse ran into me in the corridor and said, "Boy, you left just in time Saturday!" but she was gone before I could ask her what she meant. I just assumed that they'd had a rough weekend until I saw Hamilton and found out that the patient of Dr. Flagg's I had worked up just before I left Saturday was dead three hours later.

I'd seen the woman, a Mrs. Tupper, about 9:00 in the morning Saturday; she'd been in labor but not very active. Flagg had come in about 10:00 to check her and said he'd be back around noon to check her again; if she was coming along, then he'd let me rupture her membranes. I told him that I'd be gone, so he said he'd do it himself.

Well, there had been no sign of any kind of trouble when I left at 11:00, but apparently half an hour later she started having such violent contractions that the nurse called Dr. Flagg and told him she was afraid the woman was going to rupture her uterus. Now this is a significant thing; those OB nurses know enough about women in labor that they don't get all excited unless something is really alarming. I guess Flagg had wit enough to appreciate this, because he got over to the hospital fast; but by the time he arrived at 11:30 the woman was having extreme respiratory distress along with almost continuous violent uterine contractions. The anesthetist had come down to reinforce the caudal he had put in earlier, and all of a sudden the woman couldn't breathe at all and the bottom dropped out of her blood pressure; she was obviously in shock. The baby's heart sounds had stopped and the violent contractions continued, so Flagg took her into the delivery room and delivered her.

Immediately afterward she went into acute heart failure with pulmonary edema, and by 1:00 Mrs. Tupper had expired in cardiac arrest. Flagg had called Fred Kidder up to see her when she was having so much breathing trouble; I guess he arrived just when she expired, and he opened her chest and massaged her heart, but it was no good. She was quite dead.

And I guess Dr. Flagg was in a state of shock himself; there just wasn't any reason that he could see for this woman dying. He thought at the time she must have had an amniotic fluid embolus, which I'd never even heard of before, one of these one-in-a-million disasters that can happen with a terminal pregnancy. The post-mortem bore him out. Apparently an edge of the placenta had separated or torn on the inside so that the amniotic fluid around the baby had leaked into the placenta; the irritation started the violent contractions, and the pressure of the contractions forced amniotic fluid, hair, the waxy vernix from the baby's skin and a lot of other dirty junk into the mother's blood stream, so that it all jammed up in her lungs and drove her into heart failure and pulmonary edema.

Well, everybody in the hospital was stirred up about it. It was the first maternal death in the delivery room that had occurred at Graystone for several years, and Ed Flagg had to be the unlucky doctor. If it had been Goodfellow, nobody would have said anything; but with Flagg, who is a GP and not an obstetrician by specialty, everybody was yapping about whether there was anything that could have been done that wasn't, and wondering exactly what happened. It had all happened so damned fast that nobody knew which end was up, and it's true that Flagg didn't recognize what was really going on until the woman was nearly dead; he admitted it, but he's still in a thoroughly unpleasant position.

After the surgical conference Monday, he and two or three of the OB men were standing around rehashing the thing in the doctors' room. I heard their description of how it happened, and I had to open my big yap and ask why they had started an IV of plasma going if they thought she was in pulmonary edema. Flagg just said, hell, he hadn't known *what* she was in, except shock with no blood pressure to speak of. One of the OB men asked me what I would have done if I'd suspected pulmonary edema in a case like that. I said, well, I'd give her morphine first, and then get tourniquets on her arms and legs, and then digitalize her and then give her Aminophyllin, in that order. So the OB man said that all that was fine, but not one of those things would have made a damned bit of difference in this case, except maybe to have kept her alive an extra fifteen minutes. She would have died anyway, and the only thing that might have saved her would have been an on-the-spot Caesarean, right there in the labor room bed without anesthetic, the first half-hour she started having the violent contractions. And the trouble with that was that no OB man would have condoned it on the basis of what could be seen then; you could only say that would have been the right treatment if you knew what would happen later if you didn't do it.

It'll be interesting to see what is said about this at the next OB staff meeting. Any death in the house is hashed out in open meeting, and everyone has a chance to say what they think was right or wrong about the treatment. I guess they get pretty critical sometimes, too. I know back in May someone had had a patient who ruptured her uterus, and the doctor mishandled the case. The woman survived, but the case came up at the staff meeting, and a resolution was passed to censure the doctor for his handling of the case, and the record of the censure vote was sent to Nathan Slater, who is over-all chief of the surgical and OB divisions of the hospital, for entry into the hospital records. This is more than just lip service discipline, too; the Executive Committee of the hospital can rescind the doctor's hospital privileges, or even kick him off the staff, if they see fit. You rescind a GP's obstetrical privileges at the hospital and he just has to give up taking OB cases, which means a good third of his practice is shot right there.

I thought when I left Saturday that Marin's patient Mrs. Wallace would either be dead or cured of her infection by the time I got back Monday. But she was still sick, still spiking fevers to 103 and still coming up with nice little surprises for us. The lab found Gram-negative bacilli in the blood culture I had drawn on Thursday night, and they were in quite a stew trying to identify exactly what kind of intestinal organism it was.

I got to thinking about the way this infection had been behaving—the undulating fever, the surprisingly low white blood count, the over-all toxicity of the patient—and began wondering if we had a nice live case of typhoid fever on our hands. I mentioned this to Marin Monday morning, and he said, "Boy, you're cheerful this morning, aren't you?" It would be a rare and unusual thing to have turn up, but if it *did* turn out to be typhoid, we'd really have a mess on our hands. That woman had been on the seventh floor without any isolation for a week now, and almost everybody in the hospital had been near her at one time or another.

Since the meeting last Monday most of the doctors have been letting me do a little more than stand around. I'll probably end up with a total of about twenty deliveries and enough experience with episiotomy repairs and D & Cs that I will at least know how they're done. I think I could handle almost any uncomplicated delivery with outlet forceps under a caudal or general anesthetic now without too much trouble. I could probably handle a minor complication like a posterior presentation, too. There are some things I've missed: I've only seen one breech delivery, and no twins at all, but I wouldn't have been allowed to do much on such cases anyway. On the other hand, I've seen plenty of the care and treatment of threatened abortions and incomplete abortions, and altogether too many Caesareans. All in all, the service has been much better since I started screaming about it than it was at the beginning of the month, but then that could just be that the men have gotten used to having me around, too.

I was up all night Monday with fool's errands. Today was uneventful, a couple of utterly normal deliveries was all. Got off at 5:00 on the dot, for a pleasant change.

Thursday, September 29

Breakfast with Andy on Wednesday at 7:15. These breakfast meetings with Case are really getting to be a chore. You can complain, but nothing ever happens, just excuses. Case seems a little more friendly than he was, but he still is certainly an odd little bastard; you never know whether you dare joke with him or have to take everything dead serious all the time.

Up on the seventh floor I found that Marin had called Ted Van

Wert in to consult on Mrs. Wallace. The lab reported that the bug was definitely not typhoid, so that bright idea is out. The patient is still spiking temps up to 101 every day, but she's feeling and looking better. This may end up one of those cases that never really does get diagnosed for sure; you just fumble around with them and presently they get well. Van Wert didn't have very much to offer: keep her at bed rest and keep giving her the Chloromycetin.

Relatively quiet all day Wednesday, except that I had a particularly nasty job handed to me during the afternoon. A woman had delivered a premature baby over the weekend, a sick little thing that hadn't done well from the start, and Wednesday afternoon the baby died. I called the mother's doctor, an outside GP, to tell him. He wanted me to tell the mother the news and get permission for a post. I tried as diplomatically as possible to tell him I thought that this was his job, not mine, but no dice, he said she was all prepared for the news anyway, knew the baby was in trouble, so I should just go ahead and tell her. So I had to go in and give her the news.

She was a big, fat, sad-faced lady. I tried not to be any more blunt than necessary, but I suppose I sounded pretty crude. I just said that I'd been talking to her doctor and he had asked me to tell her that the baby had just passed away. She didn't say anything, just sat there with big tears rolling down her cheeks. Maybe she was prepared, but I wonder; as long as a baby is still living, no matter how sick, I don't think any woman will really believe it's going to die. She'll just keep telling herself that the doctor is wrong and that everything will be all right, so when the baby does die it's as much a blow as if you hadn't told her anything at all in advance. I sat there like a dolt while she wept, and then asked her about a post, and she gave permission. I don't know what the post will show. Maybe it's worth it, but I still think this sort of thing is about the ugliest of all jobs the intern has to do.

Things were suspiciously quiet all Wednesday afternoon. Then about 7:30 four OB patients came in back to back. One of them was Dr. Jason's patient, a twenty-two-year-old girl with her fourth pregnancy, a "NO INFORMATION" case. I thought she was almost ready to deliver when I checked her. So the nurses called Jason, but apparently I had misjudged. He thought she had a way to go yet, but he stayed around and called Miss Harrison to come in, too. This happened to be her day off, but she came in anyway, dressed fit to kill.

In fact, it was really very strange. Harrison is a pretty good-looking woman, maybe forty years old, but looks more like thirty until you look close. Last night she came in wearing the oddest getup I ever did see: a short fur jacket of some sort worn over a tweed suit with a *décolletage* clear down to her belly button and a black lace slip underneath which hung down about two inches lower than her skirt. Even more amazing, she came in accompanied by Jason's wife, a woman of about thirty-five, who was also not bad-looking. Jason himself must be fifty or fifty-five. Well, this trio sat around the labor floor all evening waiting for that patient to deliver, and it reminded me of the Mad Tea Party. Apparently Harrison and Jason's wife are very good friends, get along well. I should say Jason's second wife, or third—nobody seems to know how many times he's been married.

Well, it's none of my business, but I am just plain baffled by this guy and his *ménage*. He complains that he's paying alimony like the devil to his ex-wife; I also get the distinct impression that he's making a whale of a lot of money. He also has an awful lot of patients admitted as "NO INFORMATION" who adopt out their babies. I asked him once what happened to these babies, and he just said very offhandedly that adoptions were arranged. This may all be perfectly aboveboard; privately arranged adoptions aren't illegal in this state. But I'll bet this is one of the places where Jason gets his money. And I wouldn't be at all surprised to read in the newspaper some morning that he'd been stabbed to death with a French bayonet, under mysterious circumstances.

Dr. Bensen also had a patient, a girl who wanted to go Read. She did all right, but Bensen was no help. He is a sort of an old-maidish guy who obviously disapproved of the whole idea. He fiddled around and put in some novocaine for the episiotomy, and then cut it, put in a little more novocaine and cut a little more, patted the lady on the tummy and sort of fluttered around wringing his hands and telling her to do this and try that while she howled, and then put in a little more novocaine and cut the episiotomy a little wider, so she finally got the baby out all right. Bensen is an inoffensive little guy, but he surely doesn't exactly inspire confidence. I was glad that one was over.

I was up and down all Wednesday night with a call from somewhere about every hour. Sometimes I wonder why I bother to go to bed at all on nights like that. Finally gave up at 6:30 A.M. Thursday. A routine day until 1:00; I got an hour's sleep just before noon and then went down for a leisurely lunch. Back on the labor floor the nurses greeted me with open arms and told me that a patient of Dr. Plotzman's had just been admitted who looked like death warmed over. I went in and looked, and she sure as hell did. She was seven months pregnant and had suddenly started bleeding copiously, soaked clear through a thick Turkish bath towel on the way in to the hospital. She looked as white as my intern's jacket.

I knew we had trouble on our hands; fortunately, I didn't know how much. The girls said that Dr. Plotzman was coming in, so I went ahead finding out what I could. She was thirty-five years old, had four children and had gotten sick with belly pain and vomiting the night before. Now her uterus was hard as a rock, as though it were in continuous contraction. She was moaning with severe pain in her back and said she hadn't felt the baby move since the night before. I listened for fetal heart tones and didn't find any.

With this sort of history it had to be either a placenta previa or a premature separation of the placenta. Sometimes for no known reason the placenta just comes unglued before term, bleeds into the uterus and kills the baby; sometimes causes fatal hemorrhage for the mother unless somebody stops it. I was pretty sure this was a separation because of that hard, tight uterus. Dr. Plotzman came in, and I told him what I thought the trouble was, and he said, "Yes, I guess you're probably right," before he even went near the patient. I felt enormously relieved that he had arrived—until I discovered that Dr. Plotzman didn't have the vaguest idea what to do. He took one look at this bleeding woman and started sweating and flew all to pieces. He came in just as I finished examining her, and he said, "Well, what do you think we ought to do, maybe call an OB man to see her?" I said, "Fine, but who?" And he said, "Well, call anybody you want, just call somebody."

I just stared at him, and then I realized he meant it. He was literally paralyzed. Ordinarily if a man wants a consultant, he at least decides who he wants to call, but I wasn't going to argue, we needed somebody fast. I said, okay, I'd call somebody, but we needed some blood on hand before we did anything else, the rate she was bleeding. He said, "Well, fine, let's get some blood then. You order it." So I drew blood for typing and cross-matching, and then got an IV started so we'd have a vein open. Dr. Plotzman stood around wringing his hands. He was all over the place, all excited, asking me what we should do, and then just seconding anything I suggested. Suddenly I realized that this man was going to flunk out. He was simply abdicating, dumping this thing right in my lap, and if any decisions were going to be made, I was going to have to make them.

Well, I walked out of there and called Ben Boggs. The first thing he said was to get some blood cross-matched, so I told him I'd already done that. He said he'd be over in ten or fifteen minutes. Back in the room Plotzman said, "Why don't you do a rectal exam and see if the baby's in the birth canal?" and like an ass I went ahead and did one, the one damned thing you just should never do under these circumstances. Well, I found out it wasn't a placenta previa, I guess; if it had been, she'd have been dead right then. I could feel the baby's head down quite low, and there was no placenta in the way.

Boggs came in a few minutes later, and I told him I'd done a rectal, even though I knew he'd ream me out. He just shook his head and said, "Boy, you like to take chances, don't you?" But knowing the baby's head was down was some help, at least. Boggs went ahead with a sterile vaginal exam and ruptured the membranes. He agreed that she had a premature separation, but he thought the baby's head in the birth canal would help stop the bleeding, and then we could push the labor with Pitocin until we could get the baby delivered. Sure enough, a little after the membranes were ruptured the bleeding slowed down and the woman started having active labor pains.

By then it seemed Dr. Plotzman was getting brave again or something; he seemed to resent my having called Boggs at all. Boggs asked him point-blank who he wanted to handle the case, and Plotzman hedged, said he didn't know, and Boggs lost his temper and said, "Okay, then you take it over, and if you get in trouble, call Goodfellow or somebody," and stalked out.

Well, we sat on this gal all afternoon, or at least I did. Plotzman didn't know whether to Pit her or not, or with how much Pitocin, or whether to give her the blood that came in, or what, so I ended up doing exactly what I wanted to do and practically ignoring Plotzman, who retired back to the doctors' room and read *Life* magazine all afternoon. The patient kept bleeding by fits and starts, and by evening I finally called Goodfellow, who came to see her. He thought she was dilating, but not fast enough, so he suggested I slug her down with scopolamine and morphine and Seconal all at once, really knock her out into left field, so she would relax and bring the baby down. Then he went on to a meeting, where I could reach him easily.

It was a long pull. I was supposed to be off at 5:00, but Hamilton was tied up with trouble on the medical floor and I couldn't see leaving this gal to Plotzman's mercies. Anyway I wanted to see it through now, so I stayed over. Thought I heard fetal heart tones at one point late in the afternoon, but Goodfellow said, no, it was the mother's pulse I was hearing. When she finally relaxed, she did bring the baby's head down. When she was getting ready to be delivered, I called Goodfellow at his meeting; he said if the bleeding had subsided and her pressure was staying up that I should go ahead and deliver her. "I don't think you'll have any trouble, and the bleeding will stop as soon as you deliver the placenta. I can get over there in five minutes if you have any trouble."

By then she was having good solid contractions; I barely got scrubbed, and delivered her without trouble. The baby was dead. No stretching or lacerations, and then before the placenta came, out rolled about two quarts of old, black, clotted blood that had been sitting in there all the time. She must have been bleeding into the uterus all the night before. She didn't have any fresh blood loss, though, so I think she will survive.

All in all, it was a heartbreaking afternoon. I suppose I should be glad the woman made it; she might well not have. But I keep thinking she made it in spite of her doctors. It shook me up to see a supposedly competent doctor just fall apart in the face of an emergency, and I was in limbo myself, uncertain of what I was supposed to do or what should be done or even who to ask for help. And Boggs and Goodfellow were both disgusted and handcuffed, I guess. We sneaked by all right, but none of us can take much credit, I'm afraid.

Got out and home about 10:00; realized as I got dressed that I hadn't thought of calling Ann that I'd be late, so that contributed to the domestic joy no end. A great day.

Friday, September 30

This was my short day—merely 8:00 to 5:00—with a long weekend coming up. Not much all day, really. I saw Plotzman's patient, who is bearing up under the loss of her baby pretty well. She's really a sweet lady. I asked the nurses to move her downstairs where she wouldn't have to sit and listen to the babies crying in the nursery, and I think she was glad for that.

Friday afternoon Boggs had a D & C to do and asked me to scrub. Did it all himself, and then told me to feel the inside of the uterus with a blunt curette if I wanted to. I almost laughed in his face, but I dutifully sat down and felt around with the blunt curette, and later said, "Gosh, Ben, I sure appreciated that," and the arrogant bastard actually thought I was serious. I think it's good that I'm getting off this service. One of these days I'll just come unglued and let one of these birds have both barrels. With rock salt, not buckshot.

This evening we had Pete Carey and his wife to dinner and spent the evening talking about the hospital and the doctors. Pete and I did, that is; I guess the girls went out to look at the yard or something. Pete has been working very, very hard this month trying to hold up the Medicine II service without an intern. He looked tired and gray and got surprisingly happy on one martini. He doesn't know if he wants to stay at Graystone for another year of residency or go somewhere else. He's spent this month trying to keep Kidder, Case and Rivers happy all at once. They're the three worst perfectionists in the whole clinic, and I guess they've been riding him.

It's funny how different these guys are. Peterson and Smithers are good, sharp clinicians, probably among the best internists in the Southwest, and they're relaxed and helpful and easy to work with.

Kidder and Case are equally top-rate men, Kidder maybe even a brilliant man, yet they will ride an intern or resident into the ground. Van Wert probably works harder than any of them, but he just ignores the house staff for the most part, and he's so painfully sarcastic and arrogant you can hardly stand to be around him half the time. Trouble is, you can't pick and choose in a residency; you get the sheep with the goats. Pete's just had too many goats recently.

Anyway, it was a good beefing session. It would be nice to just take off this weekend and go somewhere. Anywhere, you name it. Instead, I've got duty, and it'll probably be a bitch since it's my last run on OB.

Sunday, October 2

A confusing and frustrating weekend. I suppose I was expecting it to be crappy, and so it was. Amazing the difference your frame of mind makes. This will be bits and snatches without much organization, I'm afraid; everything seems to have gotten jumbled together.

Saturday night Boggs broke down and let me do a whole episiotomy repair all by myself. If I hadn't been so mad, it would have been funny. He had this primip in, and he was going to some party, said to call him when she was ready and he'd get over in five minutes by cab. Well, she moved faster than we expected; at about 9:00 I called Boggs, who came rushing in with a few drinks under his belt, and struggled out of his tuxedo and studs and into a scrub suit and rushed into the delivery room in nothing flat. He was in a hurry, so there was strictly no nonsense with this delivery, none of the old patter and holding up the shoehorns and flopping the placenta around. The girl jumped up on the table, and he applied the forceps and pulled the baby out and that was that.

Then he asked me in a whisper how well I could repair episiotomies, so I whispered back that I could do it pretty good, so he said, well, fine, he was going to let me do this one. So we went up to the girl and said, "Now, the doctor is going to do a little sewing down here and put you back together again," and hustled out, then hustled right back in and whispered to me, "Now take your time and do a good job, get it good and tight." My big bid for fame.

Well, I repaired his episiotomy for him, and I got it tight, by
God—that girl is going to have a tight bottom for a week.

I know I've built up a great deal of personal antagonism for this
joker in the past few weeks, even though I have to live with him.
Goodfellow at least has followed through faithfully on the participation scheme, even when it meant some inconvenience for him;
Boggs just chucked it all out the window after the second day.
Everything is strictly 100 percent for Boggs. He could let the intern
do a lot of work if he wanted to bother; he just doesn't want to
bother. So this is the sort of guy you have to put up with.

[*Post hoc:* Years later I was discussing my distaste for Ben Boggs
with an OB man who had taken his training with him, and got another view of the man which I think was valid, although I didn't see
it during internship. "Ben can really be a shit sometimes," the man
said, "and he can be ruthless and crude, but you've got to give him
credit: he's not scared of anything or anybody. Hand Ben a rough
one and he'll ride it through to the bitter end and argue about it
later. I was with him one time when he examined a girl with an
unsuspected previa and ran his finger through the placenta. The
bed was full of blood before he could pull his hand away, she just
started to gush, and Ben just looked at her and said, 'Get me a
knife,' and had her open and the baby and placenta out of there in
two minutes flat. She would have bled to death in five, and he saved
mother and baby both. Any other man in town would have lost
them, and that includes Horace Goodfellow." So there is more to
the game than meets the eye.]

Saturday and Sunday just sort of dissolved into a blur, not so
much busy as tiring. Something was going on all the time around
the clock both days. Saturday I had mostly medical admissions, but
got called out for three or four deliveries Saturday night, neatly
spaced so that I just barely got to sleep after one before being
dragged out for the next. At 4:30 A.M. Miss Wood called me to see a
man in the Emergency Room who thought he had run a sliver of
lead into his finger the previous afternoon (he hadn't) and now had
decided the time had come to have it looked at. These are the ones
that give you unhealthy fantasies about what sheer pleasure it
would be just to shoot them through the head.

Most of Sunday I was so damned beat that all I could think of all day was getting back to bed. I'd get there and lie around for a half-hour trying to get to sleep, and just be dozing off when somebody would page me for something. By Sunday evening I was really tired, and hit one of those exhausted spells of real depression that I seem to have every now and then. I was sitting up in the OB doctors' room looking out the window at the city and the desert and watching the sun setting behind the mountains, and suddenly I felt low enough to start bawling.

I don't know quite how to handle this particular feeling when it comes on fast like that. I was thinking that I'd only finished three months of the twelve on this hitch, and it had seemed more like twenty years; it looked as though it was going to stretch on and on forever. I told myself that presently this particular weekend would be over and I would get some rest, and I knew perfectly well that after a night off I'd bounce back and everything would be rosy again. But this doesn't alter the fact that there is going to be another weekend just exactly like this one or worse, two weeks from now, and after that one another, and I can look forward to weekend after weekend like this before it's over, and it gets very discouraging.

This seems like such an endless task. It just keeps going on and on and on. You never really finish anything; there's never any real sense of satisfaction with a job completed. I'm fulfilling a function here, I guess, but it doesn't often seem like a very necessary function; in many respects I'm being used like a machine in the assembly line without being particularly liked or respected in any way. Certainly this OB service has seemed that way. I don't know if the surgical service coming up will be any different or not. I hope so. What's missing is a sense of participation, maybe, a sense of meaning to it. It's hard to grasp where it is all going or to feel that there's any real point to it. Self-pity, maybe, but this particular evening I really hit rock bottom. Finally, in desperation for something to do, I went down and worked on charts in the record room for a couple of hours, and then got called up for a delivery.

Saw Roscoe Herring at supper at 10:30, and he was looking for a crying towel, too. Dr. Slater had some very important person coming in, some rich social bitch who had sprained her ankle two days before. So. Dr. Slater had called Dr. Mel Tanner to come in, and called for the X-ray girl to come in, and then came in himself just to be sure things were really done right. Seems the woman didn't have any fracture, not even much of a sprain; they put her to bed with a hot-water bag on her foot and a pat on her fanny, but not before Dr. Slater had called in the whole damned staff and gotten every-body in a stew. So poor Roscoe was feeling put upon. I asked him why all the fuss about a sprained ankle, and he said, "Who knows? Sometimes Slater just gets a bug up his ass, that's all. You'll find out." So I guess Herring is as glad to be getting off Slater's surgical service as I am to be getting off OB.

Went to bed about 11:00, telling Miss Tuttle not to drag me out unless somebody really needed some help with something. She called me at 3:00 because a patient was about to deliver in bed and her doctor wasn't there. So I got her set up in the delivery room and was just delivering the baby when Dr. McClintock walked in. He didn't even scrub, just came in and chewed the fat with the lady while I did the repair.

Back to bed at 4:00 A.M., up at 5:00 to see a new admission of Franklin's on the fifth floor, a man with a stroke. I had him half worked up before it dawned that I wasn't supposed to be covering that service. I was finishing the work up when Herring came down looking sad and sleepless and said he'd just admitted a coronary on my service, so everybody was confused. While we were talking, the OB floor called to tell me that one of Dr. Howard's patients that I'd been waiting for all month had finally come in, crowning, and would I please come up because Dr. Howard was there waiting.

So I went upstairs and delivered Howard's patient, and by then it was 7:00, so I didn't get back to bed, just went down and ate some breakfast. And thus ended up my OB service, with a sort of a whimper. The change of service was scheduled for 8:00 A.M., so at 7:45 I walked over to the clinic for the Monday morning surgical conference, and to start my first day on the surgical service.

III

Surgery I (Slater's Service)

I had not realized, until I reread this journal years later, the degree to which the shadow of Dr. Nathan Slater fell across every service of my internship at Graystone Memorial Hospital, and especially over the two months I spent on Surgery I. Physically Slater was unimpressive: a small, wiry man with a hawk face, a sharp nasal voice and a curious resemblance to a fox. Yet of all the medical men I encountered there, Nathan Slater clearly towers head and shoulders above the rest.

Slater was a surgeon, first, last and always, and he was one of the best surgeons in the game. In a way this prejudiced me against him, for I had no interest whatever in a career in surgery, then or now. He was not the only surgeon on Surgery I, but he was the one with whom I was thrust into contact day after day, in operating room and corridor, for two long and lively months. To me at that time he was an enigmatic man, sometimes totally admirable, sometimes unbearable. Some of his curious qualities I am sure he shared in common with every surgeon of stature in the world, but some things were uniquely Nathan Slater and no one else.

As Chief of Surgery, his power over the practice of surgery at Graystone (and indeed, over the medical services as well) was all but absolute. What Slater decided became law. One could hardly consider him *benevolent* in his exercise of that power, but the fact that he wielded it with honor and decency, and above all with restraint, was a measure of his stature. I may not have liked him very well, and his service was demanding in the extreme. But I think he molded my feelings and influenced my thinking about the practice of medicine far more than I had any idea during the time I was working with him.

I last encountered Nathan Slater at Graystone Hospital only a few weeks ago. The years showed their mark: he seemed a little bit smaller, a little bit older and more tired, and a little bit more wizened than before. But there was the same quality of restless impatience, the same biting nasal voice, the same aura of coiled-spring tension about the man that I remembered so well from my intern year. Above all, there was the same uncanny resemblance to a quick brown fox—wise, sly, impossible to outdo—that had struck me the first day I met him in his own bailiwick, the hospital operating room, at the beginning of my surgical service those several-odd years ago. Some things in medicine do not change.

THE JOURNAL, OCTOBER AND NOVEMBER

Monday, October 3

Change of service may make things a little bit muddled here. According to the hospital terminology this is formally called Surgery I. Among the house staff it is also called "Slater's Service" to distinguish it from Surgery II, which is mainly the service of Dr. Arthur Emery and Dr. Matthew Meadows. Apparently there is some sort of internal warfare going on here that I don't entirely understand—a sort of pecking order or tacitly acknowledged hierarchy or some such thing, like the Lodges speaking only to the Cabots and the Cabots speaking only to God. And I gather that in this case Dr. Nathan Slater is God, except that Dr. Emery obstinately refuses to acknowledge the fact.

The arrangement of interns and residents is also confusing, except on the top levels. Ivy, Herring and I are all on surgical services this month (Schwartz is in the Children's Division now), but there are far more surgical residents than interns, some in first- and second-year residency, some in third and one even in fourth. As the intern on Surgery I, my job is to work up and scrub on Slater's cases first and Dr. Leo Richards' second; then if there is any time left over, I'll be assigned to Goodfellow's gynecological cases. Slater does general surgery, but mostly abdominal cases, while Richards' are mostly chest, heart and blood vessel surgery. But since the really

Big Name heart surgeon in the area is at County Hospital and Leo Richards is quite new in the Graystone Clinic, I guess Richards' heart cases are few and far between.

Slater has two surgical residents assigned to him alone: Fred Olsen and Henry Ruggles, universally known as "Hank." Fred is a third-year resident, but he just got married and is gone for two weeks on his honeymoon, so Hank Ruggles will be in direct charge of my activities. Ruggles is a fourth-year resident, and is Slater's Fellow—a sort of elite assistantship that goes to one favored fourth-year man each year. I guess this is considered quite a plum. Dr. Emery also has a Fellow—Dr. Virgil Aarons—and then there are several first- and second-year residents who second-assist Slater and first-assist some of the other men.

I got all this briefing by bits and snatches from Roscoe Herring, who just got off Slater's service. He didn't like it, but then Roscoe hasn't liked anything very much so it's hard to judge. Lots of Roscoe's long, sad tales of woe haven't sounded too unbearably woeful to me; so I'll just have to find out for myself.

I went down to the Monday morning surgical conference, where Dr. Calvin Cornell was talking about spinal cord injuries. It was a pretty interesting talk, but, Jesus, I could hardly stay awake through it, I was so damned tired. By exercise of will I managed to keep my eyes open and look interested.

Cornell is a tall, skinny, cadaverous-looking guy with a death's-head face and eyes that bore right through you. When he shambles down the hall, he looks like something is going to fall off him any minute. He's the neurosurgeon on the clinic staff, extremely conservative, won't operate on anybody if he can possibly avoid it. Furthermore, I've heard that whenever a patient dies on him, which is frequently, he falls into a black mood for a week and won't speak to anyone. When he's in a good mood, he has a sort of dry sense of humor and a grin that looks like it comes from the other side of the grave. All through this wretched talk he kept looking at me and grinning, so I managed to keep awake somehow.

After it was over I went up to the sixth floor. I already had the mimeographed "op schedule" they hand out each night for the next day, but the big blackboard on Sixth is more up to date, lists the surgeon, the kind of case, the time and room where it's scheduled,

and the intern and resident assigned to assist. Slater had five operations scheduled; I was assigned to two of them. One was listed as
"revision of colostomy" and the other an abdominal laparotomy—a
surgical incision into the abdomen for exploratory purposes. These
were patients that Herring had admitted and worked up yesterday
afternoon for surgery this morning, so I didn't know any of them.

Slater had already started his first case in Room I; I was to scrub
on the colostomy case with Phil Barr, a first-year resident, and Slater
would be joining us. So Barr and I scrubbed and walked into Room
II and found the patient already there and anesthetized. Or rather,
we found this little old belly protruding from a great heap of sterile
drapes, with a colostomy orifice centered right in the middle. I
couldn't even tell if it was a male belly or a female belly. We
gowned and gloved, and then a nurse came in from Room I with
the message that Dr. Slater wanted Dr. Barr to go ahead and start.

So Barr fussed around a while and looked stupid; finally he took
the bull by the horns, started a skin incision from an inch above the
colostomy orifice and carried it around and down two inches below
and started peeling back the fascia. Just then Hank Ruggles came
in and nearly went through the roof; seems all Slater wanted to do
was make a little circular incision around the colostomy to free
some scarring, and then close it up again. So Barr got sent packing
into Room I to help Slater there and Ruggles took this over, grum-
bling about turning a simple operation into a major operation, and
mutter, mutter, mutter. Ruggles is a grim-faced little guy with a
pair of the coldest blue eyes I've ever looked into. If he has a sense
of humor, he kept it tucked away somewhere this morning. I
haven't seen much of him until now, since he's usually either in the
Operating Room or over in the clinic with Slater. So I don't know
how we'll get along.

Anyway, we got this colostomy loosened up—Slater never did
come in—and finished about 10:00 A.M. I escorted the patient (it
turned out to be a lady) down to her room on Fourth with the aid
of the anesthetist, then ducked down and checked the mail. Came
back up to Sixth and found that the patient for the exploratory
was an old man about sixty-seven that Dr. Peterson had referred to
Slater. A long history of diarrhea, then vomiting and off-and-on
partial bowel obstruction, with no diagnosis. So Slater had decided

that the old boy should be looked into. Literally. Ruggles and I scrubbed, and then Ruggles proceeded to open up the man's abdomen, with me snapping the skin bleeders and retracting the fascia and muscle. Slater as yet had made no appearance whatsoever.

We got into his abdomen and found that he had nodules of metastatic cancer in his liver, so Ruggles set about looking for the primary tumor. He seemed to think he'd find it in the pancreas, but the pancreas was fine. Then down along the small intestine he found little islands of cancer all over the place. He sent one nodule over to pathology for a frozen section; it turned out to be carcinoid —a multiple cancer that might not have any primary source. The whole bowel was twisted and matted with the stuff; some even looked gangrenous.

While Ruggles was rooting around in there, Slater came in from the adjoining room and stuck his hand in, and said, "Well, there you are—now we know." He called Dr. Peterson in to take a peek in, since he was wondering about the diagnosis. Peterson asked Slater if there was anything to be done for it surgically, and Slater said, "Well, not unless you want to disembowel him completely. His gut is obstructed from top to bottom, and I don't think I can offer him an extra day."

So he told Ruggles to close the man up again, and that was that. I guess they'd hoped to find a single primary cancer of the colon that could be resected; as it is, this man has three months at the outside, and may well never recover from the surgery before the obstruction gets him.

We finished this case about 1:30 and went down to lunch. Ann thinks it's horrible to go down and stuff your face with food after spending the morning looking at some poor old guy who's rotting away inside, but when you stand on your pegs in that place for three or four hours straight, you're just plain hungry.

About 2:00 Roscoe helped me move my stuff down from the OB doctors' room into the interns' quarters again, and I hit the sack at 2:30 for an hour's nap.

Woke up at 4:00 and found that I had only one admission, which amazed me; all I've heard from Roscoe was how I would get out of the OR at 3:00 and find twenty-five new patients waiting for work-ups. This patient was a girl of twenty-eight, a patient of Slater's with a very strange story. Last January she quit menstruating and noticed her abdomen enlarging. A rabbit test was positive, so naturally everybody assumed she was pregnant. Trouble was she kept getting too pregnant too fast; by the second month she was bulging clear up to the belly button. So Slater had opened her up and found that she had a huge cyst of the ovary which had a dysgerminoma in it. This is a very rare and strange tumor which can be either malignant or benign, and you can't be sure which. You can only remove it and wait to see what happens. Slater had treated her as if it were malignant, did a complete pelvic clean-out, but now she was back because she has more masses in her belly and an enlarged spleen, as well as back pain and a dry cough. When I worked her up, she looked like she had cancer. A good-looking girl, but gray-looking, no appetite, losing weight. We'll find out Wednesday, which is when Slater has her scheduled.

Andy Case, the bastard, came in and made an ass of me while I was working up this girl. I was busy concentrating on this lurid pelvic history and failed completely to hear a heart murmur, or even notice a long scar she had on her chest. So Case just said, "What kind of a heart lesion do you think this young lady had, Doctor?" and all I could do was say, "Well, now, uh . . ." He gave me a big old grin and said, "Be careful you don't get too sloppy on this surgical service, now," and walked out. I found out she'd had a patent ductus repaired when she was twenty-one, and sure as hell she had a murmur loud enough to hear without a stethoscope. I just hadn't heard it.

I guess this may be a problem, too—the getting sloppy bit. Surgical work-ups have to be fast because I may have ten or twelve in a day just as routine, and can't do them until I'm out of the OR. Half the time, I gather, you just check the patient to be sure he's breathing. But I shouldn't have missed something like that, and it would have to be Case that caught me out. Well, maybe I'll pick up something next time that Case misses. Who knows?

Got off duty at 5:45 and met Ann waiting for me down in the lobby. I understand that I'll more likely get off anywhere from 7:00 to 10:00 on my nights off. Slater operates on Mondays, Wednesdays and Fridays, and patients are usually admitted the afternoon before their surgery, so Tuesdays, Thursdays and Sundays will be my bad days. Sunday afternoons are the real horrors, from what I hear: those boys are all rested up from their weekends, and like to have a busy day of whacking and cutting on Monday. On OB I almost always got off close to 5:00, so Ann has been coming over after work and waiting. We'll probably have to work out some other system or she'll spend an awful lot of evenings in that hospital lobby.

Wednesday, October 5

After Monday's slow start, things picked up on Tuesday and Wednesday. The operating rooms are short-handed enough for help without having somebody gone for a honeymoon, so I'm assigned to scrub with other men on the days Slater doesn't operate. Ruggles spends those days in the clinic with Slater. Tuesday I helped Good-fellow with a varicose vein ligation. He still insists on talking all the way through a procedure, demonstrating this and pointing out that. Seemed to make an awful fuss about a piddly little operation, just squeezing off somebody's veins and tying them. [*Post hoc:* I found out later in the year that this "piddly little operation" could cost a patient her leg unless the surgeon made a "fuss" about doing it right.]

I had a few minutes' break after that for a cup of coffee, then scrubbed in on a case with Dr. Jack Barley. Patient was a girl with a lump in her thyroid; he was going to do a subtotal thyroidectomy. Barley is an outside doctor with a reputation as a pretty slick surgeon, but this case was a bloody mess. Whatever he'd used pre-operatively to cut down on activity of the gland hadn't worked very well; the gland was extremely vascular and bled every place he touched it. So it was pick, pick, pick for three and a half hours. We must have tied two hundred bleeders.

This is a very busy operating suite, even though there is an awful lot of lost time between cases. While the intern helps get the fin-ished patient down to his room, the nurses have to clean and set up the operating room for the next case, and the anesthetist has to get the next patient up and get anesthesia started. Takes anywhere from half an hour to an hour. During this time you sit around the doctors' lounge, while the resident dictates his detailed account of the operation just done for the patient's permanent hospital record.

I've been a little surprised at how fussy they are about these reports. They have to be dictated immediately after the surgery, with everything described just so, and then signed by the surgeon, not the resident, after they've been typed up. Ultimately these reports are reviewed by the hospital Records Committee. This insures accurate records, and also cuts down on the amount of fishy surgery that gets done. If the description of the pathology in your "op note" doesn't jibe with the pathologist's report on the tissue you send down for examination, the discrepancy gets spotted and the Chief of Surgery wants to know what's up.

There's even a more sneaky safeguard: before any surgeon, even Slater himself, picks up his knife on a case, he's got to write his "preoperative diagnosis" down in a big ledger in the hall outside the OR. Then the postoperative diagnosis from his operative record and the pathological diagnosis go down in adjoining columns later. Of course, the preoperative diagnosis often turns out to be wrong, but if somebody takes out too many "acute" appendices that the pathologist examines and finds "normal," that surgeon has to explain sooner or later why his diagnosis is wrong so many times, and he can lose his surgical privileges if the Chief of Surgery doesn't like his explanation.

[Post hoc: Strangely enough, he may also be called to task if he's right too often! The experts say that unless about one out of four of his appendix reports come back normal, the surgeon is taking too many chances with cases of belly pain; the diagnosis of appendicitis just isn't that cut and dried. Same thing with OB men and sections: the man doing much more than 5 percent of his deliveries by section is too free with his knife, but the guy with too small a percentage of sections is taking dangerous chances, delivering some patients from below when he ought to be sectioning them for their own safety.]

Anyway, there is usually a short break between cases. The big-cheese surgeons usually get their cases scheduled early, but even they end up sitting around sometimes unless they work between two rooms the way Slater and Emery do. Slater uses both Room I and Room II and shuttles back and forth; Ruggles will start a case in Room II while Slater and Barr are finishing another in room I; then Barr closes while Slater moves through into Room II; by the time he's finished there Barr has already gotten started on the next case in Room I, and so on. How Slater stands the pace I don't know; he'll make rounds at 7:15 A.M., start operating at 8:00 and go right on through steady until 5:00 with only a half a sandwich gulped down for lunch. My legs feel like a couple of rocks after two hours.

Tuesday afternoon I went down and saw the man with the carcinoid in his belly. He seemed to be getting along, and Hank said today that he'd pulled the Levin tube out and started the man on fluids by mouth, so he may have a better recovery than I thought he would. After seeing him I went down to see the five or six new patients that had come in for surgery Wednesday morning. The work-ups on these patients are different from medical work-ups because most of them have been referred to the surgeon for a specific problem. The surgeon sees them in the clinic, schedules their surgery, and then has them come into the hospital the afternoon before they are due to go up on the block, unless extensive lab studies or X-rays are needed before surgery. Of course, some patients are diagnostic problems who require the surgery to help nail down what's wrong with them—the woman with the dysgerminoma was a case in point. They needed to explore her belly to see if she had recurrent cancer or something else going on in there.

One of the new patients was a woman with a huge ovarian cyst or something she had been growing in her belly for some time; she'd been too scared to go to a doctor to find out what it was. (She was operated this morning, and Slater found a benign cyst about the size of a volleyball in there.) Then there was Mrs. London, an extremely fat lady who had been listening to a medic program on TV that dealt with breast cancer, and she'd gone feeling around those massive breasts of hers and found a lump in one of them. Her doctor also found some swollen nodes under her arm, so she was scheduled for a "biopsy," even though Slater and everyone else was sure it would be cancer and that he would have to do a radical mastectomy—total removal of the breast and everything else within reach in the area. Another new patient was a twenty-nine-year-old optometrist in for an exploratory because of a mass in his belly.

I finished these new work-ups about 8:00 Tuesday, then chewed the fat a while with Hank Ruggles about what I'm expected to do and how Slater works. Then I went roaming around the hospital without much to do.

Roscoe Herring and I are going to try covering for each other alternate nights. He's on Emery's surgical service with the same duty nights I have, so we think we'll try a first- and second-call system. After 10:30 P.M. on one call night he'll take calls for both of us and let me sleep, and the next call night I'll reciprocate. Unless, of course, too many things break loose at once, then we'll call the other guy out. We may find that the guy on the spot is working his ass off all night so that it doesn't work out, but it's worth a try.

I met Hank Ruggles up in the OR at 8:00 this morning. The young girl who might have cancer was the first case, all prepped and ready, and Ruggles started off, making a wide abdominal incision. When he had her open, he called Slater in; Slater felt around inside for a while, clipped out a node for a frozen section, and then found metastatic tumor all up and down the girl's abdomen. Nothing to be done surgically. She will get X-ray therapy now, and Slater sounded hopeful, said if this is really dysgerminoma it may well recede or even go away because that is a kind of cancer that is very sensitive to X-ray. On the other hand, if it's chorionepithelioma (a singularly vicious cancer that can arise from retained placental tissue after a miscarriage) as it could well be with a positive rabbit test, she's as good as dead right now.

She certainly looks like a cancer patient, though I'm not sure just what is the tip-off. This girl is only twenty-eight years old, but she has the marks. There's a pale, drawn, tired look about her. She looked *sick* even though she didn't feel particularly bad, and there is a peculiar cast to her skin that seems to be characteristic of the Bad Disease. It's odd; at the beginning of this internship I didn't understand what they meant when they said a patient "looked malignant"; I didn't even believe you could tell from looks, but I do now. I think sometimes you can see it when a patient walks in the door. You just get a crawly feeling that there is malignancy there somewhere; I'm not even sure it has anything to do with what you see. It's a hateful and murderous thing there in the room with you, and sometimes it seems that you can almost smell it.

Well, that was the story with this girl: Slater called the X-ray people up to show them what was there and then went off to the next room and left Ruggles and me to sew her back up. This is a chore I could learn to hate. Slater insists on using little tiny wire sutures in the inside layers, about one-eighth inch apart so you have to put in about fifty of them in a six-inch incision, and it just takes forever. Then he wants wire for the skin sutures, too. The important part of the procedure may only take ten minutes, but you spend an hour and a half closing up.

Next we had the fat lady with the breast lump, Mrs. London. This turned out to be a really brutal job; the woman weighed about 250 pounds, all blubber, with these massive breasts. There was enough chance they'd have to do a skin graft on her chest because of the amount of skin removed with the breast that I had to scrub a donor site on her leg with surgical soap. She kind of overlapped the table on all sides, and as I scrubbed away at her leg her whole body quivered as though it were going to ooze right off the table any moment—and if it had started going, nobody in the place could have stopped it.

Once she was ready, Slater did the whole procedure. First, he took out the tumor itself, with a block of tissue around it and sent it over for frozen section. Then we all changed gloves and redraped the patient because apparently breast cancers can seed and we didn't want to carry any tumor cells to an unaffected area. The frozen section report came back fifteen minutes later, and it was cancer, so Slater started to work removing this huge breast and the surrounding tissue right down to the rib cage and into the armpit. It took him a couple of hours just to dissect through all that fat to the muscle layers, and another two hours to dissect breast and muscle away from the ribs. A frozen section on some nodes in the axilla showed tumor there, too, so we decided not to go after the nodes inside her rib cage—Slater decided, that is; nobody but Slater decides anything in these cases. Finally, he lifted this great mass of tissue out in a block, and then brought the skin back across to cover the denuded chest wall. No skin graft necessary, and just as well. This had taken so long and there had been so much blood loss that Slater didn't want to keep her under anesthesia another minute if he could help. Finally finished about 2:00 P.M. and went down for a quick lunch.

After lunch there was the exploratory on the optometrist. This time Ruggles opened and Slater came in from the other room. Found a big ulcerating lesion in the wall of the small bowel, and some great swollen nodes all throughout the abdomen. Slater thought it was a lymphoma, and this was confirmed by frozen section.

The frozen section, incidentally, is a fast, on-the-spot technique by which the pathologist can examine a bit of tissue and render an opinion about what it is then and there while the surgeon waits with the patient open on the table. You give the pathologist a sample of tissue you think may be a cancer, for instance; he takes it to the small lab at the end of the corridor, freezes it solid in a jet of carbon dioxide gas from a tank, slices a section for microscopic examination while it's frozen rock-hard, stains it, examines it, and trots back with an answer, all within ten or fifteen minutes. It isn't a good, accurate tissue examination, but it's usually sufficient to tell the surgeon whether he is dealing with a malignancy or not.

In this case, since a lymphoma is malignant, Slater removed the small bowel lesion and took out a good large chunk of small and large bowel, and closed him up. Now the man will get X-ray therapy, since the final path report will probably call this Hodgkin's disease.

Saturday, October 8

I don't know whether it will be the usual pattern or not, but the work dropped off sharply the latter part of this week. Monday through Wednesday were heavy, but Thursday and Friday were slow. Friday nights are bound to be light on admissions because there are no scheduled operations on Saturday except tonsillectomies.

Light or not, I find that the various operations seem to blur in my mind to such a degree that I have trouble remembering exactly what I did on any given day. I've been sitting here for five minutes trying to remember how we started off Thursday morning in surgery; I can remember one case on Thursday, but I can't think of the first one.

Part of the trouble is that this work is so utterly depersonalized. You may occasionally see a patient on his way up to the OR, but usually by the time you get there for the first case the patient is already there and asleep; you pay very little attention to him until the scrub nurse sticks her head into the doctors' lounge and tells you things are ready to go. Then you scrub and walk into the OR and find a bare prepped abdomen (the schedule tells you what operation is supposed to be done) and don't see the *patient* until everything is over and the drapes are removed . . . if ever. You take him back downstairs, roll him into bed, write postop orders on his chart, and hustle back up to the OR to find another abdomen staring up at you.

At any rate, I know Hank Ruggles and I did something to somebody Thursday morning at 8:00, and that Slater drifted in from the other room to administer the *coup de grâce,* and that Hank and I closed. I just can't remember what it was right now.

I do remember the hiatus hernia case with Dr. Leo Richards. Leo is about forty, an odd-looking guy with graying hair and a slouch and a face like a monkey, but so far he seems to be the most pleasant and normal person I've run into on the clinic surgical staff. He comes down and shoots the bull with us at midnight supper quite frequently, and he always has a bundle of journals under his arm. He must read constantly. Roscoe says he's very fussy and thorough with his surgery; every case is a neat anatomical dissection and nothing escapes him. The only trouble is that he takes so long to do any case that it's a trial to scrub with him.

This case figured to be a long one anyway. A hiatus hernia is in the diaphragm, way in deep. You either try to repair it through the abdomen and have to work way up underneath the ribs, or open the chest and get at it from above, pushing the stomach back down through the defect in the diaphragm and then sewing up the defect so it can't come back up through again. This was what Richards chose to do in this case, so I saw how a surgeon goes about opening a chest. You'd think it would be a very delicate, painstaking dissection. It isn't. He took the knife and went *whump,* just laid this guy open at one stroke from front to back between two ribs, about a fourteen-inch incision, and then there were just hundreds of bleeders to snap and tie. He handed Barr and me each a great handful of hemostats, and we just snapped and snapped and snapped. Then he got out a great ugly instrument that took a six-inch bite out of the eighth rib . . . *crunch* . . . and then got another little toy that looked like an earth-moving machine in there (it was a "rib-spreader," he said), and next thing you know he had a hole four-teen inches long and six inches deep into this man's chest. My job at that point was to hold the lung back out of the way with a sponge stick and my fingers while he and Barr went in up to the elbows to get at this hernia and repair it. I couldn't see what he was doing down in there, but it just seemed to take hours.

I got quite a jolt at one point, though. Richards asked me to move my fingers to lift the lung a little farther up, so I did, and thought the patient had started hiccuping because I could feel this spasmodic jerking against my fingertips. Then I realized that it was the patient's heart thumping away; I practically had my hand around it. If nothing else, I got a good look at the anatomy of the chest, a live one, not a cadaver. The lung was all nice and pink with gray splotches, the way a lung ought to look, but as I pressed it up out of the way, the part I was pressing got purple and all wrinkled up. Of course, as soon as I released it, it re-expanded and all turned pink again. But you just don't ordinarily think of the lung as a living, spongy, air-filled, blood-filled, moving organ.

Well, Richards fiddled and fiddled, and then somebody stuck his head in the door and said that somebody in another room had an internal bleeder he couldn't seem to find and could Richards come in and take a look? And much to my amazement, Richards said, "Sure, I'm about finished. Why don't you boys close up now?" and off he went. So Barr started at one end of this incision and I started at the other and we closed the guy's chest up. Barr left a huge half-inch rubber tube sticking out of the chest wall for a drain, running it down into a bottle of water to form an airtight seal. Late this afternoon I went down and saw the guy and made him sit up and cough and got a chest plate to prove to myself that that lung really did expand again, and he seems to be doing fine. I don't know why I should be so surprised; it just doesn't seem like *anybody* should survive having that kind of a hole cut into him, and the operation took five hours from start to finish.

Richards is certainly ungodly slow, but I think I'll enjoy scrub-bing with him more than with Slater, and I've heard that he lets the intern do occasional appendectomies and such things. The guy is an enthusiast, and everybody seems to like him. Slater is a different story. Nobody likes Slater, and Slater doesn't trust anybody to do anything right. He is unquestionably a very skillful surgeon, but he's a tough sort of guy to get along with.

That was the last case I had Thursday afternoon, so I went down to work up some new patients and see some postoperatives. Thursday evening was slow until about midnight. After 10:30 I had calls from both Surgery I and II while Herring went home to bed. Got called at 1:00 A.M. to see a woman who had come in with belly pain. I thought she had an acute gall bladder; found Milt Musser sitting out at the desk, and he checked her, too, and agreed with me, thought a surgeon should see her. I didn't hear any more about it, so I guess the surgeons didn't feel she needed to be opened up at 1:30 in the morning.

Then at 4:30 I was called again, a beautiful example of how much a *good* nurse can help a doctor. This was a patient of Lou Franklin's, who had been in a month and a half ago with chest and neck pain and had baffled everybody. Franklin thought he had a coronary, but nothing turned up on the EKG to even suggest it. So then Franklin began to think it might be a dissecting aneurysm—a strange business where blood under pressure splits apart the layers of the wall of a large artery and makes a false channel—but nobody would buy that either. For one thing, a dissecting aneurysm usually blows out the side of the artery in pretty short order, and the patient bleeds all over kingdom come internally and dies. Instead of that, this guy seemed to get well; his pain stopped and they sent him home three weeks ago without any diagnosis.

Apparently he'd done fine until 2:00 this morning when the pain started back. Dr. Franklin had gone out to his place and given him a hypo, but evidently hadn't found any source for the pain. When it came back in two hours, he told the man to go on into the hospital, and called to order more morphine and have him put to bed. He even said not to bother dragging out the intern, but the night supervisor just happened to notice the patient's arms were different colors: one was warm pink, the other cold and blue.

I heard that and got up on the floor in a hurry, and took about a half-minute to discover that the man had no pulse in either his right arm or his left leg. There were strong pulses in his left arm and right leg. He was having really agonizing pain in his chest and belly, and it was starting now in the blue arm, too. My diagnosis was that Franklin had been right; the guy had had a dissecting aneurysm six weeks before, and now it was extending. I called Milt Musser and told him about it, and called up Franklin, too. Got the man into an oxygen tent, with enough morphine to hold the pain, and all the time I was thinking, My God, what kind of an aneurysm could he have that would block off *both a right arm and a left leg?*

Well, I found out this morning. Ted Van Wert came in and saw the man in consultation and agreed with my diagnosis. He'd even agreed with Franklin before, I guess. Leo Richards saw him and thought he had multiple arterial clots, a notion Van Wert just sniffed at. By about noon the consensus was that Richards was right, and they took the man up to OR to do a thromboendarterectomy— a sort of heroic operation in which the blocked-off artery is opened and the obstructing clot peeled out of it to restore circulation again. Richards and Barr opened him up; I was busy downstairs at the time but got an urgent page to hustle up to the OR immediately. Half the staff was up there, with Van Wert looking smug and Richards looking unhappy. Richards had the great artery of the blue arm exposed, and sure as hell there was a dissecting aneurysm. The wall of the artery had been split between the layers, and the new channel was so large it had obstructed the main channel almost completely. It must have started down in the aorta and just dissected clear out into the arm and down into the leg, so we were just seeing the end of the dissection.

So that was that. They just had to close him up again, since there's nothing very constructive they can do. It's just a matter of hours now until the weakened wall of the artery bursts open somewhere in his arm or chest or belly and then it will all be over in a few seconds.

Friday morning my first case was at 8:30, so I got to go to the clinicopathological conference that alternates with the surgical conference on Friday mornings at 7:15. A CPC is like a guessing game. One of the bright boys presents a problem case from his files—usually something obscure and exotic, to which he knows the answer, but nobody else does. Then the rest try to work out the diagnosis from the data at hand. It can be a rough exercise, with a

whole crowd of very sharp guys bearing down on the man presenting the case and picking to pieces what he did or didn't do. Ted
Van Wert presented this case; he has a mind as sharp as his tongue,
but he got a good going over before somebody nailed the diagnosis.

Sitting there, I got to thinking of all the complaining you hear
about incompetent doctors, and I wondered how many laymen in
this city ever even dream that a crowd of about sixty of the city's
doctors gather together at 7:15 in the morning once a week, volun-
tarily, for the sole purpose of keeping themselves sharp and on their
toes. I wonder how many laymen have even the foggiest idea how
incredibly complex this business of medical diagnosis actually is,
and how much sheer accumulated knowledge and brain power a
guy like Ted Van Wert has to bring to bear every time some slob
walks into his office with the sniffles. All doctors aren't as sharp or as
careful or interested as Ted, but he's not all that exceptional either.
There are thousands like him all over the country.

After the CPC the first case in surgery was an appendectomy.
Then we had the gastric resection on the seventy-eight-year-old
man. Slater said before we started that there was no question the
old man had a cancer; the question was what could be done. We
found a huge mass of cancer the size of a baseball blocking off the
whole upper half of his stomach, which was still full of half-digested
food in spite of the tube that was down there. "Last summer's
corn," as Slater called it. Some nodes behind the stomach were
involved, but there was no sign of spread to the liver or pancreas.
Slater looked and looked, and fiddled, and then sighed and looked
at Hank Ruggles and said, "Well, Hank, what would you do?" Hank
shrugged and said, "Hell, this old man is seventy-eight years old.
What are you going to offer him? I'd by-pass the obstruction as best
I could and get out of there fast before he dies on the table, that's
what I'd do."

And Slater just said, "Well, then, you'd be wrong. He doesn't
have a chance in hell of living three months with that left in there.
Take it out and he has one chance in a million of a cure. So I'm
going to take it out, and everything near it that might be involved
—stomach, pancreas, spleen, transverse colon, the works." He
looked at the man and shook his head. "I know this is going to
create a terrible risk for this man, too. He may not even survive the

surgery, but I'm still going to do it. At least I'll let him have a run for his money."

So we dug in for a long, long procedure, over four hours of about the roughest work a general surgeon can do. Slater is fast and skillful, and he was in a relatively good mood, for Slater, but he's hard to take for four hours on a case like that. He's about forty-eight or fifty, with a sort of restless, "ready-to-blow-any-minute" tension that hits you any time you're near the guy. He's nervous as a cat all the time during surgery, fussing about this and that, snapping at people, never satisfied that anything is *quite* the way he wants it.

First today he kept riding the anesthesia resident, who was buried in drapes up at the head of the table giving the patient gas. Slater thought the patient wasn't getting enough oxygen. Said the blood was too dark. I guess this is an old, familiar theme with Slater. He would say, "Doctor, the blood is too dark down here. Are you sure this man has a good airway?" And the anesthetist would say, "Well, he looks real pink up here, sir." So Slater says nothing for about three minutes, and then: "Doctor, this blood looks awfully dark down here," and so on. This goes on for a while, and then almost invariably Slater will say, "Doctor, maybe we'd better call Don Morehouse in here," (Don being the chief of the anesthesia department) so somebody goes out and hauls Don in, and Don fiddles with the gas machine and pretends to do something, and Slater says, "Well, thanks, Don, that blood looks much better now," when actually it looks just the same as it did all along.

Then when that little canter is over—for the time being—the scrub nurses start getting it. Maggie Wren is Slater's hand-picked scrub nurse, a top-rate girl who has worked with him for years, but every operation it's the same old story. This time he was tying something with silk suture down deep in the abdomen and the suture broke, so he asked Maggie, "What size is that silk? I wanted 4-o." So Maggie says, "Yes, that's 4-o."

"Oh, are you sure it isn't 3-o? It feels too big for 4-o."

"No, Doctor, it's 4-o."

"Well, let me see the package it came out of. It feels like 3-o." So Maggie has to go fish around for the package and hold it under his nose, and, sure as hell, it says 4-o on it. So Slater says, "Well, I just can't understand it. It sure feels big, it feels just like 3-o to me."

And this goes on and on and on all the time he's working. In this case I had a pair of retractors to hold while he was sewing the esophagus to the duodenum, and I couldn't see anything down in there because he was between me and the patient, and it just seemed like he was going to go on sewing indefinitely—sewing and sewing and sewing. For three-quarters of an hour something was going on in there that he and Hank were all excited about that I couldn't see, and I just thought he was never going to finish. By the time it was finally over, my legs were so sore I could hardly stand on them, and then there were all those tiny wire sutures to close the man up with, about 135 of them that had to be tied just so and cut just so. So Slater said, "Very nice case, gentlemen, very nice case," and bounced out to rustle up something else to do. I could just about stagger to the door.

Bit by bit I'm seeing some other interesting little sidelights to this man's personality, too. Today Maggie had some nice new needle holders that grip a curved surgical needle very nicely. Before Slater came in Hank saw them and said, "Say, these are nice needle holders." And Maggie said, "Yes, I'd like to get some more, but I don't dare because Dr. Emery likes them, too."

Hank said, "Well, don't tell Dr. Slater that Dr. Emery likes them. Just hand them to him, and when he compliments you on the new needle holders, just say, 'Yes, aren't they nice? Maybe I should order some more,' and he'll tell you to go ahead."

Well, I couldn't see what difference it made to Dr. Slater whether Dr. Emery liked a particular kind of needle holder or not, so I asked Hank what the story was. It appears that Dr. Emery and Slater don't like each other; they work side by side in the same clinic, but they hate each other's guts. Emery used to be the big-cheese surgeon at the clinic when Slater came there as a young upstart; now Emery is getting older and Slater has built up a national reputation Emery never came close to, and they hardly speak to each other. If Emery does something one way, Slater won't do it that way for anything. Dr. Emery, for instance, uses silk to close up the subcutaneous tissue, so Dr. Slater insists on using wire. Recently Slater had some removable and sterilizable handles installed onto the operating lights in his two rooms so that he could reach up and adjust the light himself with gloves on—the light, of course, is never right. So Dr. Emery won't have these things in his OR, and even refuses to use either of Slater's rooms.

I guess this childish bickering between these two guys is an old, old story around here now, with both of them acting like little children. Hell of it is, they are deadly serious about it. You don't joke about it when Slater is around. You don't even mention Dr. Emery's name, and you don't mention to Dr. Emery that Dr. Slater exists, because I guess this is really meat and drink to both of them.

The man with the carcinoid tumor is not doing so well; he obstructed again as soon as he tried to take anything by mouth at all. I doubt he'll make it through the weekend. Other patients doing well. At 10:30 I turned call over to Roscoe and got a full night's sleep. This morning I got up, had a leisurely breakfast and made rounds with Hank, then got off for the weekend at 9:30. We looked in on the aneurysm patient, wondering when he's going to blow out an artery. He knows something bad is wrong, but doesn't understand what. Maybe that's just as well. At least he isn't having a lot of pain; a quarter-grain of the poppy every couple of hours takes care of that.

Tuesday, October 11

The man with the carcinoid survived the weekend, even looked a little better Monday, but he still can't get anything to stay down so he's living on IVs. The aneurysm man died Saturday night. The artery blew out somewhere in his chest, and that was that.

The first case Monday morning was an old man Dr. Gillies thought had cancer of the stomach. He did, but it was spread all over the place, including the liver, so there was nothing to do but make the diagnosis and close him up. I took him back downstairs and wrote his postop orders. By the time I got back Slater had already started his second case, draining a pelvic cyst by means of a long needle through the floor of the vagina. Finally, there was a woman who had been admitted Sunday with a lump in her breast for Slater to biopsy. Apparently this looked and felt like a cancer clinically; Hank was sure of it, and the OR was all set up to do a radical mastectomy, but it turned out to be a large benign cyst. This was very gratifying, after all the cancer we've been seeing on this service. You get the feeling that every patient that walks in has got the Bad Disease. There are many breast lumps that are not cancerous—in fact, the majority turn out to be benign—but this one had seemed so large and scarred down that everyone thought it would be a bad one. So this gal had a lucky break.

That was my last assigned scrub for the day. I had lunch and went down to quarters for a shower and shave. About 3:00 P.M. a patient came in with a bleeding ulcer. He'd had a massive hemorrhage from it three years before, and today he had fainted at work and then vomited up a lot of bright-red blood. Hank saw him and ordered up some blood; then about 4:30 Slater saw him and decided that the time had come to resect his stomach as an emergency procedure. So everyone started running in all directions. Got the patient into the OR about 5:00, actually made the incision at 5:25. Slater did it with me and Barr grudgingly assisting. It was a long, tiresome procedure; Slater found the ulcer all right, and took out two-thirds of the man's stomach, the part that makes acid, and then explored to make sure nothing else was wrong in there. Finally finished at 7:45, and Barr and I went to the diner down the street for hamburgers, since the cafeteria was already closed.

When we got back I had a patient in that made me wish I hadn't eaten anything at all. This woman was a real mess. She'd had a carcinoma of the uterus last spring, and had deep radium therapy for it, and the radiation had broken down her vaginal wall top and bottom, so she had false channels into both bladder and rectum, and was passing stool out her vagina and leaking urine all over the place, and now had a purulent bladder infection on top of it, and you could smell her clear down the hall. I went in and saw her. God, what a repulsive creature. She weighed about 250 pounds and had a huge filthy gauze pad stuck down across her belly to cover a big draining sore above her pubis. I did a work-up as fast as I could, but I didn't try to do a pelvic; by then I just wanted to get out of that room. I called Dr. Peterson, who had sent her in, and he agreed to let the pelvic go until somebody could get her cleaned up and over to the clinic on an examining table next morning.

It was my night for double call, so Roscoe slept and I had a lively night. At 10:30 the nurses on Second called to say that the man in 203 we'd operated on in the morning was not doing very well, and had a temp of 105. He was having trouble breathing. I got him sitting up and dangling his legs, and he coughed up a big plug of green mucus from somewhere down in his chest, and that relieved the breathing some. I still didn't like the fever and called Hank about getting a chest film, but Hank didn't sound very interested and said wait until morning and see if he was still around. So I checked another patient or two and went to bed at 11:30. Beginning at midnight I started getting calls every half-hour on the half-hour, mostly pill calls and nonsense. Some nurse called to say that a patient wanted a hypo and it was ordered for every three hours, and it had only been two hours and forty-five minutes since the last one, and could she go ahead and give it anyway? This at 3:00 A.M. I nearly tore the phone out of the wall on that one.

At 4:30 they called me again about the man in 203—more breathing trouble and still a temp of 105. I told them to put him in oxygen, and then lay there thinking that maybe the old goat would just up and cool and that I should really go up and see him again in case there was anything more to be done. This time the old conscience won; I crawled out and went up to see him, got him pulled back upright in bed again, got him to cough up some more crap out of his chest, and he did feel a little better.

Another call at 5:15; my old friend Hattie Stevens, who has been back in again for some time, had just expired. So I went up and saw Mrs. Stevens, and this is the end of that story. She had come in with frank kidney failure finally; Dr. Franklin hadn't been able to keep her blood pressure much below 280 over 200, and she had been going steadily downhill in uremia, and now just quietly died. I felt bad because I had been meaning to go up and say hello to her ever since she had come back in, and hadn't done it. She was just a very sweet woman with a dirty disease, and I felt lousy about it.

Got back to bed from that at 6:30; at 7:00 the nurses on Second called to tell me the man in 203 had just died, so I went up and pronounced him, too. Met Slater and Ruggles just coming in the door at 7:15 and told them. Slater seemed to think it was a blessing, but I still don't understand exactly why he expired. Maybe, with the terminal cancer he had, the surgery sucked up the last fragment of physical reserve that he had left, but I know that isn't a very satisfactory clinical cause for death.

I'd been scheduled to scrub with Goodfellow at 8:00, but by that time I didn't feel like scrubbing with anybody on anything, so I dragged my feet getting post permission on the man in 203 until I was sure Goodfellow had started without me and then called the OR and told them, sorry, but I wouldn't be able to get up there. Between 8:30 and 10:30 I went around taking out sutures and did a couple of redressings and then went down to quarters and hit the sack for a couple of hours.

Got up at 1:00 and had a little lunch—I wasn't very hungry— and then just roamed around the hospital until the new patients for Slater started coming in around 3:00: an abdominal exploratory and a woman for a breast biopsy. That babe was a real pill; she greeted me at the door with "Well, what the hell do *you* want?" and permitted me to listen to her heart and lungs, but refused to let me examine the breast lump, which was the only damned thing I was interested in at the moment. She was really snotty about it, and I wasn't particularly pleasant in return either—just finished up my work-up as quickly as possible and stalked out mad. I suppose the poor woman had had her breast squeezed by fifteen different strange men since this thing had turned up and was getting pissed off about it, but I was so dead tired by that time that she just made me sore.

About 5:30 or so Hank Ruggles turned up, and we changed the dressing on Mrs. London, the fat lady who had the radical mastectomy. She's doing fine; her main trouble right now seems to be keeping that other remaining huge breast somehow tucked down into her Ace bandage. Hank asked her with a perfectly straight face if she had any trouble now listing to the left when she walked around. She looked up at him real sharp and met that flinty look of his for a spell, and then giggled and he even broke down and grinned. I was glad to see something perk her up a little, she's been so quiet and sad since the surgery. Also glad to find out that Hank does have a sense of humor stuck away somewhere in that shriveled-up little hulk of his.

Wednesday, October 12

Today and tomorrow are both short days because Alec Ivy and I are switching call; he's taking my call tonight so that I'll cover his on Friday night and let him have a long Friday-night-through-Sunday weekend. Seems like a hell of a lot of bother for the privilege of a whole fat two-day weekend, but that's how it is. I was scheduled to help on Mrs. Du Pré's breast biopsy this morning—the woman who was so snotty. Slater was sure it was going to be a radical, and it was. The frozen section showed that the lump was carcinoma. It was a long, long job; Slater did the radical mastectomy, and then biopsied her axillary nodes, and then went into her chest and biopsied her intercostal and internal mammary nodes, and did a skin graft, and we didn't get out of there for five hours. I suppose I should be all eager to scrub on cases like that, but these long ones just kill me. I thought we'd never get through with this one.

After lunch I made rounds and redressed Mrs. London's breast again and took out some stitches. She's a good-natured lady, and Hank and I both get a kick out of her. If all goes well, she'll probably go home Monday.

Monday, October 17

Since I covered for Alec on Friday night, my long weekend on duty really started Friday morning and ended this evening, about eighty hours later. Ann got over to the hospital for supper Sunday night; otherwise I didn't see her, nor get home, nor get any journal dictated since Wednesday night. So if things sound a little disconnected, that's why.

I don't remember much about Friday except that it was long. I was in the OR scrubbed in on one case or another from 8:00 until 4:30. There was a gall bladder case, and a rectal stricture that Slater repaired, and two or three other things. Very hazy now. And I think Friday night was quiet except for a couple of outpatients. Oh, yes, a woman had ruptured a varicose vein in her leg and bled all over the kitchen floor, nearly scared her and her family to death, but by the time she got to the hospital the bleeding had stopped and all there was for me to do was to cover the bleeding area with a Band-Aid.

Saturday morning I got up early to make 8:00 rounds with Hank. We'd planned to see everybody very carefully, and then take time to get squared away on some questions that have been bothering me on this service. But Slater outfoxed us, turned up with Barr just as we were starting and said, "Well, boys, let's make rounds!" and took off down the hall—so we made rounds with Slater at his usual galloping pace.

This business of rounds with Slater is really something to behold. His patients are about evenly distributed between fourth, third and second floors, so he starts off on Fourth, at a dead run. One of his underlings is supposed to have all of his fourth-floor charts already out and in order so that as soon as Slater walks out of one room he gets the next chart shoved into his hand along with the patient's name and room number, and he goes down the floor, click, click, click, like a general on a fast inspection tour. When he gets to the last patient or two on Fourth, the underling is supposed to dash madly down to Third and corral those charts so that the first one goes into Slater's hand the minute he gets downstairs. And the same with the second-floor patients. He sort of sweeps down the corridors this way and sees patients in thirty minutes. And if the underling isn't quick enough with the charts, or gets them out of order, he gets a sarcastic blistering from Slater through all the rest of that day's rounds.

Well, this whole business seemed silly to me, and I said so to Hank once; why did Slater run around and see these people at all? But Hank said that Slater gets a lot out of his rounds, clinical things he needs to know, and that he's so fast and sharp that he doesn't miss a thing—urine output, Levin tube draining, temperature, respiratory problems, everything. "You may think he couldn't notice anything going around that way," Hank said, "but you just try omitting something once and he'll be on you like a hawk, every time. He just can't stand making social calls on these people, that's all." Then he grinned and said, "That's my job, I'm supposed to take care of the public relations. To Slater rounds are just plain surgical business and nothing else."

The amazing thing is that the patients eat it up. They literally idolize Slater; you'd think he was Christ Incarnate. They sit around all day holding their breath waiting for Dr. Slater to come see them, and then he swoops in and grants them a whole fat twenty-five seconds' audience and then swoops out again, and it's as if God had reached down and touched them. Well, I don't pretend to get it. I don't know how he does it. I don't even really think it's anything he tries to do, or gives a particular damn about; it's just there. But it is indeed there.

Anyway, Saturday morning we leaped from floor to floor trying to keep up with this guy, and then Slater took off for the clinic and Hank and I drank a cup of coffee and talked over the service in general and my contributions to it in particular. It appears, for some obscure reason, that Slater likes me. Which is nice, since I gather he doesn't usually like his interns, and I wasn't even sure he knew I was around—though I had noticed that he invariably addresses Alec as "Dr. Ivy" but usually calls me by my first name. Hank said my work-ups on the admissions and my follow-ups on postop patients have been okay. Slater wants Hank to do the "important" follow-up—deciding when to pull tubes, doing the first redressings, etc.—and I'm not to do any of those things unless Hank delegates it. As with Mrs. London: I am specifically to change her dressing each day now until Monday.

I also asked him where Slater gets all these people. He said about 80 percent come by referral from other clinic doctors or up from Mexico. The local outside doctors know Slater is a top-rate surgeon, but don't want their patients going to the clinic if they can help it—afraid they'll get into the habit, I guess. So when a case comes from an outside doctor, it's usually a real bitch, according to Hank— something somebody has really botched up, or a patient in really bad trouble or something. Or one they don't think is going to survive the surgery anyway.

When we finished talking, Hank took off for the weekend and left me in charge. Most of Saturday was taken up with crappy little things—starting IVs, putting down Levin tubes, etc. Roscoe left me with double call Saturday night, but for once had practically no calls from 11:00 until 6:30 A.M. Sunday when second floor called me to pronounce a medical patient, a coronary, who had just died.

After breakfast Sunday morning I was just finishing complete rounds on Slater's patients when Hank came in. I guess part of the "weekend off" for Slater's Fellow is coming into the hospital both Saturday and Sunday to make rounds. He only saw a couple of people, though, and went back home. No problems to speak of. From 10:00 until 2:00 I just loafed, read a little, took a nap, didn't budge from interns' quarters.

You get an almost fatalistic feeling about these little luxurious pockets of quiet that turn up, as if being tucked away somewhere and not on display will somehow prolong the period that you're not bothered. Especially on these Sundays: the ax is hanging up there, ready to drop, and you know that sooner or later the first of Monday's surgicals is going to turn up and that once you set foot out on the floors you won't get back again, but that if you are *very* quiet the ax will stay up there a little longer without dropping. In some curious way this applies to times when I'm scrubbed, too; I can be scrubbed on an emergency case in the evening, say, and there won't be a page for me, not *one,* all the time I'm in the OR, and then the very minute I pull off my gloves the page starts hollering for me in an endless succession of calls. And it can't be that the nurses know I'm scrubbed in on a case and therefore can't come to the phone—nobody tells them that. They just seem to smell it. Psychic emanations or something.

Well, this Sunday, like all the rest, the closer it got to 2:00 in the afternoon, the higher the suspense, until about 2:45 when they paged me for the first new admission, and between the new surgicals for Monday and about a dozen outpatients, I was running full tilt from then until midnight.

One of Slater's preoperatives was a woman with recurrence of a breast cancer, generalized spread of the tumor which had occurred since Slater did a radical on her in January. Now she was scheduled to have her ovaries and adrenals removed in an attempt to slow it down. Trouble was, she also had heart disease, with borderline failure that Van Wert had been trying to get under control in time for surgery. I thought she looked like a sorry operative risk Sunday night when I saw her—pulse flitting all over the place, and gasping for air every time she moved. Van Wert and Slater both came in to see her, and then had a big flap about the impending surgery.

Slater wanted Van Wert to take responsibility for the surgical risk, and Van Wert, who thinks this kind of an operation is a stick in the wind against recurrent breast cancer anyway, wanted Slater to be responsible. At first it was just an intellectual discussion of the relative merits of heroic surgery in hopeless cancer patients, but finally it boiled down to the fact that Slater didn't want to operate on this woman unless Van Wert would guarantee that she wouldn't die on the table from her heart disease. He didn't exactly use those words, but that was what he was driving at.

Van Wert, of course, wouldn't buy this at all, wouldn't make any such guarantee, and Slater just got furious. Kept saying, "Ted, this procedure is the only thing in the world we have to offer this woman," and Van Wert planted his feet and said, "I'm sorry, Nathan, but I am no goddamned magician with a wand to wave over this woman, and you're going to have to take your own surgical risks, I'll be damned if I will," and then wrote, "I can see no justification for surgery until this patient's heart failure is controlled, if then," and signed his name and walked out. So Slater spluttered and beefed to Hank and me, and went in and saw the woman again, and ordered another EKG, and spluttered some more, but this morning it seems the case was canceled.

So instead of that one, Monday morning I had the joy of scrubbing on a Whipple resection—a radical excision of pancreas, stomach, duodenum, gall bladder, etc., etc.—in a patient with an early cancer of the pancreas. This is a procedure they save up for the patient who has a single localized lesion that is cancerous but has no sign that it has spread yet. I guess the theory is that if they can get it before that magic split second in the natural history of the disease when the first dirty cell breaks loose from the mother tumor and seeds into the liver or somewhere, they have a cure. They take out all the surrounding organs in hope that if there *has* been some spread they can't see, maybe it is still localized enough that they can get it. It seems like a forlorn hope, but who can say? They *do* get cures, sometimes. Not palliations, or prolongation of life, but *cures*. Sometimes. But the procedure was long and tedious, especially because Slater planted himself right in front of me for most of the four hours it took so I couldn't see anything that was going on. I just hung onto the retractors for dear life and wished he would get it the hell over with. Started late and ended late, so this was a pretty disgusting day.

Oh, yes, we sent Mrs. London home today after a final dressing change this morning. We'll miss her; she's fat and good-natured, with a baby face and big blue eyes, and she would call me "dearie" whenever I came in to redress her or take out stitches. She never did solve the battle of that other breast, I guess. The nurse and I were debating devising some kind of uplift bra she could use to support that remaining bosom sufficiently that we could get a bandage to stay on her, and she just said, "That's all right, dearie, I can stand it," in a martyred tone.

Had a very interesting example here, though, of the way doctors and their patients react to each other. Mrs. London and Mrs. Du Pré, the other woman who had had a radical mastectomy, had adjoining rooms. After my first unpleasant encounter with Mrs. Du Pré, I hadn't seen much of her, but Mrs. London gave me a running report on how Mrs. Du Pré was doing. One day when they were talking about the doctors, Mrs. Du Pré had confided that she liked Dr. Slater very much and she liked Dr. Ruggles, too, but she just didn't like me at all. I got to thinking later that in all truth I hadn't been particularly nice to Mrs. Du Pré, and got to feeling quite ashamed of myself. It certainly must be a horrible blow to a woman to come into a hospital with a lump in her breast ostensibly to have a little biopsy (although she is warned in advance that something more may have to be done) and then wake up from surgery to find out that that breast has just been peeled off right down to the bone. No real reason she should be pleasant to anyone about it. The way the doctors treat her in spite of her being unpleasant must make the blow much worse or much better.

Turned up a kind of sickening thing over this weekend. I was up on third floor about 10:00, and one of the nurses, middle-aged, who's on the 3:00-to-11:00 shift came stumbling into the chartroom and nearly fell over me trying to get a chart out of the rack. I'd noticed before that this woman kind of tottered, very unsteady on her feet. This was Sunday evening, and Herring came by just as this woman was grabbing the counter to steady herself. He called me aside when she had gone on down the hall and told me that this nurse is a dope addict, and that she was pulling tricks all the time—taking morphine or Demerol hypos down to postop patients and squirting half into a bottle for herself and only giving the patient half, or else taking the full ampule of Demerol when only half is ordered and hiding the rest. Apparently, this has been going on for some time, and she's been stacking up quite a supply of drugs and comes in to work at night thoroughly hopped up. The head floor nurse on Third noticed it first, and notified the nursing supervisor, and the doctors are being notified, but so far nobody has been able to nail her with it. She's been discharged from other hospitals on suspicion of narcotics addiction, but never has actually been caught flat-footed.

Later Roscoe and I were talking about this at midnight supper when one of the nurses came down; she confirmed this story, said the woman was very clever about it, and that it was hard to find a way to catch her, since there are always postop patients that complain that their hypos aren't working, or want another sooner than they ought to need another, and it's practically impossible to tell whether this is due to the low pain threshold of the patient or to the simple fact that the last hypo happened to be a little weak. I asked the nurse why in hell they didn't fire her, or at least have someone else give the medications, and she said the nursing office had talked it over with the hospital administration and agreed to try to give her rope and catch her, as long as it didn't get too bad, and then prosecute her and get her license revoked. Otherwise she would just go on victimizing hospitals forever. So we all are supposed to be keeping an eye on this babe to see if we can't pin her.

Wednesday, October 19

Yesterday was one of Slater's clinic days, so Garvin and I scrubbed with Goodfellow on two vaginal hysterectomies. I'd never seen one of these things and couldn't quite visualize how it could be done; this is where the surgeon removes the uterus through the vagina without making any abdominal incision at all. Allegedly this method is faster for the surgeon and not so hard on the patient, but it seems to be very tricky to do. I know that Hank Ruggles did one last week for Slater and ran into an awful lot of bleeding, spent half the time just trying to get hemostasis.

Goodfellow is the acknowledged expert on vaginal hysterectomies around here, and I must say these were very slick jobs. The first took him no more than thirty-five minutes from beginning to end. It all looked very simple: he propped the patient up in stirrups as if for a pelvic exam or a D & C, put a clamp on the cervix to draw it down, peeled the vaginal mucosa away from it all the way around, then went in on either side and clamped and tied the cervical arteries, and then just literally twisted the uterus upside down and delivered it top first, clamping and tying the ligaments and blood vessels one by one. Goodfellow lectured all the way through, identifying structures and all, and everything went snicker-snack.

The second one took a little longer, about fifty minutes, because there was a known pregnancy in the uterus and he had to be a little more cautious how he handled it. This was a woman with a history of severe Rh trouble with two previous children, now two and a half months pregnant and already running an alarmingly high anti-Rh titer. Goodfellow had called for consultation and everybody had agreed that the pregnancy should be stopped. This is one of the few indications for a therapeutic abortion that everybody agrees with, I guess, and removing the uterus is a guarantee against the same trouble in the future.

By the time these were over the new patients were coming in downstairs, five patients for Slater and a couple for Dr. Richards, all scheduled for Wednesday.

After dinner Wednesday I ran into Fred Olsen, who is back from his honeymoon now. Technically, he is supposed to be my boss, and assign me to scrubs and so on. He's a tall, thin guy in his third year of surgical residency, and seems too pleasant and normal to be a surgeon. Maybe that's just because he got married so recently. This is one of these romances that is so much like a bad TV script that it is laughable: up-and-coming young surgeon falls in love with beautiful nurse on the surgical ward, secret whirlwind romance and sudden dramatic revelation after the wedding—all the trimmings. Hell of it is, this "typical hospital story" is so untypical that it amounts to about a million-to-one chance. Fred was about the only unmarried doctor around this place; the girl was head nurse on Third, and about the only really good-looking nurse in the hospital—most of them are ugly as sin—and a good, sharp, competent nurse as well. If things had been "typical," he would have married somebody down in the typing pool and she would have married a stock broker somewhere. As it was, nobody knew they were even going together until they were married, mainly because Fred is shy and didn't want to be razzed about "Young Doctor Kildare" all the time. So the "typical hospital romance" makes a great story, but it never happens. Well, hardly ever.

Tuesday evening I got called to admit a real pain in the ass, some rich Americano woman who had flown up from Mexico City, supposedly in great pain. When I rushed up to see her, it seemed that her chief complaint was that she hadn't been given a private room; they'd thrown her into this three-bed room on Fourth which she had to share with these two swine in the other beds, and it was just more than she could bear. She was about forty and fat, with enough perfume on to fell an ox. It actually took me ten minutes of coaxing to get this woman to tell me what the hell brought her up here in the first place. Apparently she had had a kidney stone before, and thought she was having another attack. She was antagonistic as she could be, said she'd come two thousand miles to see Dr. Slater, and she wanted to see Dr. Slater, not some miserable cur of an intern— oh, hell. I just turned and walked out while her jaw was still flapping. I told the nurse to give her some Demerol every three hours if she had pain, and check her urine for blood, and I didn't even bother Hank with a call. I hear in the morning that Slater saw her for twenty seconds and referred her to the urologists right on the spot.

I suppose there must be some better way to deal with that kind of person than to just get mad at them, but I don't know what. You hear from a lot of people that they don't like this doctor or that doctor; they sure don't mind telling you all about it. Many times patients will drift from one doctor to another, see one they don't like and go to somebody else without even bothering to cancel an appointment. But I think that people don't quite grasp the simple and fundamental fact that the doctor may not like them either. I think most doctors generally like people and get along with them, enjoy talking with them or dealing with them. If they didn't, they wouldn't be doctors. But I'll bet every doctor alive has certain patients that he simply can't bear. It can be a terrific job even to be ordinarily civil to some of the people that come drifting through this place, yet I'm sure patients never imagine that such a thing could be. They just naturally assume that any doctor they choose to honor is automatically going to think they are great.

Ann brought up one question that I should say something about: with all these accounts of breast cancer I haven't mentioned what the surgeon tells these patients before surgery or after. Mrs. Du Pré is a good case in point. Dr. Peterson had found a lump in her breast on a routine physical exam. He sent her over to Slater, who thought it was probably malignant, from its appearance. He urged her to come into the hospital as soon as he could get her scheduled, for a breast biopsy; she was actually operated on three days after the thing was found.

Of course, Slater didn't tell her he was sure it was malignant. He just said that any time something like that appeared, it was almost always benign, but it should be removed and examined because of the remote possibility that it might conceivably have an early cancer in it, and he didn't dare to take any chances with a thing like this. He described what the biopsy would be—just a small incision, an overnight stay in the hospital, etc.—but said that if it *should* turn out to be malignant, they would know it right then and there while she was in surgery, and in that case he would want to be free to go ahead and remove the whole breast right then, since in a case like that he wouldn't want to lose even a day in getting rid of it for her.

Mrs. Du Pré had agreed to this, reluctantly. I guess some do and some don't. Some have to think about it for a while, or want a second opinion, and this is perfectly okay, but in such cases the surgeon leans a little more heavily on the possibility that the lump might be cancer, because it is quite literally true that every day counts and you cannot guess what day is the day the thing first starts to spread. Then during surgery, if the frozen section shows cancer, you not only remove the breast but try to determine whether it has spread or not by examining nodes fom under the arm and between the ribs and even inside the rib cage by frozen section. That determines whether to recommend X-ray therapy after the surgery, or hormone therapy, or what.

Of course, it's a shock under these circumstances for a woman to wake up after a hopefully minor biopsy and find a breast gone from armpit to navel, but apparently if you bear down too heavily on this possibility, you scare away some who might be curable and keep them scared away until there's no hope at all, so it is a kid-glove business.

Mrs. Du Pré was terrifically distressed and frightened when she woke up, and I wondered what Slater would say to her the first time he saw her after surgery. I found out on rounds with him next morning, and I can't imagine any more kind and thoughtful thing than what he did. He walked into her room just beaming from ear to ear, and shook her hand like a long-lost friend, and looked her straight in the eye and said, "Madeleine, congratulations! We found a tumor there, but we found it in time and removed it completely, and you are cured." No equivocation, no ifs, ands or buts.

Afterward Slater said that half the time he *knows* he's lying, but he thinks this is very important to tell the patient, whether there was any evidence of spread or not, not only because of the physical and psychological blow of finding the breast gone, but because having an incurable cancer is the one thing these women are really afraid of, and the only way you can relieve them of that fear is to tell them point-blank that they're cured and make them believe it. Later, when they're back on their feet, is time enough to explain that it may take time to find out for *sure* whether they're cured or not; tell them that to start with and you just torture them when they have nothing to fight back with.

The real surprise to me was that Slater even thought about these things. He sometimes gives you this feeling of being the perfect, dehumanized operating machine, all cold steel and precision, and then he surprises you.

When I got down for midnight supper about 11:00 Tuesday, there was practically a staff meeting going on down there. Andy Case was there, and Leo Richards and Milt Musser, and Roscoe Herring, Pete Carey and a couple of others. We all sat around and chewed the fat for an hour before it broke up. Case was in one of his affable moods, and he can be very pleasant and human when he's feeling affable. I think all of us feel a little more at ease with him now, but there are some around who just don't like him for beans. Milt is one. I don't know exactly why, but on a couple of occasions I've heard him refer to Case as "that black bastard" with more than his usual contempt. At least they weren't fighting tonight.

Wednesday we had a horrible operating schedule with Slater; he had about eight cases, and kept dashing back and forth from one room to the other, and agitating to get the next patient in, and getting more and more irritable all day. Part of it was that a couple of these cases were planned to be Hank's. Quite a number of cases are planned that way, I guess, right from the time the patient is seen in clinic; but whenever Hank has cases like this, Slater just gets all tied up in knots. It's completely irrational, and he must know it; after all, Hank often actually does cases that aren't planned for him, with Slater just coming in to look into the abdomen and stick his hand in, and discuss what ought to be done, and maybe taking a stitch or two, and then telling Hank to go ahead and finish up while he goes into the other room to start another case, and with this he's cool as a cucumber. But give Hank one that's all Hank's and Slater is in and out, and fretting, and pacing around, and asking Hank if he's sure it's going all right, and asking him if he's sure he's not having any trouble, and telling the anesthetist that the blood looks too dark, and so on and so on.

Well, this is nonsense; Hank is in his fourth full year as surgical resident, and has first-assisted or actually done thousands of cases, and is a perfectly competent surgeon. He doesn't have Slater's really outstanding and amazing technical skill, and he doesn't have Slater's years of experience or Slater's judgment, but he also doesn't hesitate for a minute on one of "his" cases to call Slater in and *ask* his judgment. Furthermore, one reason that a Fellowship year with Slater is such a plum for a resident is that Slater has a staggering volume of surgery, and *does* turn a lot of work and responsibility over to his Fellow, and Hank wouldn't have had the position for two weeks if Slater didn't actually trust him as implicitly as he can trust anybody—which sometimes doesn't seem very far. Surgeons only learn by doing their own cases, really; you can learn so much by assisting, and then pretty soon you have to have it all in your own lap or you don't learn any more. And most surgeons want, really, to train new men and to help them learn; even those who don't want to teach need their residents quite desperately for assistance, follow-up, coverage and relief from some of the load, and recognize that the price of having a resident around is to give him work to do.

I'm sure Slater really wants his Fellowship to be a top-rate training experience for his Fellow; I'm sure he wants it to *mean* something for a man to say "Well, I was Slater's Fellow before I took my Boards," not only here but in the national world of surgery. And the fact is that it *does* mean a whale of a lot. To anyone who knows surgery, it means that that man has had top-rate surgical training with one of the leading surgeons, probably one of the great surgeons, in the country. But, ideally, the surgeon will step down a notch in order to let his resident do a case. Ideally, the surgeon will first-assist the resident regularly, and only take over if a particularly difficult problem appears, or be ready to take over if trouble really develops. Not Slater. He can't do it. I've seen him try, and he fidgets and fusses, and complains, and just can't keep his hands off, and invariably, when he first-assists, he has taken over before the case is half-done, problem or no problem. So on Hank's "own" cases there seems to be a tacit agreement that Slater won't put on gloves. He just parades around fuming.

Anyway, Hank's two cases weren't anything exciting: a hernia repair first, then an ovarian cyst. They'd planned for Hank to use one room and Slater the other, but you can't predict the length of cases; Olsen was first-assisting Slater in Room I, and most of the time Slater was in Room II. On each of these cases Slater came in and peeked, and told Hank to go ahead, but then he would come back and look, and stew around. Hank works slowly, and Slater was coming in and saying, "Jesus, Hank, are you still working on that case?" and later, "Good Christ, have you got your hand stuck in there or something? What's taking you so long?" and then he would sort of half-laugh and say, "No, you just take your time and do a good job . . . but why the hell don't you hurry up and get out of there so I can get my next case in?" and so forth and so forth.

It was really just maddening, irritating beyond words, or would have been if it hadn't been so damned funny, with Hank working placidly along, plod, plod, plod, and Slater fluttering around like an old mother hen. Even Slater could see the humor in it, I guess. At one point on the second case Hank had the patient's abdomen open and the ovarian cyst exposed, ready to remove, and Slater came in and peered at it and said, "See? That's just what I thought from the pelvic exam. Damned thing is as big as a grapefruit," and Hank said, "Gee, I don't know, that's pretty small for a grapefruit," and Slater said, "Well, I was talking about a *Florida* grapefruit."

To add to the fun, we had Ole Bjornson as anesthetist all morning. There's been a sort of a running feud between Ole and Hank ever since the time a long way back when Ole allowed a patient to come up too far out of anesthesia while Hank was trying to close the abdomen, and the patient's muscles got so tight that Hank couldn't even pull the peritoneum together to get it sewed up and Ole had to almost completely reanesthetize the patient. Ever since then Hank has called Bjornson "Old Tightbelly" and needles him without mercy.

So today Slater was needling Hank, and Hank was taking it out on Old Tightbelly; they were using one of the new anesthesia machines that does everything but think for the anesthetist, and Hank was giving me this stuff about somebody someday inventing a gas machine that would dispense with the anesthetist altogether, and then we wouldn't have to put up with people like Old Tightbelly around the operating room. So when we were closing the cyst, the patient *was* tight as could be, and Hank said, "Jesus, Tightbelly, you've got to loosen her up a little bit for me here," and Old Tightbelly said, "Well, I don't know, some surgeons can manage to get a belly closed up without complaining to the gasman all the time."

Maggie Wren was scrub nurse, and all of a sudden we found Maggie taking Tightbelly's side in the argument, very sharply indeed. This surprised us. Usually she just sniffs and ignores the banter, but this time she began sticking up for Bjornson. So Hank and I started jumping on her for taking his side, trying to get her to say why she was all of a sudden standing up for him, and Maggie got red in the face, and madder and madder, and finally said, "Well, I just don't think it's dignified to call him names like 'Old Tightbelly!'" We asked her what she thought we ought to call him, and she said, "Well, at least you could call him *Doctor* Tightbelly." So we called him "Doctor Tightbelly" all the rest of the day, and that made Maggie all the madder.

Incidentally, I suppose people would be scandalized if they heard the standard operating room give-and-take. People think of surgery as a grim, tense business with the surgeon snapping "Scalpel!" and "Clamp!" and everything going along in dramatic silence except for the click, click of the instruments. This is just a lot of hogwash. About half the time the surgeon is telling dirty jokes with the fixed intent of embarrassing the scrub nurse—who, if she has been in the

game any time at all, is the closest thing to a totally unembar-
rassable female that is known to man—and the rest of the time
there is bickering, or gossip, or talk about how things were last
winter out in Palm Springs, or how many suction cups on a squid's
tentacles, or whether a woman has an orgasm at the instant she is
hanged, or other things of dubious relationship to the surgery at
hand. Of course, there are times when you just shut up and work,
and there are times when things *are* just plain tense, and the conversation never interferes with the concentration on the work nor
even approaches it, but an uninitiated observer would think that
these people were doing nothing more important than playing with
an erector set under all those drapes.

Saturday, October 22

Since Thursday was Slater's clinic day, Olsen assigned me to scrub
with Goodfellow on an abdominal hysterectomy. This turned out to
be quite a wild affair. After he got the woman open he did the
routine exploration of her abdomen prior to taking out the uterus,
and found she had a great big tumor mass under her diaphragm on
the left. He explored further and found nodules of it all over her
belly. So Goodfellow didn't know whether to go ahead and do a
quick hysterectomy and get out of there, or just what; he was sure
this was an unsuspected cancer he'd found. Dr. Emery was still in
surgery across the hall, so he asked Emery to come in and take a
look, and Emery thought it was a tumor, too. Emery scrubbed in,
and they took a piece of this tumor out for a frozen section, but
ten minutes later the report came back that it wasn't cancer at all, it
was a talcum powder granuloma.

Emery could hardly believe it. This gal had had an operation
fifteen years before, in the days when surgeons were still using talcum powder on their gloves, and they had gotten enough talc scattered around to start off this massive foreign-body reaction that had
just kept getting bigger and bigger all this time. Emery said he's
never seen anything like it in his life, but he thought it might keep
piling up scar tissue forever and eventually cause a bowel obstruction. So he advised Goodfellow to go ahead and do the hysterectomy, and let the woman recover from that, then bring her back in

a couple of months to take this other thing out. Couldn't do the two
things at once because the bowel might get opened getting the
granuloma out, and the surgeon wants a special preop bowel prep
done any time that is likely to happen. So we went on with the
hysterectomy and left the granuloma sitting there.

After lunch Friday I got an hour's nap, and then made rounds.
Dr. Gillies' old patient with the stomach cancer finally died, after a
period of studied neglect; after the first couple of days postoperatively, Hank and Slater pretty much just ignored the poor old goat,
just wrote minimum IV orders and waited for him to die. Maybe it
was the kind thing to do, but it annoyed me. They were eager
enough to operate on him, but everybody lost interest as soon as
they knew he was terminal.

Things may be slow for a while; Slater is leaving for Chicago next
week, going to some big surgical society meeting. He'll be gone for
ten days, and Hank says the service just dies when Slater is away.
We'll see.

Thursday, October 27

Hank was right; things have really been dead. No new patients
on Slater's service at all, and the inventory shrinks as his postop
patients go home one by one. Not even a good juicy postoperative
complication to keep us busy. I've been scrubbing on odds and ends
of cases with other doctors, but with the Hot-Shot gone the service is
very quiet.

Thursday morning I scrubbed with Olsen and Ben Boggs on an
abdominal hysterectomy. They found an ovarian cyst, too, or
thought they had, but when they had the pathologist come in and
cut it open they found it was a dermoid cyst—one of those disgusting things all full of hair and grease and skin. Sometimes you even
find teeth in them, but this one turned out to be toothless.

I was dead tired by the time I got out of the OR, so I went down
after lunch and slept from 12:30 to 3:30. Woke up feeling just as
tired as when I went to sleep. I don't really get much sleep during
these afternoon naps anyway; people are pounding in and out of
the interns' quarters, and the loudspeaker keeps blatting, so I usually just teeter along half-asleep and half-awake.

Just before I went off this evening a patient was admitted under Dr. Slater's name, though I guess Leo Richards will take care of it. This woman from some little town across the state, who found a mass in her breast a month or so ago. Ten days ago her doctor did a biopsy on it, somewhere out in the sticks where there wasn't any pathologist, so he sent the lump to a pathologist in Albuquerque for examination. Seven days later the report came back that it was a malignant tumor he'd pulled out, except that apparently he'd cut right through it, just chopped a chunk of it and left the rest of it in there. And meanwhile the wound had become infected, so now this poor creature is here with a big, hot, swollen breast, all inflamed and draining pus from the incision, with a great deal of pain, and a breast cancer sitting right in the midst of this mess. She'll have to have a radical mastectomy, of course, but the mean part is that if the cancer hadn't yet spread at the time of the biopsy, it sure as hell has spread by now, thanks to some backwoods jerk who was either too stupid or too greedy to send her where the job could have been done right in the first place. There's just no excuse for excising a breast mass without doing a frozen section on it right there. If you don't have the facilities to do a frozen section, you have no business even touching the breast, you send the patient somewhere else. Well, what could have been a clean case and maybe a cure of breast cancer has been turned into a dirty mess now. Richards wants to operate her as soon as possible, but probably won't be able to touch her until the infection is controlled. And meanwhile the cancer goes on growing.

This has been a lazy, dull week. I don't know which is worse, running my butt off on an overloaded service or sitting around bored on a slow one. I could be doing a lot of medical reading, but I'm not. I was thinking last night that I'm reaching a point now where I need to pull myself in a little tighter or something. I'm getting used to seeing things and dealing with problems, and I'm recognizing some of the patterns of medical practice that I didn't recognize before, but I find I'm also getting sloppy and taking the wrong mental attitude toward things. I remember how furious I was a few years ago as a corpsman in the Naval Hospital when I called an intern to see an old man who was dying of lung cancer, and had to wait twenty minutes for the doc to get out of bed, and then he didn't even go look at the patient, just sat down at the desk and started making out a death certificate. I thought this was inexcusable negligence and callousness then; yet last night when they called me to see some eighty-year-old man with a stroke who was choking on his own saliva, I sure didn't rush up there with any eagerness. Sure, I tried to suck him out and do what I could, but I know I was thinking, Jesus, this old guy isn't going to survive another couple of hours, why bother? Why not just let him choke and get it over with?

Well, that's what I was thinking, all right, but it's not a good attitude to have around this place. Maybe there isn't a hell of a lot you can do in a case like that, but it's still your job to try. I don't mean that you should try just because that's what the rules say; I mean it's your job as a doctor, any doctor, to try. And it isn't just these terminal cases that bother me; my whole attitude toward patients and the internship has degenerated to a certain degree since I got onto this surgical service. I don't think it's the service that's to blame. Maybe it's just laziness or overconfidence. Maybe every intern gets bored along about the end of his third or fourth month, but something is different that I don't like. I don't get excited about the patients the way I did before. I resent getting called up to see them, and get sore at the nurses when they "bother me" with problems that don't seem important, and try to deal with too much over the telephone in order to avoid going up to the floor in person and so forth. This is not a good way to be, and the fact that I'm on a service that I really don't like very much doesn't justify doing a sloppy job on it.

Well, we'll see. It may be a matter of reinforcing my diligence a little bit, but I think the time has come for a little soul-searching and re-evaluation of what I think I'm doing here, and what I thought was important earlier in the internship compared to what seems important now, and why. Maybe I'll talk to Roscoe Herring or Hamilton and see if they are worrying about the same thing, or whether I'm just bored and depressed. I suspect that working with Slater has a lot to do with it. I find him a rather revolting individual to have to deal with, most times, yet I'm nailed with him whether I like it or not until December 1st.

Tomorrow I may actually have a morning without any scrubs at all. Richards may do this dirty breast case, but probably not; and Garvin wants to scrub on Richards' other case. So I may just have a day to loaf around in.

Monday, October 31

A very strange weekend, this last one. I wonder if it's the phases of the moon or something. I didn't dictate anything Friday night when I was off; Ann decided that if I had weekend duty coming up, we were by God going out for once, so we went to the movies and really splurged, stopped for hamburgers and beer on the way home. The kind of gay, exciting date a doctor's wife looks forward to, like they say on TV. Now it's Monday night, and there still isn't much to comment on. I haven't had such a stone-dead weekend yet; the place was like a tomb. About three calls all day Saturday and two on Sunday. I don't know if all the doctors got tired at the same time and quit admitting patients or what.

As I expected, Leo Richards scratched the breast surgery Friday morning and put the woman on pen-strep and Chloromycetin and all the other antibiotics he could think of instead. He doesn't think she'll be operable for at least a week with the amount of infection she has in that breast. Slater is still gone, so I had no Friday morning scrubs. Then Saturday and Sunday I wandered around quarters and read a couple of murder mysteries and watched the Big Eye and went up on the floor to pinch nurses and generally wished something would happen, but nothing did.

Correction—there was one case that came in Saturday night that stirred the place up a bit, even though I didn't really get in on it. It's all very hush-hush except that every doctor in the place is talking about it. This patient was a girl who has been a long-time cocktail waitress down at the Hacienda, who was sent in by Dr. Frank Harlow, one of the really top-rate outside surgeons. This in itself was funny, because Harlow does most of his surgery at St. Christopher's and rarely indeed brings anybody here—I guess on the theory that there's not room enough for him and Nathan Slater in the same hospital. Anyway, this gal came in by ambulance, and the nurse called me, all confused; Harlow had called ahead to schedule emergency surgery, but he'd said specifically *not* to call out any intern or resident, he'd come in himself. He wasn't there yet, and the patient was, and the nurse said the woman was obviously having a lot of pain and she didn't know what to do.

So I went up to the floor, but before I saw the girl, who should come buzzing in but Hank Ruggles and Harlow together. Apparently, Harlow had called him to scrub on the case with him as a special favor. And they both were very vague and insisted that I needn't bother to scrub.

That was about 7:30 P.M. Saturday. About 11:00 I was down at midnight supper wondering if I was really hungry enough to try the hot pot or not when Hank appeared, so mad he was actually swearing under his breath, and he told me what the story was. It seems this woman had a varicose vein ligation done at St. Christopher's Hospital about a week before by some general practitioner—Hank wouldn't say which one. Anyway, a day or so later she had developed this sore, swollen leg and complained of pain in the leg and cramps when she walked; she'd called the GP on the phone, and the GP had told her not to worry, there always was some pain and swelling after a vein ligation and it would go away. Next day it was worse, so the woman went to the GP's office, and the doctor ordered some quinine for her leg cramps, and said, "There, there, my good woman, everything's going to be all right," but was too busy to examine her leg.

A couple of days later the leg was so painful that the woman went back and this time insisted that the GP call another surgeon in for a second opinion. This time the doctor looked at the leg, and then called Harlow in because he discovered that the leg was blue and cold from mid-thigh on down. Harlow had shipped her in to Graystone on the spot, and set up emergency surgery, and he and Hank had opened up the incision again and discovered that the GP had ligated the woman's femoral artery just below the groin, so she had no arterial circulation to her leg for four days. So Hank and Harlow had just finished doing a thromboendarterectomy, cutting out the ligated section of the artery and sewing the ends back together again, and then had the anesthetist give her a splanchnic block, which helps dilate the blood vessels in the leg, in hopes of opening the circulation back up again. There on the operating table, after they joined the artery together again, the leg turned pink down to the knee, and after the splanchnic block it was pink to the ankle, but the foot stayed slate gray. It now looks as if the girl may have to have an amputation just above the ankle and lose a foot, all because some jackass couldn't tell the saphenous vein from the femoral artery.

Well, it sounded incredible to me that any doctor could make a mistake like that in the first place, and even more incredible that he could just ignore the woman's complaints, particularly those complaints, for four days postoperatively. If the mistake had been picked up within twenty-four hours, chances are her foot could have been saved. And now neither Hank nor Harlow know what to tell the woman; she's sitting on a $100,000 malpractice claim and doesn't know it. Hank said the GP would probably lose his surgical privileges at St. Christopher's for a while, or at least have them limited, but he didn't think the woman should be told that she was the victim of incompetent surgery compounded by negligence. I got sore as hell at this, told Hank it seemed to me that the gal should sue for every nickel she could get and that every doctor in town should be with her right down the line.

Hank just shook his head and said, "It could be you next time just as well, and then what?" I said, "Well, I wouldn't do a vein ligation without looking at what I was doing, for one thing, and nobody in his right mind could get that big pulsating artery confused with a vein." Hank said, "My ass they couldn't, I've done it myself. I had a big, fat 2-o silk tie around a femoral artery once, all set to pull it down and tie it before somebody noticed it and hollered. You just can't nail the man for making the mistake, and as for negligence, there isn't a doctor alive that isn't negligent one way or another every week of the year. So how can you crucify this guy just because he happened to get caught? You go pointing fingers and you may find yourself in a very slippery spot sometime with a whole lot of fingers pointing at you."

Well, I can't agree with him, or at least I don't think I can, but I'm not so sure about it as I might have been before I came to this place. I guess nobody is going to say anything much, just tell the woman that this was an unfortunate complication of her surgery, and see what happens. I mean see whether she actually needs an amputation or not, and see what she does. And I know about it, but

I don't think *I'm* going to walk in and say to her, "Gee, you ought to sue that bird for everything he's got," either.

I came down to a very dull Monday morning CPC this morning, then scrubbed on a thyroidectomy with L. D. Kaiser, a very nice job. Kaiser is not a clinic doctor, but most of the clinic men seem to like him. He interned here, and later came back as Slater's Fellow two or three years ago. Now he's trying to get started in private practice, sort of loosely teamed up with Dr. Jack Barley. The interns and residents here try to give Kaiser and Barley a boost when they can. When we see an outpatient at night for something that should be followed up by a surgeon, and the patient doesn't have a private doctor, we will refer him to Kaiser. There's no point sending them to a clinic man; the younger clinic men are on salary, and the old boys like Slater and Emery couldn't care less whether they have another patient more or less. With Kaiser one referral can be next week's bread and butter. It's a rough way to build a practice, for him, because most of these things turn up about 2:00 A.M., and it's a matter of dragging the poor guy out of bed for something piddly, and he's always so very willing to come to the hospital to see someone at the drop of a hat that you feel a little guilty picking on him when you know it's nothing very lucrative. On the other hand, when a guy sees a surgeon because of a cut finger, he's liable to go back to him with his next gall bladder attack, so Kaiser is happy enough to come no matter for what.

Anyway, I was impressed that Kaiser was a quick and careful surgeon; he laid the thyroid open like a neat anatomical dissection, and then out it came, snicker-snack. He's a very pleasant guy, and honest as well, from what I've heard. One night at midnight supper Leo Richards was down chewing the fat and talking about how he came to the clinic and was just as glad he wasn't starting off solo in surgery in this town. He maintained that we have very little trouble with scabby practices here, particularly fee-splitting with surgeons, because most of the young guys starting off won't play ball, but apparently there are a number of men in town who keep looking for one who will. Every new guy who starts off in general surgery apparently gets approached by these guys to see if he will kick back part of his fee in return for a referral, or promise to let the referring doctor assist in the OR, which can amount to the same thing. Sometimes the approach isn't direct, but a GP, for instance, will send three or four nice juicy cases to a new surgeon, make him think, Gee whizz, this practice is really taking off nicely, and then approach him as the price of keeping it up.

Fortunately, Richards said, there aren't very many of them in this town, and the surgeons get the word about them early, so the town stays pretty clean. Also, apparently Slater is personally instrumental in keeping these guys, referring doctors or accepting surgeons, off the Graystone staff; he's got an amazing amount of power in this hospital, and whenever something suspicious of a fee-splitting setup turns up, Slater rises in fury and drops the ax, and nobody dares argue with him even if they would like to.

This is the last of October, and now we have the service shuffle again. Not for me; I stay right where I am on Slater's service for another month, but Roscoe Herring is going over to the Children's Division tomorrow, and Schwartz comes back from Children's to go on Medicine I, so two of the three medical services will not be covered and Hamilton and I will be covering Surgery II and Surgery I, respectively. This may shoot our "double call" arrangement, since it would mean one intern covering both medical and surgical service on the same night, which might prove to be an excessive load; we'll have to see how it works out.

Regardless of that, Alec is going to pay back the call night he owes me this Friday so I can take off for the weekend Friday at five; Ann and I are tentatively planning a desert camping trip. This means I'll have to take call Tuesday, Wednesday and Thursday nights in a row, so I don't know what I'll do on the journal or when, the rest of this week.

Sunday, November 6

The woman with the foot had her amputation Friday A.M.; they've kept her kind of sequestered away, and have been using splanchnic blocks twice or three times a day and gradually the foot got a little pinker, but not pink enough. The whole lower part of the foot was getting gangrenous, so I guess Harlow finally gave up trying to save it. Now the question is whether the circulation to the stump—it was a mid-calf amputation—is going to be good enough to keep it from breaking down into gangrene when she starts walking on a prosthesis. They try to amputate as low as possible, but might conceivably end up having to take this gal's leg off two inches at a time over the next year or two.

One interesting case turned up last week, a really spooky one. This was a man who came in on Dr. Cornell's neurosurgical service. At the age of fifty-two this patient had suddenly begun having Jacksonian seizures, a peculiar kind of convulsion which in this man's case involved only his right arm. He would be sitting and reading and suddenly his thumb would start to twitch, and then his fingers, and then his wrist and then his whole arm. Then after a few moments with his arm shaking violently, it would all stop, but would recur again in an hour or so in the same fashion.

Cornell saw him in the clinic and felt sure that the seizures were caused by a fast-growing brain tumor which might be operable. But then the X-ray people reported that a chest film showed that the man had a large tumor in his right lung. So Cornell put on the brakes; this looked like a lung cancer, probably bronchogenic carcinoma, which commonly seeds to the brain. Cornell called in Leo Richards, and Wednesday morning Richards opened the man's chest. Found a bronchogenic carcinoma all right, and removed the whole upper lobe of his right lung, cancer and all. Pretty massive surgery; the man is good and sick, may not even make it through the postoperative recovery period. If he does, Cornell then wants to go in after the brain lesion.

He claims there are rare cases in which there is a single metastatic lesion in the brain and no more. I don't know; bronchogenic carcinoma is one of the really vicious ones that grow fast and seed all over kingdom come. I just can't imagine that a single cell could break loose and lodge in the brain to grow a single metastatic lesion without others doing the same thing at the same time, but on the other hand, his life isn't worth a plugged nickel without the brain surgery, that is 100 per cent sure, so maybe Cornell is justified.

Things were slow enough that I got out of the hospital on the dot of 5:00 Friday; Ann stopped by for me, packed and ready, I got out of my scrub suit and showered and shaved, and we headed down into the desert for a weekend of camping and exploring. When you get good and sick of people, go to the desert for a couple of days. It's good for the soul. We had already picked a spot about sixty miles out for our Friday night camp. Cooked steaks on a sagebrush camp-fire, and then spent Saturday and Sunday on back roads without seeing another soul. It was great.

Tuesday, November 8

Back to the hospital this Monday morning and found Slater back at work. Eight scheduled cases, and cranky and impatient as ever. So it looks like we'll be back on a normal schedule again. I just didn't realize how delightful it was to have him gone.

A couple of nonmedical things to catch up on here. The ax finally got dropped on the nurse who has been stealing dope on the 3:00-to-11:00 shift on Third. The hospital had hoped to nail her—catch her flat-footed—but no such luck. Finally, they felt they couldn't risk having her around any longer and just sacked her. Trouble is, they would have to have *proof* to accuse her. A narcotics charge can just wipe out a nurse's career and livelihood, and if you can't make your accusations stick, you could be sued for lifetime support on grounds of slander and defamation of character and malicious mischief and false arrest and every other damned thing. So there was no accusation, but one night last week the woman came in so hopped up she could barely stagger down the hall and a couple of patients were scared silly because she came in talking nonsense to them and waving a syringe and needle around at them. I called the nursing supervisor and said, "Look, let's get this babe home before she kills somebody." So she was sent home "sick" and was then just quietly discharged. Nobody knows which hospital she'll pick next.

Duty Monday night was pretty noisy—sick people must have gotten word that Slater was back in town—and I was up most of the night. Slater had a patient in with biliary colic that he finally did this morning; Ike Isaacs sent in one of his drunken delights with low back pain and a lot of abusive language, gave me a pain in my low back, I mean down *very* low in my back; and Flagg had a threatened miscarriage that came in bleeding like a stuck hog, so the night was jolly. This morning I scrubbed with Goodfellow on a vaginal plastics—no kidding, that's what they call it, repair of a rectocele and cystocele. I can't remember when a case seemed so utterly long or so utterly boring; I just about fell asleep in the middle of it all.

We have things lined up tomorrow for Slater's "first real day of surgery" since he came back. I don't know what he thought Monday was, a sort of a warm-up, maybe.

Thursday, November 10

Well, the honeymoon is certainly over. It took Slater a couple of days to really get back into the scrap again, but by now he's made it. He must have had fifteen major cases so far this week and another half-dozen scheduled tomorrow. It's still a mystery to me how he can turn the flow of patients off and on like this, but he sure manages to do it.

Wednesday was his operating day, and we had a steady stream of cases, with Slater shuttling back and forth between Rooms I and II like mad all day. There was a thyroidectomy and a hysterectomy and the breast biopsy, which turned out to be a radical. That one was at least a little cheering; the frozen section showed a cirrhous carcinoma, one of the slower-growing cancers that doesn't spread so early or so fast. Which means it may be one that was *really* cured by the radical. And it's double lucky, too, because the idiot woman noticed the lump some three months ago and has been waiting around all this time hoping that it would go away. As Slater said, "She's probably been sitting around squeezing it every day for the last three months, too," which isn't exactly choice therapy. Even so, she may do all right.

After that was over, I went down to see new patients coming in. One was a man who had part of his colon removed for diverticulosis a month or so ago. Now he is spiking fevers for several days, and has a mass palpable in his rectum that feels very much like an internal abscess getting ready to drain through into the rectum. Talk about sore—I went to examine him, and the damned fool didn't tell me that Slater had examined him the day before in the office and nearly sent him flying through the clinic roof, so I examined him and nearly sent him through the ceiling of 316. He just rose up like Lazarus.

I had to hand it to Slater, though. The first thing he said was:

"Well, it could just be an abscess from contamination, but I could
have left a sponge in there, too," and he sent Hank packing for the
old operative record and sent the guy down to X-ray for films. The
surgical sponges all have radio-opaque tags on them that show up
unmistakably on X-ray. None showed up here, and the sponge count
had been correct and confirmed, but at least Slater admitted it
could happen even to him. The man will probably have the abscess
drained tomorrow.

Nothing much Wednesday night. Hamilton, who is on Medicine
I, took double call, and I got a full night's sleep. This morning I
scrubbed with Boggs and Olsen on a pelvic exploratory that certainly illustrates how incredibly stupid some patients can be, and
how little you can believe what they tell you. This was a woman
who had been trying to have a baby without success, and had had
some X-rays taken with contrast medium* that had showed that
both her tubes were obstructed. The surgery was planned to find
out why, and we found out, all right. Boggs got in there and found
that she'd had a bilateral tubal ligation, both tubes had been tied
years back, a little fact that this babe had somehow neglected to
mention! And sure enough, looking more closely, there was a tiny,
barely discernible half-inch scar in her lower abdomen that nobody
had seen. So Boggs cut out the ligated segment of each tube and
tried to reopen them by inserting polyethylene catheters. Said this
was like trying to unburn a burnt bridge, that the odds were a
hundred to one against it doing any good, but now that he was in
there he might as well try.

We got out of the OR about 3:00. I found that the guy that had
the carcinoma of the colon which Slater had removed about three
weeks ago was back in. Now he seems to have a bowel obstruction,
but he looks too sick for just that, doesn't look good at all, in fact.
He's forty-five years old and should have bounced back from surgery
better than this. You can't help wondering if the malignancy wasn't
farther along than it seemed to be. There wasn't any evidence of
spread at the time of surgery, and Slater was feeling very elated
about it, insisting that here was one that we had cured, and the
path report showed no sign of microscopic evidence of spread, but I

* A substance opaque to X-rays (iodine, for example, or barium) which can
be injected into various parts of the body to show the shape of internal organs.

was really quite startled to see how sick and debilitated he looked now. Of course, it could just be a slow recovery, but it could also be that the Bad Disease had its hooks into him deeper than we thought. We'll find out soon enough, I guess.

Slater also has a thyroidectomy, a hysterectomy, the rectal abscess and a gastric resection lined up for tomorrow. I don't know how he does it. That's a good week's worth of surgery right there for a busy surgeon, and he's got it all scheduled for one day. Now that things are rolling again, I'll have more to do in making rounds, and working up new patients and helping keep things under control, so it looks like I'm through loafing for a while.

I found out a little more about Hank Ruggles today when Olsen and I were chewing the fat. Hank was a Dartmouth man, then studied medicine at Jefferson and married a woman from a very wealthy family—which may be why he can afford four years of surgical residency. Slater's Fellow, the best-paid resident in the place, gets a whole $250 a month. Hank is a little, short, skinny man with a sallow face and thin cheeks, kind of bulging eyes and pock marks—altogether a sinister-looking guy. He reminds me of the little spook who played one of the Terrified Villagers in the early Frankenstein movies. Especially when he gets on his overcoat and his brown felt hat with the brim he pulls down all around, he looks like a small-time hustler or somebody you'd find down on skid row trying to sell you dirty pictures—certainly anything but a highly competent surgeon. And you'd think he couldn't smile if he had to, even though he has a very pleasant smile when he feels like using it ("Once a year, at Christmas," he once said deadpan). We've gotten to be good friends during the past six weeks. He rides me a good deal, but he also gives a lot and goes out of his way to help or explain things. He strikes you as being a very cold, noncommittal sort of individual when he really isn't. His looks are against him, that's all.

Friday, November 11

This was my biweekly short day today. Slater had a D & C on a woman this morning and put a probe right through the uterine wall. So it can happen to the best of them. He didn't do anything about it but watch her blood pressure like a hawk all day; if the probe had gone through a major vessel he'd have had to open her up, but she's been doing fine.

Slater and Olsen also opened up the man with the fevers and rectal pain today and found he did indeed have a big abscess pressing on his rectum, secondary to the colon resection of three weeks ago. They got it drained and closed him up, and he will probably do okay now.

Things are beginning to get onto an even keel again now. The service is active, and I may have a busy weekend. The man with the bowel obstruction is doing better; Slater ordered some water and salt by IV, and he just picked up miraculously in twenty-four hours. So maybe obstruction is all that's wrong. Slater isn't planning further surgery for now, at any rate.

I got off at 5:30 after making brief rounds with Hank and Fred; then home for supper. Ann and I talked about tightening up the budget a little, because we are down to scratch, just about. She is getting about $250 a month take-home pay and that isn't much, even with my $125 a month from the hospital thrown in. This car is going to go *queep* and die one of these days just as sure as shooting, and I don't know what we'll do for another one. I guess we are both disgusted and discouraged. Seems we have to weigh the cost of going to a movie, and even the gas for a camping trip weekend puts us behind for three months. I know Ann is damned sick of typing this journal on my duty nights, and equally sick of having me squat here on my can dictating it after supper every night I have off. I'm usually bushed enough by the time I get home that I want a good stiff drink and then dinner and then the journal and then to go to bed and sleep as soon as possible, and the less yap from anybody the better. Then we leave by 6:45 in the morning again to get me to the hospital by 7:15.

Well, so much for the delights of the gay, exciting life of an intern's wife.

Monday, November 14

A busy weekend, as I thought it was going to be. Between Slater's patients and the emergency room I really was hopping most of the time. Started at 8:30 Saturday on rounds with Hank Ruggles. The woman with the infected breast biopsy is finally scheduled for Wednesday, hopefully, at last. We took the last stitches out on the two thyroidectomy patients and sent them home. Those patients seem to have just a three-day hospital stay. You take half the stitches out twenty-four hours after surgery, and the other half out after forty-eight hours. They have a sore neck for a while, but they have less scar showing on the throat that way, and they seem to do all right.

We didn't finish rounds until 10:45, and then a steady succession of outpatients started turning up. A big fat girl who had had her purse snatched on the street took a swing at the purse-snatcher, missed, lost her balance and fell down, whacking her head on the curb. Life is full of hazards. The X-ray man found a hairline fracture of her occipital bone, so we put her to bed to watch for any sign of intracranial bleeding. She already had a great shiner on the right side, and she was so mad that I had to interrupt a running stream of indignation every now and then to find out if she was hurting or not. By Monday morning she was doing fine except that by then she had a shiner on the other side, too.

Saturday evening the clinic doctors and their wives were throwing a potluck supper for the house staff in the clinic lounge, which was very nice except that I had to drink ginger ale while everybody else became convivial on better stuff. Even Slater made a brief appearance, though he didn't stay long, just long enough to exhibit his social charm, which is different from his operating room charm. Ann says he reminds her of a fox, in both appearance and manner.

Slater also drank ginger ale, I noticed; Hank once said that Slater won't take a drink, not even a beer, any time he's within telephone contact of the hospital, no matter what the occasion. It's not that he's a teetotaler—he'll have a drink at Surgical Society meetings in Chicago, for instance—but if he's where he might conceivably be called at any time, he just won't. Claims that even one beer impairs a man's judgment a little, maybe only by 2 percent, but that that 2 percent might make the difference between making the right decision or the wrong one on an emergency case at 2:00 in the morning sometime. He doesn't make a pious point about this or try to cram it down anybody else's throat. He just quietly doesn't drink himself, thank you, because that's how he looks at it.

Ann arrived at the hospital just before the party was to start, and then had to wait while I saw an outpatient, some old man who could speak only German. He had just that day arrived from the old country to visit a son in the city, and had opened a door and fallen down the cellar stairs thinking it was the bathroom. No serious injuries, but finding out what had happened in the midst of all that German was tough, and we were an hour late to the party.

Finally got back to the hospital about 11:30, leaving Ann to drive herself home. I'd thought it was just luck that I hadn't had a single call all evening, then found out that the girl on the switchboard hadn't known where to reach me, so she had turned all the calls over to Miss Foulkes, who had a stack of goodies waiting for me when I got back.

I got to bed about 1:00, but I didn't sleep well. Not because of calls—I only had one—I just kept waking up and tossing and turning. Finally got to sleep at 5:00 or so and slept through the alarm, awoke with a jolt at 9:00, to my horror since I was supposed to meet Hank at 9:15 for rounds. I piled out of bed and shaved and dressed and started to catch a bite of breakfast hoping that Hank would be late, but at 9:20 sure as hell there was my page: Hank was on Fourth to make rounds, and where the hell was I? Finally at 11:00 I got combination breakfast and lunch and went back to interns' quarters to wait for the Sunday afternoon onslaught.

It started at 1:30 with a call to see a man with an incisional hernia that was strangulated. This guy was in addition to the ten-odd patients I was expecting in for surgery in the morning, and I ended up spending most of Sunday working with the fat old goat. His name was Mr. Horner, and he'd had a gall bladder operation eight years ago, with peritonitis and an infection in his incision. Four years ago he'd come back with a rupture into the incision, right down the middle of his abdomen. At the time of the original operation he had weighed 220 pounds and they had tried like hell to get him to reduce but he would not stop eating. So when the hernia appeared, Slater had decided not to repair it until he'd lost fifty pounds of fat or so. He'd promised faithfully and then disappeared, just never came back.

Now he was in again; he had his big hernia protruding from a pad of fat that must have been six inches thick at least. He was short and stubby and sort of spread out on the bed like a big mound of Jello. Through all this fat I could feel this rupture about the size of a cantaloupe, very sore and tender, and he'd been vomiting for almost twenty hours straight, so he was bone-dry. Had to get him moved over flat on the X-ray table—he couldn't get all that weight hoisted over there himself—and took the flat plate. Then I had to strap him down and support him while the motor tipped the X-ray table up for the upright film. Reminded me of the old Frankenstein pictures where the Monster is being lifted upright to launch him; if Mr. Horner had just tottered off stiff-legged saying, "Ugh, I go kill," it would have been perfect, but all he was saying was, "Oh, mercy me. Oh, mercy me," over and over and over.

After all that work we couldn't tell a goddamned thing from the X-rays except that he was full of gas from one end to the other. Took him up to bed and started fighting to find veins for his IVs—four of them had been ordered in the first twenty-four hours—and started a fight that lasted all afternoon, in between admitting other patients and running up to Mr. Horner's room to restart an IV that had infiltrated. He had these tiny little veins that just wouldn't take or hold a needle.

By 8:30 or 9:00 Sunday night I had about half the ten or twelve new admissions worked up. If I worked uninterrupted, I could finish the last one up by about midnight, but then Hank trouped in to see Mr. Horner. He'd gotten about one of the four liters of fluid into him by IV by then, and he didn't look very good. Hank thought he might have developed acidosis from his prolonged vomiting, and called out the lab girls to get electrolyte studies done on him. I'd already done the blood count and hematocrit, which just told us what we already knew, that he was dehydrated as a dog biscuit. Well, there are times you just can't win. Nobody could get a blood sample from him, and finally Hank said, "Hell, we could keep this up all night, and he's got to get water into him. Let's cut him down."

So the nurses brought in a cutdown set, and Hank scrubbed the skin on the man's ankle and cut down to find a vein and threaded a polyethylene catheter into it and tied it in place good and tight, so we got blood and got a stable IV running at last. I don't know why I hadn't done it hours ago; I draw back from doing cutdowns because they seem so much bother and always give the patient an irritated vein and a sore leg, but it would have saved half a day if I'd done it at 3:00 in the afternoon instead of 10:00 at night.

Oh, yes, we'd also been trying to get a Miller-Abbott tube down him. This is a long rubber tube-within-a-tube with a little bag of mercury on one end which you slip down into the stomach like a Levin tube, and then by positioning the patient correctly and moving him from side to side and advancing the tube a little at a time you try to coax the end of it out of the stomach into the small bowel. It's great for decompressing gas down there—when you can get it through the pylorus—but you have to sort of personally nurse the thing along hour after hour. If you leave it up to the nurses, they always seem to forget when to turn the patient over or when to advance the tube.

Once we got the cutdown done, Hank went down with me to midnight supper while he waited for the electrolyte reports to come back. He thought the man might have to be opened up right then and there, and was afraid he might be in such bad shape that he wouldn't be able to stand the trauma of the surgery. By the time the electrolytes had come back, however, Hank had talked himself out of a midnight party, just planned to run the man into the schedule first thing in the morning unless he started getting worse during the night.

Monday morning everything went wrong. Mr. Horner was first on the schedule, but with all the trouble getting blood out of him, Hank had forgotten to order blood typed and cross-matched for surgery, and I hadn't even thought of it. So they got him to OR all ready to anesthetize and there wasn't any blood on hand. Slater wouldn't start him until the blood was right there in the operating room, so they sent over to the blood bank for 3 units, and then brought another case up, a gall bladder, to start on while they waited. This error and snarl-up irritated Slater no end, so all day long he wouldn't let Hank do anything at all. By the time the blood came we were well into the gall bladder case, and the patient's gall bladder was full of little tiny rocks and gravel, so there had to be an exploration of the common bile duct, too, which is like a second major case on top of the first, and involves getting the X-ray people up into the OR with a portable machine and sterile-draped plates to take films during surgery to show whether the common duct is free of stones or not before you quit. So all this took until 11:30, with Mr. Horner lying there on the table in Room II with his belly sticking up into the wind.

So finally we got going on Mr. Horner, opened him up and found about five pounds of gangrenous bowel incarcerated in his hernia—about a foot and a half of small bowel involved—and Slater was ranting and raving that we should have done him last night, and that now he was going to have to do a bowel resection, and with all that fat pad Mr. Horner was going to get a wound infection, sure as hell, and so on and so on. We had old Tightbelly passing gas for us—pardon, Dr. Tightbelly—and something wasn't right with the anesthesia, so Slater fought with Dr. Tightbelly, and finally wanted Don Morehouse to come in, but Don was tied up somewhere at that particular instant, and I guess this was just the wrong day to stick needles into Slater because he slammed his needle holder down and said that by Christ he wanted Don Morehouse in that operating room and he wasn't going to make another move until Don Morehouse was there. So finally Don came in and thank God had wit enough to keep his mouth shut, and we finally finished Mr. Horner about 2:30.

Then there was an appendicial abscess, a case I could have done myself in about fifteen minutes, but Slater had to do that personally, and then went in to start a gastrectomy at 4:30, and still had a colon resection to go. He asked Hank very sarcastically if he thought he could manage to close the abdomen on the patient with the appendicial abscess, and Hank meekly said, yes, he thought he probably could. After that there was a man with a fatty tumor on his abdominal wall that Slater allowed Hank to do.

I was about full to the ears with Slater by then and I guess Hank was, too; he was riding Olsen just as hard in the other room, closing up the gastrectomy at a quarter of six as Hank was doing the lipoma. There was a staff dinner that night, and I was determined to get to it and told Hank so. Hank said, "Well, if we drag our feet on this lipoma, they may get scrubbed and start on the colon in there before we finish; otherwise you're nailed." So we made a three-quarter-hour project out of a piddly little fifteen-minute case, and Slater and Olsen were just scrubbing for the colon at 6:30, and I took the man with the lipoma down to his room and wrote his postop orders and then went down and disappeared into the bowels of the hospital where nobody could find me. Waited for a half-hour until I was sure the colon was well started, and then changed my clothes and washed up and went over to the staff dinner.

I sat with Dr. Compton, Luke Hamilton and Virgil Aarons, who is Emery's Fellow, and we spent the meal arguing about how carcinoma of the cervix should be treated.

After the dinner I went over to the surgical section of the staff meeting, and there was Slater finished with his colon resection, spry and chipper as could be, reviewing the surgical deaths for the month of October as though this had just been another ordinary routine day. No admissions on the service, so I went home after the staff meeting.

Wednesday, November 16

For once Olsen had not assigned me to an 8:00 scrub on Tuesday, so I made rounds with Slater and Ruggles. Slater seemed to have forgotten all about his troubles of Monday. We saw old Mr. Horner and found that he was still alive, but not in very good shape. Whatever Don Morehouse had given him for anesthesia, he was still out in left field from it. Most of the rest of the patients we saw seemed to be in pretty good shape. These were business rounds; we didn't stop to talk about anything to speak of.

Mr. Horner was a little more responsive that evening and beginning to look better. The gastric resection from the day before was having a lot of pain and discomfort but was feeling good enough to complain. All Tuesday evening I had a multitude of little calls; got to bed by midnight. A couple of pill calls, and then at 3:30 I got called to go up and take a look at Mr. Horner's IV cutdown. This simple-minded nurse couldn't tell me over the phone what was wrong with it except that it wasn't working right—couldn't say whether it was leaking, or stopped altogether, or infiltrated or what. So I went up and found that it was leaking but still running. This time I didn't fool around with it; I just reopened the incision on his ankle, put another tie around the catheter after shoving it on up the vein another couple of inches, irrigated it with a little saline, and it ran very nicely. In fact, it ran nicely all day. By 3:00 Wednesday afternoon he was talking and laughing and could even take some fluid by mouth, feeling much better, so maybe we are out of the woods with him.

Wednesday morning I slept through breakfast with Andy. Just about got up in time for rounds with Slater at 8:00, then up to the OR to scrub on the thyroidectomy-plus-gall-bladder case. Slater did the gall bladder first, then started the thyroid while Hank closed up the abdominal incision. Very neat, clean job on both of them. After that we had a second cholecystectomy (gall bladder operation), which would not have been bad except that Slater insisted on doing an incidental appendectomy through the same incision. You'd think it would be simple, but it isn't; finished up in the OR about 3:15 P.M.

No new admissions on Slater's service, so I got home on time. Tomorrow Fred has me assigned to help him assist some outside doctor with a breast biopsy and possible radical mastectomy. The guy is a surgeon, I guess, but the case or two I've seen him do have been the clumsiest, bloodiest messes I've ever seen anywhere. So I hope it's just a biopsy.

Looking at the record of some of these days that Ann has been typing up, it certainly sounds like an assembly-line business, this surgery. And from the intern's point of view, I guess it is. All I see is the *coup de grâce*, the bare bones of the surgical procedures and the acute follow-up period postoperatively. Actually, there is a great deal to a surgical case from the first discovery of something that requires surgical correction to the final stage of recovery that I just don't see at all. All the preop work, and most of the follow-up, goes on in the clinic offices and I never see it. So from my standpoint this surgical service seems like an endless succession of surgical scrubs on an endless succession of inert, anesthetized bodies that roll in one end of the operating suite and out the other. Which, of course, is not by any means all the game involves; it just seems that way.

Tuesday, November 22

Back to work Monday after a strictly do-nothing weekend off. I was anticipating a rugged schedule for the week, but so far it hasn't turned out quite that way. Slater's service is down sharply from usual; Monday he had just three cases scheduled, hardly worth getting out of bed for. A hernia repair, a gall bladder case, and a removal of a sebaceous cyst from somebody's scalp, and that was all. I was surprised; I guess I'd just assumed that Slater always had a full load of surgery piled up, a sort of a backlog to draw on, but Hank says, no, mostly he is working on current cases and sometimes even running in cases that have just been referred to him a day or so before they are scheduled.

All the same, Monday was a strange and peculiar day in the operating room; in fact, Slater put on one of the oddest performances I've seen yet. I mentioned some time back that part of a resident's training in surgery depends on his actually doing cases himself. First-assisting the big cheese is fine up to a point, but the most important part of the training is actually having cases to do on your own responsibility, ideally with the surgeon first-assisting. And this doesn't set well with Slater; he gets nervous, and when anything the slightest bit difficult turns up in the course of a procedure, he grabs it away from the resident right there and finishes it himself.

Recently Fred Olsen has been agitating for some cases. Slater lets Hank do some things, but always makes excuses to Fred, never turns a case over to him. He'll say, "Gee, Fred, I'd let you do this one, but the patient had a lot of trouble with anesthesia last time," or "You could probably do this just fine, Fred, but I'm a little bit nervous about this case, so I'd better do it," and so on.

Well, Monday Slater was apparently nursing a sore hand he had whacked with a hammer; he let Hank do the hernia repair from start to finish, didn't even scrub on it, just came into the OR to watch and chat. In the course of it Hank made some remark about how Slater ought to let Fred do more, how competent Fred was in the operating room and how faithful he was on rounds and follow-up, and so forth, and Slater said, yes, he knew he ought to give him more work, but every time he did he just got so nervous he had to take over in midstream even when Fred was doing fine, and he didn't like that to happen because then Fred thought he was doing something wrong when he wasn't at all.

In any event, Slater must have mulled this over through the closing of the hernia and all the time they were getting the gall bladder case ready in the other room. He and Fred and I were scrubbing together for the case when Slater started complaining loud and long about his hand, and when we came in to do the case, Slater said, "Well, Fred, you go ahead on this one if you want to, I'll just stand by in case you have any trouble."

So Fred did the gall bladder, but Slater didn't first-assist. I first-assisted, and they dug up Barr to second-assist. Slater pulled a stool over to the side of the operating room and sat there through the whole procedure, gowned and gloved, with his back to the operating table. He just sat huddled there, shivering, with the sweat pouring down his face, and I'd have sworn he was suffering agonies, but he let Fred go through from beginning to end. Once when Fred was all set to remove the gall bladder, Slater came over and took a look at the dissection and remarked on how nice it looked, and then went back to his stool again.

Well, it was a very strange thing to see. This was the second or third major case I've seen Olsen do. He's a third-year resident now and really a competent surgeon. He knows exactly what he's going to do; he's obviously up on his anatomy and technique before walking into the operating room at all. That gall bladder case took an hour and a half to do; it was a very nice job and Slater complimented Fred very sincerely on it when he was finished, but all I could think of was what torment Slater went through. You would think he was turning his own grandmother over to an intern to do.

Later I talked to Fred about it, and he said Slater couldn't help it, it was just the way the man was made. I asked Fred if he expected to move up into Hank's spot as Slater's Fellow when Hank leaves in January, but Fred said, no, the spot had already been promised to a fourth-year surgical resident who had been over at the Children's Division for the past six months, a guy I don't know at all. Fred may go on into general practice next year and try to gather a little money before going on with his fourth year of surgical residency somewhere else. It's too bad, in a way; apparently Slater's service is the only service worth staying on as a fourth-year resident at Graystone. Emery just doesn't give the resident enough work to do, and there are too many first- and second-year residents wanting to get their fingers in the pie there anyway.

After the gall bladder case Monday I went down for lunch, then made rounds on some of the patients who came in over the week-end. Mrs. London was back in; her breast incision had broken down and gotten infected, so she will have a skin graft, probably on Wednesday if we can get the infection cleaned up enough by then. Mr. Horner was coming along famously until Monday evening, when the nurse called to say he was spiking a fever for some reason. Hank didn't like that a bit; in fact, seemed very much upset by the news. I asked him why, it was only one degree of fever, and he just said, "Well, you saw that six inches of fat we had to cut through to get into his belly, didn't you? If he's getting infection in that in-cision now, we're in for a long, tough haul." He went up with me, and we went over Mr. Horner's chest and abdomen carefully, but couldn't find the trouble. He just said, "Let's just hope there's pus in his urine. That'll explain it," and told me to be sure to check his temp again in the morning, and not give him any aspirin, which might mask a fever if he had one.

Monday evening was relatively quiet. Had to start a Miller-Abbott tube on a patient of Dr. Richards' who's in for a thrombo-endarterectomy tomorrow. Got up at 7:00 to make rounds with Fred. Mr. Horner's temperature was still up to 100.4 degrees. No other major problems on the floor now.

Fred had me scheduled to scrub with Leo Richards on the thromboendarterectomy, and I sure wasn't looking forward to it very much. This is this business of opening a major artery to remove a clot or obstruction of some sort, and then sewing it back together again, or grafting in a new section of artery. It usually takes Leo at least six hours to do this kind of a procedure, sometimes eight or ten. This man had had diabetes for some time, and recently devel-oped obstruction of the arteries in both legs. X-rays showed that the obstruction was high up in the abdomen, near the place where the aorta splits into the two common iliac arteries, sending one to each leg. Well, it is tricky to do anything about this, especially on a diabetic, but we went into this guy.

Leo cut an incision from breastbone to pubis and laid him wide open. Finally dug down to the great artery that runs down the back of the abdomen and found that the whole aortic trunk was calcified solid from the level of the kidneys down to where the iliac arteries branched, and then down both iliacs all the way into his legs. Leo saw he would have to take out the whole lower aorta and both iliacs en masse, and replace them with graft, and he still couldn't be sure that there wasn't more obstruction down lower. He called Ted Van Wert in, and Ted agreed not to try it. Richards did remove a chain of sympathetic nerve ganglia from either side of the rear abdominal wall in hopes that this would dilate what good arteries were left, but it is a pretty forlorn hope, I guess. I'm afraid the man ended up not much better off than before his operation.

It was a long, tedious procedure, going from 8:15 to 12:30 even without doing anything. Leo was obviously disappointed that the trouble was as extensive as it proved to be, but he remarked as we were closing that at any rate it was good practice for another case tomorrow. He has another patient, a Mr. Martin, who has a large abdominal aneurysm just above the iliac bifurcation, with multiple little aneurysms along both iliac arteries, too; these are like air bubbles on a tire, areas that are bulging out under pressure and presently will blow out if something isn't done. On this man Leo is going in to see if he can't chop out the whole lower aorta and both iliacs, aneurysms and all, and replace them with a graft from the frozen-artery bank.

This is a pretty ambitious undertaking. Dr. Richards told me he had done everything he could to talk this man out of the procedure, told him he might die on the table, and that he would have a long stay in the hospital, and that at best he'd be very, very sick and might not survive even if the operation itself was completed all right, but he still wanted it done. Of course, the man knows that if the surgery isn't done he is going to die for sure in a matter of a few weeks or months. Having this condition is like sitting on a powder keg with the fuse lit; when an aneurysm blows, it blows, and then it's too late to do anything at all about it. I just hope I can escape scrubbing; the case may take eight or ten hours straight. I guess I'm just not a surgeon at heart.

Got off at 5:00 on the dot again tonight. I've been lucky on this score, but I guess my good luck will come to an end in a week or so when I go onto Emery's service on December 1st. Emery and Meadows between them have more patients than Slater has, so I'll have to work harder, I guess. I've heard that Matt Meadows in particular puts in a really butcherous operating day, going from

8:00 A.M. until 9:00 P.M. or something like that. But we'll see when the time comes.

Friday, November 25

It finally dawned on me why the last three days had been so slow when Pete Carey asked me on Wednesday morning if Ann and I had any plans for Thanksgiving dinner the next day! So naturally nobody has been too eager either to schedule surgery or submit to it over Thanksgiving weekend, a little detail I'd forgotten completely. Talk about living in a fog.

We did operate Wednesday morning, but Slater's hand was still bothering him so he let Hank do a gall bladder and Fred do a thyroidectomy. Same stool-sitting routine as before, except that he didn't seem so nervous, and got up and left as soon as Fred was ready to start closing.

By Wednesday also we knew the fat was in the fire with Mr. Horner. No pun intended, but he had infection in his incision, big as life. He was spiking fevers to 102 and 103. Hank and I were able to get a little pus draining from the bottom of the wound, but not much. We took a culture of what we got, and the lab reported a whole batch of skin and bowel organisms, mostly Staphylococcus aureus, E. Coli and Aerobacter aerogenes. Then Friday morning, when still nothing would drain out, Slater himself came down in gown and gloves and took all the skin and subcutaneous sutures out, and reopened the incision right down to the peritoneum. That six-inch-thick fat pad fell open and this great puddle of foul-smelling green pus welled out, just spilled over the edges of the wound and ran down the man's sides into the bed and down between his legs and all over the place. I never saw such a God-awful mess in all my life, and it smelled like somebody had opened a cesspool. There must have been a quart and a half of pus in that big, blubbery wound. Slater débrided the skin and the fat all around, and then laid a soft rubber drainage tube along the bottom of the wound and hooked it up by a slow Murphy drip to a bottle of antibiotic solution—sort of like soaking a lawn continuously with a perforated sprinkler tube—and packed the wound loosely with Aureomycin gauze and left it open. This we will have to change now twice a day.

Slater said this was the way they treated dirty gangrenous shrapnel wounds in the field hospitals during the war, that unless you established real drainage the infection keeps right on festering. He seemed to feel that Hank should have spotted the trouble and opened the wound sooner, and Hank seemed sincerely chagrined. Slater wasn't angry or vindictive, just pointed out that with sterile operating techniques and all the antibiotics to lean on it's easy to forget what a dirty mess a wound infection can be until one sneaks up and kicks you in the balls. "You young guys just need a year or two on a battlefield somewhere," Slater said, "working in a field hospital where you haven't even got any soap around, much less any antibiotics. You'd find out all about infection."

Thanksgiving Day I had duty until 1:00 P.M., then was relieved for the rest of the day. The Careys had asked us for dinner, along with the Herrings. A very nice dinner, and we got to talk to Pete, whom I haven't seen except occasionally for a long time. We got to discussing plans for the future; everything in this internship is so much yesterday, today and tomorrow that I haven't really given half a thought to what comes next. Pete is planning to stay on for a second year of residency in medicine at Graystone if his wife doesn't get pregnant and have to quit work. Roscoe has Navy duty coming up when his internship is over. I don't have service to worry about, but I still don't know what I'll do come next July. All I'm sure of right now is that I don't want to be a surgeon.

After dinner we sat around talking until almost midnight, and it was medicine all the way. It was almost funny; you could change the subject to the state of the world or some other scintillating topic time and again, but the conversation always drifted back to some patient's breast abscess in about five minutes. Sometimes I think the girls must get damned sick of it, but they're married to it, so what are they going to do?

Monday, November 28

Got in to the hospital Saturday in time for early rounds with Hank and Slater. Lots of odds and ends of work to do: redressing Mrs. London's skin graft; redressing Mr. Horner's infected wound, which was looking much cleaner and smelling better, too; a lot of piddling little things. Didn't finish rounds until 11:00, and I really wished Slater hadn't come in that morning before we were through. I swear that every time I get to thinking that I really do like and admire that man after all, he has to pull some shitty little trick or another that just makes me sick.

This particular incident involved a case we did Friday: there was this little eighty-two-year-old grandmother who had been referred to Slater because she'd been collecting fluid in her abdomen, almost certainly from a cancer of some sort. Slater had decided to make a little two-inch abdominal incision, get the fluid out and try to make a definitive diagnosis in the rather forlorn hope that it might prove to be something treatable. So Friday morning he made the incision, got out over two gallons of fluid from her abdomen, and found that she had widely disseminated carcinoma of the ovaries. It was all over the place, just peppered all over the inside of her abdomen. He just took a bit of the tumor for pathological examination, drained the fluid out for temporary relief, and closed up the hole again.

Well, it was a sad case and a sad, sweet, little old lady, but apparently Slater didn't see her family at all on Friday, and Saturday morning her son and daughter were standing around her room down at the end of the fourth floor near the stairway that goes down the back end of the hospital, the outside stairs with bars instead of windows where the wind goes blowing through full speed all the time. They saw Slater as he came breezing through on rounds all in a great Saturday morning rush, and called to him out in the hall. Finally caught him as he was starting down the stairway. He didn't even know who they were until they told him and said they'd hoped to see him yesterday to hear what he'd found at their mother's surgery and all. So he told them very briefly and impatiently that he'd found cancer all over the place and that maybe the X-ray people would be able to do something for her after they got the pathology report back, but that he doubted it, and on down the stairs he went. And I just noticed that the girl was standing there in that cold doorway, shivering in the wind, with tears in her eyes, and I thought with this sort of thing why couldn't Slater at least have been a little gracious about it, just taken five precious minutes to sit down with them and give them the story with a little more kindness than that? It isn't every day you learn your mother is dying of cancer, and what a hell of a way to have to be told.

Well, I could think up excuses, I suppose, but I guess basically that may be the difference between being a top-rate, skillful surgeon and being a great man. I don't know.

The rest of Saturday was taken up with little things. Sunday we spent all morning making rounds again. Started off with Hank about 8:30; we were just finishing on Three when Hank was paged with the news that Dr. Slater was in the house to make rounds and couldn't find us. Well, he knew perfectly well where to find us, but Hank just heaved a deep sigh and we trotted back up to Fourth to start rounds all over again. Didn't finish until 11:30, much to my disgust. I went down for lunch, and then went back to quarters, knowing full well that the next time I trotted up onto the hospital floor I wouldn't get off it again until dawn. I read the Sunday paper and took an hour's nap, and got called at 1:30 that the first new patient was in on Fourth for surgery in the morning.

After I'd worked up that patient I got a look at the OR schedule for Monday and almost flipped. There were twenty-one cases scheduled, sixteen of them for me to work up. I guess Slater had just been saving them up. He had seven new admissions, including three gall bladders and two thyroids. I never saw so many patients all at once in my life; they were tripping over each other coming in the door. I started working them up at a dead run; by suppertime I was halfway through and feeling very low. And on top of the routine preops there were some problem patients that came in. Some outside doctor had a patient with severe jaundice and belly pain, referred to Slater without any work-up at all, so I had to do a full medical work-up in the middle of the rush. Another patient, who was scheduled for an exploratory in the morning to find the cause of her partial bowel obstruction, was so violently ill it looked as though she might have to be opened up sooner. I got to do the lab work on her, and then spent half the evening tucking a Miller-Abbott tube down her until finally at midnight Hank decided that she'd probably hold until morning and just ordered up IVs for the rest of the night.

Then, just to make things jolly, around 2:00 A.M. Hank called to say he was sending in a lady who was hemorrhaging and would I see how bad and call him back. I thought he was kidding at first, but he wasn't. The woman had called and said she was pouring blood all over the bathroom floor and soaking up pads as fast as she could get them on, but he didn't want to come back to the hospital unless it was the real McCoy. So she arrived, by ambulance yet, and they paged me frantically and I dropped everything and ran up to see her as soon as they got her in bed. Could have broken her neck, too; she had a spot of blood about the size of a quarter on the pad she was wearing with no sign of active bleeding. It was totally impossible to tell how much she'd *really* bled; it could have been a teaspoonful or a gallon. But she wasn't in shock and her blood count was okay, so I called Hank to tell him to drop dead with his hemorrhaging women, but found that he'd gotten cold feet or a guilty conscience or something and had already left home for the hospital to see this babe himself. Later he apologized for sending her in but said he couldn't see anything else to do, because she might have been bleeding as much as she said she was, and women get very emotional about vaginal bleeding.

[*Post hoc:* Greater truth was never spoken, and I have since learned the hard way that when you get a story like that you just can't take any chances. I later met an old doc who used a fascinating yardstick to gauge the extent of vaginal hemorrhage reported to him over the phone: he asked the patient if she had bled enough that it ran down her legs and filled up her shoes. "If she says yes to that," he told me, "it's time to start worrying."]

Wednesday, November 30

So this is the record of my last two days on Slater's service, Surgery I. After Monday's horrible schedule, Tuesday was something of a breather. I didn't have a scrub assigned until noon, a gastric resection with Dr. Edward Eldridge. I spent the morning making rounds. Mr. Horner's wound infection is healing, and Hank even pulled the edges of the wound closer together with tape. Still a long way to go before all that fat heals together again, but he will make it all right. I took some stitches out of the two thyroids we did Monday, and then went around spreading good cheer among the rest of the patients.

I didn't know who Dr. Eldridge was at first; he hadn't been

around much. I gather he was Slater's Fellow several years ago, now practicing general medicine and surgery. His patient was this old, old man with a history of severe bleeding ulcers, so he was going to take his stomach out. We scrubbed about 12:30, and it turned out to be a four-and-a-half-hour procedure. Everything went along fine until Eldridge got the ulcer in the duodenum peeled away from the surrounding tissue and then put the clamps on the stomach to close it off prior to resecting it. The guy had a stomachful of something or other; Eldridge was trying to decide whether or not to open it with a little incision and empty it under control when the clamps slipped and the stomach fell open all over the place. What he had a stomachful of was grapefruit sections, of all things; I don't know where or when he'd gotten it, but he was just loaded full. So we had grapefruit and gunk spilled all over the inside of his abdomen and had to clean it out section by section, irrigate and clean out some more, irrigate and clean out some more, and still find more tucked down in some nook or cranny somewhere else before we could go on.

So we finally finished this up about 5:00, and I went down to see my old friend Ed Arnquist, who was back in on Leo Richards' service. This is a big Swede admitted in July, a forty-four-year-old man who was complaining then of unsteadiness and loss of balance. He's had a very bizarre story since, and now has everybody in a big flap, especially Cal Cornell and the radiologist, who is really standing on his ear. Seems when Ed had been in before, Cornell was called for a neurological consultation. He had examined the man carefully then, but couldn't find any explanation for his balance loss, couldn't find anything wrong with him really except that he couldn't keep his balance when he stood on one foot, and had nystagmus—an odd kind of involuntary jerky movement of the eyes when he looked out of the corner of his eye. They'd sent him home without a diagnosis then; even though Cornell knew he had something going on in his brain he couldn't find.

Later, after I was off the service, Ed Arnquist came in again because the balance loss was getting steadily worse, and this time an electroencephalogram showed changes suggesting that he had a mass lesion in his brain somewhere. Cornell then did a ventriculogram— a sort of grisly diagnostic procedure involving introduction of some air into the interior chambers of the brain that are normally filled with cerebrospinal fluid—and these studies showed the outline of a brain tumor located in a place Cornell could get at. So Cornell had opened Ed's skull and peeled out this big tumor that was growing there. The thing was so sharply defined and peeled out so neatly that Cornell was certain it was benign, and had one of his rare days of elation when he thought he'd cured a patient. Everybody was happy for Ed for about three days until the pathologist got a careful look at the slides of the tumor and declared that it was a metastatic cancer that looked very suspiciously like bronchogenic carcinoma under the microscope.

Well, this was in October, and Ed had had many chest X-rays, all reported normal, so they hauled him back down to X-ray for some special chest films including stereos and sectional tomograms, and, sure enough, without any question there was a tiny little soft-tissue mass in the upper lobe of his left lung. The thing that jarred everybody was that once this soft fuzzy shadow was located and he knew where to look for it, the radiologist got out all the old films of Ed's chest that he'd read as negative and found the barest sugges-tion of this same lesion visible on a chest film taken back in July, and still present on all taken since. The X-ray man was all shaken up; six months lost on a lung cancer is dreadful, and it practically *has* to be an X-ray diagnosis early. But he insisted that to spot this shadow on the film at all you not only had to know that it was there; you also had to know exactly where to look for it. Of course, now *everybody* can see it.

Unfortunately, all these little niceties are all the same to old Ed. He had a carcinoma of the lung which has been sitting there for well over six months, and has seeded to his brain. Leo Richards now wants to do an exploratory and take out the lung lesion. He feels that Ed's only possible chance would be if the brain lesion were somehow a single metastasis, and that by taking out the lung tumor he might catch the cancer before it has seeded anywhere else. Of course, the odds against a single metastasis are just astronomical, but I guess with that disease even a million-to-one chance is worth taking. Very probably they'll find a chestful of metastatic nodes along with the primary cancer, and that will be that. But if they leave the thing in there, Ed's odds for survival are 0.00 . . . to a hundred decimal places; with it in there he is already dead and just hasn't quit breathing yet. Anyway he's to be done on Thursday.

[*Post hoc:* I was obviously shaken up about Ed Arnquist, as were most of the clinic men, especially the X-ray man. And Ed *did* have metastatic nodes in his chest, and died of his lung cancer about four months later. At the time I know I felt that the radiologist had made a hideous and inexcusable error, and thought he was just making excuses for himself when he said the lung lesion couldn't have been identified in July unless you already knew it was there and where to look for it. Curiously enough, those films of Ed Arnquist's chest have since become teaching classics; they have been presented in clinical conferences on chest disease all over the country, and repeatedly the best and most experienced X-ray specialists, without exception, have missed the fatal shadow that was visible on the July films until it was pointed out to them. And this was under conditions where they *knew* something was funny about the chest film because it wouldn't have been shown to them if it were really as normal as it looked. They still couldn't pick it up.

So I suppose this vindicates the radiologist insofar as it vindicates anybody in a case like Ed Arnquist's. More than anything else, though, I think it points out the kind of fight medical men are up against constantly, and are totally aware of constantly, with every patient they see. Every practicing doctor has more than one Ed Arnquist on his record that he blames himself for, rightly or wrongly. In a way, you could say it points out the guile and craftiness of the Enemy. I think now that Ed probably had the best, most expert, careful and interested medical care he could have gotten anywhere, and the Enemy whipped even the best. Medical students joke about the "almost-visible chest lesion" or the "almost-audible heart murmur." They laughingly define a "Grade I" murmur as the murmur you can hear only if the Professor of Medicine insists that it's there. And they laugh because they know that that "almost-visible chest lesion" is no joke at all, that it happens to be very real; it is the cancer of the lung that they are going to miss one day until it's too late, and it is better to laugh than to think too much about it.]

Wednesday morning the place was crawling with visiting firemen attending a big Surgical Society meeting in town, and all the visiting surgeons had been invited to Graystone Hospital to observe the local surgeons doing the day's surgery. Quite a carnival atmosphere. I was just starting up to the OR at 7:45 when I heard someone paging me and Hank. It was Slater, of course; I found him up outside the OR door wandering around looking worried. He said he hadn't seen Hank yet. Where was Hank? Had I seen Hank? I said I hadn't, but I was sure he would be on his way up there directly. So he asked me to tell Hank to get the abdominal hysterectomy, the first of three cases he had scheduled, started the minute he got up to the OR, the patient was already on the table and asleep, and then he rushed off to shake hands with the visiting firemen.

About two minutes later Hank came up, so we got into our scrub suits and got the hysterectomy started, and passed the word out to let Dr. Slater know Hank was opening his first case, and the race was on. Maybe it was just that this was my last day on Slater's service and I just didn't give a shit any more, but that morning was a scream. There were forty or fifty visiting surgeons wandering around the place, free to choose whichever case they wanted to watch. So only five came in to watch Slater do his hysterectomy. Slater was nervous as a cat, even though everything went all right; he kept talking about what he was doing, and putting on a big show, as if an abdominal hysterectomy were somehow very difficult and exciting surgery. When we finally got to closing and the visitors had gone on to another room, Slater said to Hank, "Well, how did it go?" and Hank said, "Oh, it looked fine, it went along just fine," and Slater was all upset about whether or not it really went so well.

He'd been in a big rush to get this case out of the room and get his second one, a gastric resection, started because Dr. Hal Piedmont's big case was coming up (he's the big heart surgeon in the area, imported from County Hospital for the occasion), and Slater very clearly wanted to get going on his case first so that he'd get the audience instead of Piedmont. So he closed up the woman's abdomen himself after the hysterectomy was done, saying that Hank was just too damned slow, and he used silk to close, not wire, and kept shouting at the circulating nurse to know if someone had gone down to get the next patient yet, had the next patient come up from the floor yet, did the anesthetist have the spinal block in yet, was the next patient ready yet, etc.

Well, he finished that hysterectomy in an hour and five minutes, at 9:05, which was some kind of speed record for Slater, and by 9:30 we were making the incision on the gastric resection while Piedmont's case was still on the elevator coming up to the OR, so Slater got his audience all right. He was tense as an ingénue on opening night; he was all over the place, talking, calling attention to this thing or that, showing off how his sterile overhead light handles worked, asking me to give the patient's history (which I did without flaw or fumble, having been forewarned by Hank) and so on. He kept fooling with those damned lights until he had them both pointed at the patient's feet while he was saying "See? This way you can control them yourself perfectly," while the poor circulating nurse worked feverishly to get them aimed back at the patient's belly again.

Finally he got started and found a posterior ulcer, duodenal, not badly scarred down, so it should have been a lead pipe cinch of a gastrectomy, but when we went to put the clamp on below the stomach, he got the clamp right across the lesion. So when he opened the duodenum, nobody could see the ulcer. Then he put the big clamps on the stomach in order to do the resection, and one clamp slipped off, and he had trouble getting it reclamped. Then in order to show the boys that there really *was* an ulcer there, he took the clamp off the duodenum, and the ulcer was there all right—it immediately began bleeding like Billy-be-damned, with blood spurting up and splashing off the overhead lights, and he was fighting the bleeding all the rest of the way through the procedure. One bleeder he tied off three times before he could get it to stop. In general, it turned out to be a thoroughly messy job; later I heard Olsen say they hadn't had such a bloody gastrectomy in months, but Slater managed to get through it in an hour and three-quarters, compared with Eldridge's four hours the day before.

When we finished that, it was noon, and Hank and Fred and I had some lunch, then came back to do the third case, a hernia repair, while Slater went out to lunch with the visiting surgeons. I don't know what was wrong with Hank, but I thought this patient was going to die on the table for sure—of old age. It was the longest, dreariest, *slowest* hernia repair I'd ever seen, and I was just bored to tears. Olsen and Ruggles were both scrubbed on it, and I don't know why the hell I had to be in on it anyway, because I didn't have one damned thing to do but stand there.

Finally finished that up about 3:00 and I went down to see a couple of new admissions, one for Richards and one for Jack Barley. And dear old Alec tried to hand me the shaft when I came up on Third to see if I had any patients there. A nurse came up to me with an admission card on a new patient just admitted for Dr. Piedmont, said the card said it was assigned to Dr. Ivy, but Dr. Ivy had said that must be an error, it was supposed to be my patient because it was a chest case. I just handed the card back to her and told her she'd better try to get through to Dr. Ivy that I just wasn't about to work up any of his patients for him, no matter what he said they were, and walked off. If Alec didn't try that so often, I might get kindhearted and let him sneak one by as an honest mistake; as it is, it just galled me beyond words.

Ann picked me up at 5:00, and we went home and had two good stiff martinis apiece and horse meat steak for dinner, all in honor of Nathan Slater, surgeon, *ave atque vale*. Tomorrow I start my sixth month of internship, going on Surgery II, the service of Dr. Emery, Dr. Meadows and assorted others including Cal Cornell—only it won't be Cornell after all, it looks like. Dr. Fuller slapped him in the hospital yesterday with a suspicious attack of indigestion, and the word is out today that he's definitely got a coronary.

IV

Surgery II and III
(Emery's Service and Orthopedics)

With the changeover from Slater's service to
the second surgical service, I came to the low point of my entire
internship year. I was tired of surgery and discouraged with my
training. Entries in the journal during this time were sporadic and
brief; there was no disguising my own weariness and boredom, no
hiding the sense of futility I felt in my work with Dr. Arthur Emery
and his associates on Surgery II.

Looking back, I suppose part of my discouragement could be
charged up to the "mid-year doldrums"—the sag that every intern
feels when he knows that half of that year is gone, yet sees six more
long months stretching out before him. Part was related to the
holiday season, always a low point in hospital admissions and medical activity, and the intern's first experience, perhaps, with the un-
Merry Christmas of the practicing physician (I have never since
spent a yuletide holiday unmarred by calls and demands of medical
emergencies; I can remember three Christmas dinners interrupted
midstream by pregnant women demanding to be delivered, and two
years running I was called out of church on Christmas Eve to deal
with accident cases—all, I tell myself, a part of the game). Part of
my discouragement was undoubtedly my own growing distaste for
surgery, particularly for the intern's-eye view of surgery: a world of
endless scrubs, mechanical rounds and the never-ceasing succession
of small, necessary, but generally unpleasant jobs that were dropped
in the intern's lap because it was "safe" for him to do them, and
because nobody else much wanted to.

But in retrospect I think the main reason that this was the low

point—though I blush to admit it—was because I missed Hank
Ruggles and Fred Olsen and the brisk, clean unpleasantness of
Nathan Slater himself. Although it covers three long months, I find
that this section of the journal is surprisingly brief. None of the
surgeons I worked with on Surgery II and III could approach
Nathan Slater's personal magnetism. None had Slater's infinite ca-
pacity to infuriate. Even so, each of these men had their own little
moments of humanity and greatness, a fact which shows clearly
through the humdrum weariness of this section of the journal. It
was a long stretch, but the routine of days and nights passed
quickly, and I learned. Day by day, I learned.

THE JOURNAL, DECEMBER, JANUARY AND FEBRUARY

Saturday, December 3

Started off Thursday on the new surgical service, which is spoken
of freely as "Emery's service" although other surgeons are also involved. Arthur Emery is the senior surgeon here, second in rank to
Slater among the clinic surgeons. Matt Meadows is Emery's junior
associate, a younger member of the clinic staff. Other clinic surgeons
on Surgery II include the two members of the clinic urology department.

As for the resident setup, Virgil Aarons is Dr. Emery's Fellow, a
fourth-year resident who works for Emery the way Hank Ruggles
works for Slater. Then there are two underling residents on the
service: Phil Barr, a second-year resident, and Bob Mankovitz, in
his first-year residency. Bob is a Canadian boy, who studied and
interned in Toronto. I don't know where Barr studied; I've wondered sometimes whether he studied at all. From what I've seen of
him so far he doesn't seem to be good for anything but getting in
people's way.

Actually, I haven't seen a whole hell of a lot of any of the surgeons on this service yet, mostly because I got involved with a
patient of Dr. Piedmont's on Thursday evening, a thoroughly nasty
case that gulped up practically all my time from then until I got off
this morning for the weekend. Don't ask me how; that's just the way
it worked. Thursday morning neither Emery nor Meadows had any
cases, so I was assigned to scrub with an outside surgeon in removal

of lipoma from a man's back. This was supposed to be a ten-minute job, but it ended up taking an hour and a half; once the guy got started pulling out this little fatty tumor he just couldn't seem to stop, it was like pulling the stuffing out of a teddy bear. Later I scrubbed with L. D. Kaiser on a resetting of a wrist fracture, and then went downstairs to see what patients I'd inherited and what kind of shape they were in.

Thursday evening after supper I was fiddling around, starting IVs on this person and that person around 9:00, when the nurse on Fourth asked me to come see a patient of Hal Piedmont's who needed a pint of blood started. The patient was a doctor, she said, and he insisted on having a house doctor come do the job. Ordinarily this would have galled me; doctors can be the most horrible patients in the world, and we've run across a couple of snotty sons of bitches from time to time who came into the hospital and pulled rank. But I'd seen this guy briefly Wednesday night with Slater and knew he was one sick, miserable cookie.

His name was Dr. Paul Merritt, a man who has been practicing surgery in town for some time. Some three years ago he had a bad case of infectious hepatitis; he'd recovered, but the disease beat the hell out of his liver and he developed such a severe cirrhosis as an aftermath that the scarring had blocked off his portal vein—the big one that carries blood from all the digestive tract back to the liver— almost completely. As a result of the obstruction, he very rapidly developed huge distended varicose veins in his esophagus where it entered his stomach, and these esophageal varices are the ones that can blow out and bleed so fast and violently that a patient can exsanguinate in thirty minutes if you don't find some way to get the bleeding stopped in a hurry. The really nasty part of it is that there isn't any good way to get at those veins to stop them from bleeding. This poor man had had five severe hemorrhages in the past, and had had a total of five major operations to stop the bleeding and prevent it from recurring, all done by some big-wheel surgeon in Boston. They'd tried everything: tried shunting the blood from the obstructed vein into another vein that would by-pass the liver, tried ligating the varicose veins themselves, everything, but the varices had just gone on getting bigger and bigger.

Now Dr. Merritt had been admitted here on Peterson's service with another severe hemorrhage. They'd poured blood into him, and finally gotten the bleeding stopped by putting down a sort of a medieval torture device called a gastroesophogeal pressure bag. This is a hideous-looking affair, looks like a half-inch-thick soft rubber hose with a long, sausage-shaped inflatable bag built around the business end of it. You shove the tube down with the bag deflated, just like a stomach pump tube, until the bag is in the patient's stomach; then you blow up the bag like a balloon inside the stomach and pull it up tight against the top of the stomach so that one part of it actually wedges tight into the esophagus, and then hook up the tube to a rope over a pulley at the end of the bed and hang a two-pound weight on the end. The idea is that the balloon can't come up because it's too large to slide up the esophagus when it's inflated, but it wedges tight in the area where the varicose veins are and presses them flat, and thus (theoretically) prevents them from bleeding. Great in theory, but the damned thing is sheer physical torture to have to have inside you, feels like it's trying to pull your whole insides up and out through your mouth.

Dr. Peterson had gotten this bag installed and got the bleeding stopped and then had asked Slater to see the guy Wednesday night to see if there was any further surgical help for him. He was a weird-looking sight, a little skinny guy lying there in bed with his head cocked to one side and this huge rubber tube coming out of his nose—straight out, horizontally—and hooked to pulley and weights at the end of the bed. I'd never seen one of those gadgets, though I'd heard about them, and what hit me the most was how acutely uncomfortable the guy looked.

Apparently Slater felt an operation might help—a fairly new procedure in which the stomach and lower end of the esophagus could be cut off, varicose veins and all, and a loop of small intestine brought up and attached instead, so that the blood supply to the varices could be cut off, and food would go directly from esophagus to small intestine, completely by-passing the stomach. They call the procedure an esophageal-jejunal transposition, and it's a massive operation involving opening chest and abdomen up wide and root-ing around in there for hours. Apparently Dr. Merritt had refused to let Slater do the surgery, and asked for Dr. Piedmont instead.

Piedmont saw the guy and told him he wouldn't think of operating until the man was in better physical shape, as long as the hemorrhaging could be controlled, so they were temporizing.

So it turned out that just about everybody was looking in on this man, one way or another, and this evening I happened to get the gold star when his blood transfusion infiltrated and the nurses needed somebody to restart it. I thought I was just getting into a fifteen-minute job when I went up there at 9:00; actually, it was a long, hard night-and-day's work.

The gastroesophageal bag was out when I got up there, had been for twelve hours or so, and the bleeding apparently had stopped, and everybody had their fingers crossed. Dr. Merritt was obviously scared sick that he'd start bleeding again and have to have the damned thing put back down. He looked like death on crutches—a pale yellow, dried-up, scrawny little man with a three-day beard on his chin, short crew cut, graying hair and kind of yellow-green eyes. He just looked kind of cornered and desperate all the way around. He started apologizing for making me come up to restart his IV; Peterson and Piedmont didn't want him to have to tighten up his belly muscles or bear down in any way, since this made the varicosities balloon out from internal pressure, but he was so sensitive to pain by now, even to IV needles going in, that he involuntarily tightened up unless the needle just went in zip.

Well, I guess he didn't draw any prize picking me to do the job. I tried an arm vein and fumbled it, just couldn't get the needle into it, and then I tried a nice accessible vein on his foot and this time the needle screwed me up, the plastic tube around it began wrinkling and twisting and I couldn't get it in. Finally I got a vein on the other foot, got the needle in and anchored well and the blood running again.

All this took me until almost 11:00. While I was working at the IV, this special nurse he had (who couldn't have been more stupid if they had gone out and dragged the streets for one) remarked casually that his blood pressure seemed to have been falling for the past two hours or so, and did that mean anything? I asked her how much, and she said down from 160 to 135. That gave me a jolt; it could mean that he had started bleeding again inside, and it suddenly dawned on me that the fat could really be in the fire with this guy. I checked the pressure myself and found it was 120, so I told the nurse to call Piedmont and tell him that I was putting the bag down again.

Well, I didn't know what to do; the guy obviously didn't want the thing back down there, and I didn't know how to *get* it back down, but while I was fiddling around looking at the thing and thinking maybe we could temporize a bit, Dr. Merritt proceeded to vomit up 400 or 500 cc of blood, all of it bright red, which meant a new hemorrhage, and obviously I was soon going to be temporizing over a corpse if I didn't do something about it.

I said, "Well, I guess it's got to go down again," and he nodded yes, and, God help him, he lay there and patiently told me step by step how to work the thing: which lubricant to use, how to pass the tube so that it was less irritating and he didn't gag so much, how much water to let him swallow to help get it down, when to take the water away from him so he didn't swallow too much. Once we got the uninflated bag down, he told me how much air to pump into it to inflate it properly, so I did that and pulled it up tight. He said that two pounds of traction was more than he could stand at first, just to start with one pound and then ease the second pound on gently a bit at a time when the pain eased up a little. After that he told me to hook up the suction to the tube that went through the bag into his stomach and try to suck all the old blood out of his stomach I could get, explaining that that way we could tell if the bleeding was controlled by whether any new blood began appearing. This didn't work so well because his stomach was full of old, black, rubbery, clotted blood that didn't want to come up through the tube. I worked and worked at it and finally gave up on it about 2:00 A.M. At least I wasn't getting any fresh red blood up.

While all this was going on Piedmont came in and assessed the situation and shook his head and said, "Well, Paul, I'm sorry, but it looks like we'll have to take you upstairs and try and fix this if we can." Dr. Merritt just nodded. Then Piedmont asked me to notify the OR crew and have them set up as fast as they could, said he'd need two residents and an intern to help him. By 2:30 A.M., Barr arrived and then Mankovitz. While we waited to scrub we sat around the doctors' room talking with Piedmont. He seemed very calm and collected, but when Barr asked him what he thought the guy's chances were, he just shook his head and said, "Don't ever ask me questions like that."

Finally, at 4:00 A.M. we went into the operating room and started this procedure. It took eight solid hours. Piedmont made an incision from the guy's left armpit clear down to his umbilicus in one swipe, just laid him wide-open. And started feeding blood into him, pint after pint. Everything in that mid-portion of his body was vascular, and he just bled and bled, everything you touched started bleeding, and his blood pressure started to drop, and we kept pouring more blood into him, actually pumping it in under pressure—I think at one point we got a quart into him in a matter of about three minutes. Just dissecting out the stomach and esophagus with all those distended blood vessels in the way was a horrible job, down in the bottom of a great hole in his belly, with blood welling up from the bottom like a fountain. The varicose veins didn't look very impressive at all once they were clamped off; all I could see was a little ulcerated mucous membrane there. It certainly didn't look like the sort of vicious thing that could do this to a guy.

Finally Piedmont got going on the new hook-up of small intestine to esophagus, and that took forever, and then there was the long, long job of closing. Finished at the stroke of noon, and I was dead on my feet. Went down with Barr and Piedmont to eat a bowl of soup for lunch. It was just incredible; Piedmont had two more long cases scheduled at County Hospital for the afternoon, and he was as fresh and chipper as could be. You'd think he'd just come back from a three-week vacation instead of a grueling eight-hour job after a night without sleep. I decided that if anybody wanted me badly enough for something they could damned well call me, and went down to quarters and went to bed.

And got called half an hour later to go up and give somebody an enema. From 1:00 until 5:00 P.M. I slept uninterrupted, then got up and had supper. I'd had double call Thursday night, but I'd had to call Hamilton out since I was working the whole night with Dr. Merritt and I guess Luke spent most of the night up, too; he'd come into the OR about 5:00 A.M. to peer over my shoulder and didn't look like he'd had much sleep.

After supper Friday—I guess it was Friday; it seemed like Thursday had never quit—I went up to Fourth and found that Dr. Merritt was still with us so far. I forgot to mention that he'd been given *twenty-two pints* of whole blood during the operation to replace what he was losing, which meant that almost his total blood volume was blood-bank blood that wouldn't clot, and near the end of the operation he was bleeding from everything that would bleed. Some IV calcium gluconate helped that, I guess, but then sometime during the afternoon he had a mild transfusion reaction and the blood had to be stopped. It's hard to see just what else could go wrong and still have him survive.

Friday night I took second call. Felt guilty about making Luke Hamilton face a second sleepless night in a row, but apparently it was fairly quiet. I think he got hooked on a fracture case about 3:00 A.M., but nothing much else.

This morning—Saturday—I made rounds with Mankovitz and Aarons, still dog-tired, and got off about 10:00 A.M. Went home and slept until almost 8:00 this evening, which shoots the weekend pretty much right there. Seems like this is the pattern of home life for weekends off duty: I get off Saturday morning, go home and sleep most of the afternoon, eat supper, maybe whack down some grass around the house and go to bed early; we sleep in for a late breakfast Sunday morning, maybe go to church, and it's noon, take a nap in the afternoon, fiddle around and pay bills or something until dinner, and get to bed early because Monday is always a bitch of a day, and the week always starts with a Monday. And then this journal dictation stuck in there somewhere.

Well, I suppose I'm feeling low again about the hospital and the internship and everything else; Friday evening it was getting so I was cursing out loud every time that damned page sounded off for me. I do hope we have a quieter time next week. We've just seemed to have a whole bunch of sick people, all requiring a lot of time and attention. And I still don't know anything about Emery's and Meadows' service because most of my time was spent on other patients. I also hope to find that Dr. Merritt is still alive when I get back Monday. The thing we were all dreading, of course, was that he would die on the table just about the time we were finishing up eight hours of surgery on him, an extremely discouraging prospect from the surgeon's point of view. To say nothing of the patient's.

Tuesday, December 6

One of the first things I learned Monday morning was that Dr. Merritt was dead. He died sometime Sunday morning. His blood pressure had kept dropping and dropping in spite of the transfusions, and finally he just shuffled off without any particular terminal incident. Also learned that Mr. Martin, the Y-graft case Leo Richards did ten days ago, which took them eighteen hours in the OR, went out Sunday. He'd had a lousy postop course, developed a clot in the grafted artery, and then threw a big embolus from it to his lung and went out like a light early Sunday afternoon. So it must have been a great weekend.

I was scheduled to scrub with Dr. Emery on Monday, a cholecystectomy and operative cholangiogram. This babe turned out to have a common bile duct full of rocks, so Emery spent all morning digging them out. This was my first real scrub with him, and he is certainly a weird old boy. He must be pushing sixty, tall, gray hair, face full of wrinkles and a pair of thick convex glasses that magnify his eyes about five times so that whenever he looks at you, you see those great big, *big* eyes staring out at you. He must be almost stone-blind without those glasses. But he seems to see all right at the operating table.

Emery is a different man from Slater in the OR or outside of it, and I'm not just dead sure I like the difference so much. I was beginning to get used to Slater's idiosyncrasies, I guess. Some of them, at least. Slater might have been frankly snotty about half the time, but Arthur Emery is spooky. He seems far more pleasant and personable than Slater at first, but he also seems more sarcastic and sneaky. He's very strongly opinionated, I gather, and if something irks him on morning rounds, it seems to color his thinking completely for the rest of the day. Tuesday on rounds somebody made a remark about some magazine article defending intermarriage and miscegenation, whereupon Emery took off on a half-hour tirade against the current Administration in Washington. And then he went on to blame everything else that he didn't approve of all morning long on the Administration, right down to some poor lady's postoperative wound infection. And I'm not sure that he wasn't dead serious about it.

At least Emery doesn't gallop through rounds the way Slater does. He stops and talks about this case and that case, even seems halfway interested in teaching somebody something. He smiles occasionally, too, which is nice. He is also extremely sarcastic a lot of the time. I've noticed already that he seldom criticizes straight out, seems to go at it hind side to. In the OR he works very swiftly, but gets all excited whenever things don't go exactly the way he wants them to, which they never seem to do. He's never satisfied with the angle of the lights, and keeps wanting instruments that he knows perfectly well aren't there, and generally runs the scrub nurse ragged. It was almost funny to watch, because it went on all day Monday in the OR, and all day Tuesday, too; he acts as though the scrub nurse ought to just naturally know exactly what he's thinking. He'll stick out his hand to ask for a clamp, so the nurse will give him a curved clamp, and he'll slam it down and say, "No, for Christ's sake, I want a *straight* clamp!" Or if he gets a straight clamp, it'll be a curved clamp he wants. Of course, it's true that to be a good scrub nurse you've got to be one step ahead of the surgeon, know him and the procedure well enough to understand what he's doing and what tool he's likely to want for what and when. But reading minds is something else again.

I finished in the OR about 2:00 on Monday and went down to admit patients for Tuesday. I'd already heard that we were going to have a horrible operating day, and new patients were just crawling out of the woodwork down there, six or seven patients for Emery and Meadows, another three or four for the urologists. So I spent until almost 10:30 on Monday evening working them up. Meadows is one of these eager guys who schedules seven or eight major cases on one operating day, I've heard, operates from 8:00 in the morning until 9:00 at night, and would be perfectly happy to go on until dawn except for running out of patients. I suppose I'll find out if this is true or just one of Roscoe Herring's complaints.

Monday night was another one of Miss Wood's menstrual evenings; I got eight or ten pill calls between midnight and 4:00 A.M., and she hadn't screened a one of them. Then at 4:00 a patient of Silver's came in, a girl of twenty-three with acute belly pain, and I had to get up and work her up and run a white blood count. Looked to me like either an ectopic pregnancy or an acute appendix. While I was working on her, Silver sent in another acute belly, this one an eighty-three-year-old man Silver thought had blown out an ulcer, perforated it. So by breakfast time those two were hanging fire as probable surgery, too.

I was scheduled to scrub with Meadows and Barr, but somehow I ended up scrubbing with Emery again, and all day a very heavy schedule. There was a thyroid first and then a gastrectomy, then two gall bladders back to back and then Silver's eighty-three-year-old ulcer case. Found that he had an ulcer the size of a dime that had perforated right through the wall of his stomach; Emery thought sure it was a cancer, but the frozen section said no, so he just did a gastrectomy. Then another gall bladder and common duct exploration. And all this wasn't shuttling back and forth between two rooms either. Emery personally did each and every one of these cases with Virgil Aarons and me assisting. Got out of the OR finally at 5:00, worked up a couple of new admissions, made rounds with Aarons and Mankovitz on about forty patients, and my butt end was dragging down the stairs, bump, bump, bump, by the time I got off at 6:15.

Thursday, December 8

Wednesday morning I found out that I had no scrubs at all scheduled for the day. Emery makes Grand Rounds on Wednesday mornings, so we went around on all of his patients. And got some more of his views on the Administration in Washington. He still hadn't gotten off that kick.

In the afternoon I actually had an hour or so free, so I sat around and loafed for a while. A few new admissions for Thursday, otherwise a quiet night. One oddball case came in on one of the medical services that I got involved in sort of peripherally, though Pete Carey and Floyd Schwartz were actually taking care of the guy. This was a man of about thirty-eight, a chronic alcoholic, who came in with all sorts of agonies: belly pain, couldn't breathe, cramps in his legs, etc., etc. He insisted that he'd been throwing up blood for four days and had drunk nothing but milk since this had started. Pete pumped his stomach and got up almost a quart of greenish-black gunk that smelled like acetone, and sure as hell the lab said it *was* acetone. And as the evening went on, the man had more and more trouble breathing, then began going blind, then began convulsing, and then suddenly died, quite abruptly, about 9:30, just like that. We still don't know what he'd been drinking. He had no family, and the coroner took the body and probably won't do a post on it, so we won't ever know what he drank. Pete thought it might have been wood alcohol, or maybe cleaning fluid, which seems to be a favorite potion around this part of the country.

Got to bed fairly early Wednesday night, and had a quiet night. Had one notable patient to admit this afternoon. This lady was complaining of a multitude of things, including itching of the brain, for which I did not have any antidote to suggest. God, but you get some weird stories from people about what is bothering them. Like the lady who told Pete Carey once that she had firebirds in her uterus, and was passing clogs.

Monday, December 12

The weekend duty was strictly humdrum, though quite busy. Emery came in for rounds Saturday morning and got started talking about indications for thyroidectomy on the way down from fourth floor to third, and he stopped there on the stairs and talked about it for two hours straight. I was about ready to drop in my tracks before he quit. Once he gets going on something he sure seems to have trouble getting stopped again.

Sunday wasn't too stiff a day; I had only eight or nine surgical admissions for Monday and actually had planned to go home for dinner around 9:00 in the evening if I had them all worked up. Then at 8:30 I got word that Piedmont was expecting a patient in from somewhere downstate by ambulance, a man who had blown out an abdominal aneurysm. Piedmont turned up about 9:00, and I had visions of another all-night stand in the OR, but at 9:30 word came from the State Patrol that the patient had died en route. This didn't seem to sadden Piedmont any; he just said, "Well, that saves us from being the executioner on this one." I had always assumed that when a great artery like that ruptures it just kills the patient instantly, but he said, not necessarily, very often the patient lives for another five or six hours, so you have time to go in and close up the tear. It's just that most of them either die on the table or in the

immediate postop period, so that the surgeon gets blamed unless
he's lucky enough that they die before they get to him.

Routine scrubs on Monday, but a long day. Got out of the OR
about 4:30 in the afternoon to find some fifteen new patients for
Emery and Meadows waiting to be worked up. So I didn't get off
until almost 10:30.

Thursday, December 15

I got my real initiation to Matt Meadows on Tuesday; I was
assigned to scrub on his cases, and he was whittling away all day
long. Meadows is young and skillful and sarcastic and arrogant and
has this South Carolina drawl that makes me want to disagree with
almost anything he says regardless of what it is. He also has the bad
habit of using his operating team as a sort of captive audience for
sounding off on his various bigotries, of which he apparently has
quite a selection.

He started things off merrily on Tuesday morning with a collection of flannel-mouth jokes, which went over big with Mankovitz as
his resident and Miss Lopez as his scrub nurse; so when these fell
flat, Meadows seemed to consider this a challenge and went on to
tell us all about what was wrong with the Southern Negro and
how the Negroes have ruined the South for everybody. I don't know
if he blames it all on the Administration in Washington or not; he
didn't say. Anyway, it was a long, tedious day all the way around;
there seemed an endless stream of patients to be operated on.
Maybe they're trying to wind up all the available surgery in the city
before Christmas.

Tuesday night a boy was admitted on Meadows' service with a
tumor in his right cheek, a parotid gland tumor that had been
biopsied by another surgeon fourteen months ago and found to be
one of these slow-growing dermoid carcinomas, malignant but not
likely to spread very soon or very far. The surgeon had taken out all
of it he could get, and now fourteen months later it had grown back
again. It was scheduled for Meadows at 2:00 Wednesday afternoon,
and I thought, Ha! just a quick simple job to peel out a little old
tumor, so we went in at 2:00 and spent until 1:30 A.M. whittling
away at this wretched thing. Two main trunks of the facial nerve
went right smack through the middle of the tumor, and had to be

dissected away a bit at a time, tracing the nerve trunks back toward the ear and peeling tumor away from them in hopes of saving the nerve.

It was a beautiful bit of surgical skill and patience, I had to hand it to Meadows, and he wasn't about to be hurried with it, but, God, what a tedious affair! Apparently did save the nerve, too, although it still had tumor under it and around it on all sides by the time he decided to quit. It's such a low-grade cancer that the kid will probably be able to live with it for a long, long time, but it will keep right on growing, and he'll have to keep having pieces of it chipped out from time to time. And God help the next surgeon that has to go in; we spent half the time fighting our way through scar tissue that had formed from the first operation. The next time the surgeon will be lucky to be able to identify the nerve at all. It was a long, dismal job, not very rewarding, and I was about dead by the time we finally got out of there. It was the longest scrub I've personally encountered, and the second longest scrub that's been in the OR since I came on the surgical service.

Today—Thursday—was fairly routine, and not much excitement. Scrubbed with Emery on a gall bladder, the fastest damned gall bladder I've seen yet, forty-five minutes from start to finish. I keep hoping that by some miracle we might have a nice quiet time from now until Christmas, figuring that after that it will be just another week until January 1st and then this miserable surgical internship will be three-fifths over with at any rate.

Forgot to mention that after the parotid tumor case Wednesday night I'd gone down for supper, and then up to change out of my scrub suit, and found Meadows there with the boy's parents in the OR office, very gently and patiently trying to explain to them how it was that even after such a long operation the boy still had cancer in there, and why he would have recurrences, and what this would mean. It's hard to tell people something like this and make them understand, but Meadows was doing the best he could at it, and not just on the run either; they were all having some coffee and they were asking him questions and he was answering them as kindly as he could. I went down to see the boy today, and when I asked him to open and close his eyes he could close both of them, so at least that trunk of the nerve is okay.

I guess that's about all I can think of right now. There seems to be a direct relationship between the interest I have on a given service and the eagerness with which I dash home to talk about it. This service has really been a flop, as far as I'm concerned. I miss working with Hank and Fred; I get along okay with both Meadows and Emery, I guess, but I don't like Virgil Aarons worth a damn. I guess Emery doesn't either, because he never lets Aarons do anything, won't even let him close a belly unless he's practically forced to. Mankovitz is such a quiet, colorless guy that he just seems like a cipher, and as for Barr, the more I see of him the more I wish, if he has to be around at all, that he could just keep his big yap shut. I don't quite know how to describe him except as a muddle-headed, pompous ass. Most of the time he's brown-nosing Emery or Meadows or one of the other surgeons, and he's so clumsy that it gets acutely embarrassing for everybody, including me.

Unfortunately, I have to scrub with him most of the time and be around him most of the time, and you just can't turn him off. I've even said point-blank, "Barr, why don't you just for Christ's sake shut up?" and he just puts on this stupid grin and keeps right on talking. On rounds I don't have much to do; Aarons writes all the orders, makes all the decisions, and there's practically no discussion of any of the cases. As intern I have no real responsibility for anything, except to be on hand for the scrubs I'm assigned to, and since I don't care for the scrubs much I haven't knocked myself out to do much else. I suppose this works both ways, too; nobody under those circumstances is leaping forward to bury me in responsibility either.

Ah, well. Ann and I went out to dinner tonight for the first time in over a month, and we had a relatively relaxing evening.

Tuesday, December 20

There wasn't much of anything doing Friday, one short scrub on a thyroid case, and then I sort of doped off the rest of the day and had a fairly quiet night on duty without anything particularly remarkable happening. Got off right at 10:00 Saturday morning and Ann picked me up; took a couple hours' drive, then came home and just loafed all weekend.

I found on Monday that Dr. Emery was in the hospital with a

strep throat or something, so all his cases were canceled for Tuesday. Also, with Christmas coming up the service has slowed up a good deal. Only the real hypochondriacs want to be sick at Christmas. Even so, Meadows had another hideous schedule Tuesday: a cholecystectomy, two abdominal hysterectomies, two hemorrhoidectomies and a varicose vein stripping all scheduled for one day. Even that wouldn't have been so bad except that when he got into the gall bladder case he found the patient had a big obstructing mass in his pancreas, so the simple cholecystectomy he was going to whip off in an hour turned into one of those vast Whipple resections, and it wasn't until he got the Whipple all finished—all six and a half hours of it—that he had a frozen section done on the mass and discovered that it was simply a big pancreatic abscess and not a cancer at all. The mass had looked like a cancer and it was obstructing the duodenum, so Meadows just assumed that it was. I don't know how he goes about explaining to the patient that half his insides are now missing in a case like that, but the case knocked the rest of the schedule into a cocked hat. We were in the OR until 8:30, and even at that postponed the last two cases until tomorrow.

Sunday, December 25

Wednesday morning we had a laparotomy and several other things; no new admissions, though, and a quiet night. Meadows had only a case or two on Thursday, and Friday was pretty slow.

I scrubbed with Dr. Ellis Martin in the morning on a prostatectomy on an old fellow with the kind of benign but obstructive prostate enlargement that lots of men get in their fifties and sixties. Martin seemed inordinately pleased that this old guy had finally yielded to the knife, said he's been trying to talk him into this procedure for years. So I asked him why, if it took the guy all that time to make up his mind, he had to pick two days before Christmas to have it done. Perfectly logical reason, as it turned out: the guy was a rancher from Oklahoma and his wife had come over for more or less urgent gall bladder surgery, so he decided that if he had to be around the hospital anyway he might as well have his job done as well.

[*Post hoc:* The extenuating circumstances may have been relatively incidental. A perfectly amazing number of people who have been putting off some elective surgery for years will decide one day out of the blue that they want to have it done; when they do decide, it doesn't matter if it's 9:00 P.M. on New Year's Eve, they want it done *now*, not tomorrow.]

Friday afternoon I had four new patients to work up. About suppertime there was a mass paging for all the house staff to come down to the mail room, and we found Andy Case there handing out envelopes as Christmas presents from the clinic doctors: $10 bills for the interns, $25 for the residents, which was very nice. Later on L. D. Kaiser came by and presented each of the interns with a bottle of Old Charter Kentucky bourbon as a Christmas remembrance from him and Jack Barley. I felt more pleased at this than at the $10, I think, because we all knew that it was not even remotely necessary, and was quite pleasantly unexpected.

Saturday morning, Christmas Eve, I went to work at 8:00 to relieve Alec Ivy so he and his wife could go off for a Christmas skiing weekend. A quiet morning, with rounds and a few other odds and ends to catch up on. About 10:30 I got together with Luke Hamilton; we decided that I should take first call for the rest of the day until 10:30 P.M. so that he could have the day free. Then he'd relieve me at 10:30 so I could get to midnight church and have most of Christmas day; then I'd relieve him at 9:00 Sunday evening for first call all night. Monday was to be holiday routine, so he would be off Monday, and I'd be relieved by Alec at 8:00 Monday morning. This way we could split up the weekend, always assuming that the weekend would be quiet enough to manage that way.

Saturday afternoon there were a few admissions, most of them just annoyingly silly. One lady came in with a case of shingles that she had had for two weeks and finally decided she couldn't stand for another minute, so she came in on Christmas Eve. Then there was the ninety-year-old man whose chief complaint was that he hadn't had a bowel movement in four days. He was admitted, but before I could even get up to see him he'd gone to the john and proceeded to deliver a nine-pound stool specimen, whereupon his pain and distress cleared up completely. So we sent him on home again. Sometimes just walking into the hospital can be therapeutic.

Midafternoon Dr. Rivers sent in a twenty-year-old girl for Slater's service with a hot appendix, just a classical textbook case. So Hank came in about 4:00, and at 4:30 we did an appendectomy on her. It took about thirty minutes, and Hank left me to finish closing her up and get her downstairs. He was feeling very sad; he had the sniffles and a sore throat, and said that all three of his kids were sick for Christmas Eve, and he wished to Christ he could just once in ten years have a Christmas holiday without having to do an appendectomy right squat in the middle of it. So I guess I'm not the only one who gets to wondering if it's really worth it or not.

Between suppertime on Saturday and 10:00 there were multitudinous little calls for this, that and the other thing. Some nurse on Fourth called me, all frantic because a postop patient of Dr. Eldridge's was spiking a temp of 104. And no wonder either; Eldridge had ordered a heat cradle over his abdomen, which was fine except that they had outfitted the cradle with eight large light bulbs on the inside and covered it with three blankets on the outside, and it was hot enough in there to bake a pizza. It was just radiating heat all over the room. I ordered the cradle off and told the nurses to use a hot-water bottle instead, and that seemed to solve the problem nicely; by 9:00 his temp was down to 99.

Very quiet from 7:00 until Luke relieved me at 10:00 P.M., so I showered and got dressed and met Ann and went off to church. Slept in this morning, Christmas Day, and now it is 2:00 in the afternoon and no distress signals yet from Luke. I won't plan to go in until 9:00 this evening unless it's real busy, but I'll probably give Luke a call around 6:00 to see. If he's been working hard, I'll go in a couple of hours earlier to relieve him.

Thursday, December 29

I seem very happily to have forgotten about this journal for most of the week; the hospital has been dead—no scrubs to speak of, no emergency work that I've been involved in, or involved myself in, which is something else. I've just been doing what I had to do and making myself scarce the rest of the time. So I suppose I'll pick this up again more actively after New Year's and the change of service. If I had another month on this service, I think I'd blow my cork. Right now I just feel the less said about it the better, it's depressing even to think about, so I'll try again next week. Maybe the next couple of months on orthopedic surgery will be more interesting; it's hard to tell. I hate to admit that I miss working with Slater, but I do. I guess.

Tuesday, January 3

This week marks two important milestones. First, and probably most important from the standpoint of this journal, is the completion of the first six months of this internship year as of January 1st. The job is half-done, and perhaps this is a good point to take an objective look at how I feel about it now compared with the early months. Second, it marks the end of my activity on Dr. Emery's general surgical service, the most dismal service I've encountered yet and—I hope—the most dismal I'm going to encounter. I never did feel that I had any significant contribution to make on the service except to hold retractors in the OR, and, frankly, a hook in the wall could have done that job just as well as I could.

Even more, though, I think there's been some element of midyear doldrums; I've been bored with the work, tired of the daily routine without a break (especially around Christmastime when everyone else is having vacations), far enough into the internship to know that I'm going to make it but not far enough in to be able to see the end in sight. Sometimes I find myself just counting days, thinking that every day past is one less to go—convicts must do something like that. Other times it seems that this six months has just been interminable, and the thought that there is just as much still to go is depressing beyond description.

I suppose, too, part of it is the lack of any sense of reward in this stretch of work. On the medical service there are depressing failures and some dreadful and foolish mistakes, but there also are some correct guesses, some feeling that once in a while I won one, and that at the least I was learning something and getting somewhere. This has been a squirrel cage, and the squirrel has been getting both winded and tired of it all.

The new service may give me second wind. Surgery III covers two major groups of doctors: the clinic orthopedic or bone surgeons, Dr. Archie Everett and Dr. Mel Tanner, and the outside general surgeons. Mostly it will be orthopedics, because the surgeons outside the clinic don't use this hospital very much. It's not really their fault, nor do they have anything against Graystone; it's just that Slater, Emery, Meadows and the other clinic doctors monopolize the OR so completely that the others get crowded out. The outside men often have trouble scheduling their cases at all, and then have to accept afternoon scheduling much of the time.

Oh, yes, I will also be assigned to neurosurgical scrubs. Dr. Carlo Ronzoni in particular does neurosurgery around here. Cal Cornell is back now seeing some patients; apparently his coronary was fairly mild. He probably won't be operating very much, however. Which suits him; he never seemed to like to operate very much anyway.

I think the orthopedic men are going to be fun to work with. Both of them are at least agreeable people to be around. Mel Tanner is a man in his early forties. Kind of an old maid, tall, austere, proper, with rimless glasses that add about fifteen years to his age. He acts as though he feels it's his professional duty never to smile even if he feels like it, so he has a peculiar way of peering at you soberly through those old-maid glasses, which I thought at first was a rebuke but have learned is actually his substitute for a smile. Archie Everett is the senior man, one of the original founders of the clinic along with Armand Fuller and Arthur Emery. He is older, a little, gray-haired teddy-bear kind of man who is very soft-spoken and pleasant to his co-workers, but usually gruff and grouchy in the OR. I've heard that there is a sort of permanent state of warfare between him and the OR nurses, and he just has a terrible time. The scrub nurses call him "Bloody Archie" and hate his guts, and he always has the lousiest, raunchiest scrub nurses available assigned to his cases, so he has all sorts of troubles, which may or may not be of his own making.

Certainly the orthopedic service is busy enough. Much of their work is emergency: closed and open reduction of fractures and dislocations, that sort of thing. Some is elective: corrective bone surgery, etc. And then there are laminectomies and fusions, done to treat vertebral disc problems. There'll be quite a variety.

The first case I saw on the service was actually on Friday night before I changed services: a dentist's son, about twenty, who had been skiing in the mountains north of the city and broke his left tibia. The ambulance brought him in at 7:30 P.M., and I took X-rays. Tanner came in and we took him up to the OR and put a Steinman pin through the bone above and below the fracture and then put a cast on from toe to thigh to hold the broken bone still. Monday night a twenty-one-year-old girl who had also been skiing broke her left tibia and the fibula as well. This is actually a more serious fracture, yet when Everett came in Monday night to see her he didn't feel a Steinman pin was necessary—just put a long-leg cast on her.

This morning we had another, a seventy-year-old diabetic man, the children's cop at the crossing at one of the nearby schools. He is one of these guys who stands out in the street at noonday wearing a bright yellow jacket and cap you can see six blocks away, helping little children cross the street. Some jackass came barreling through the crossing in his car and knocked the old guy flat, broke his leg. This was a nasty one; a fragmented fracture, in a man his age with the diabetes to contend with, too, is no delight for anyone. Got X-rays in the afternoon and got him up to the OR at 5:00 to fix the fracture. In this one Everett used a pin through the top of the tibia, got the cast on, took postreduction X-rays, and then didn't like the position of the fracture, so he cut the cast off again and started from scratch: reset the bone, recast it, and finally, grudgingly, decided it looked all right to suit him.

I didn't get off until 9:00, thanks to that one, and I gather a lot of orthopedic work is going to be unscheduled, with lots of late off-duty nights and botched-up days on the service. People don't break their bones for the convenience of the surgeon, it seems.

And trust me to get on the orthopedic service right in the heart of the skiing season. It had never occurred to me that you would have skiing in desert country, but the mountains north of here are covered with snow and there are six or seven booming ski areas busily sending broken bones to Graystone.

Friday, January 6

A very busy couple of days, too busy to try to outline them in detail, and very interesting days, too. Apparently some of the orthopedic men are going to let me do something besides stand around and watch, and I find some of the patients are coming into focus, too, once I start to have some degree of responsibility for what happens to them. On Emery's service, I was really the Invisible Man; the business of the service went on around and past me as though I were a stump in a stream. On this service Frank Gloucester is the resident now, and he *expects* me to make my own business rounds of the patients and take care of some of the routine work without bothering him except for problems.

I've been given some things to do in the OR, too, which is really a novelty. On Wednesday Dr. Everettt had another fractured tibia, this one from an auto accident. He got the fracture reduced, and took an X-ray and seemed satisfied with the reduction, and then said, "Why don't you put the pins in? Then you and Frank can cast it up." So he first-assisted me, showed me the landmarks to pick above and below the fractures for placing the pins, and then I put the Steinman pins through. It was a good example of the difference between watching something done and actually doing it.

You'd thinking that driving a 3/32-inch pin through a leg bone would be something very dangerous and difficult, and in fact it's a lot like putting a knife through butter. You take an old-fashioned brace-and-bit—the kind you drill holes through a board with—and using the pointed Steinman pin as the bit, stick it into the skin until you come to bone and then start drilling your way through until it comes out on the other side. Then you clip off both ends so about three-quarters of an inch protrudes from the skin on either side. With one of these above the fracture and one below and the whole mess held tight in a plaster cast, that broken bone couldn't move if it wanted to. And it doesn't even matter exactly where you put the pins through, as long as you're roughly in the right place. But it does give you the most God-awful feeling to do this until you realize from actually doing it that (1) they can't feel it going through, being anesthetized; (2) it won't hurt them when they wake up; and (3) you're not ruining them for life in the process.

Anyway, I've been getting a little experience doing things like this, and I think it's very good. Certainly makes a case more interesting by a factor of 10.

Thursday I scrubbed on two disc cases—laminectomies and fusions—one with Archie Everett, one with Carlo Ronzoni, the outside neurosurgeon. The purpose of this procedure is to find the ruptured disc between the vertebrae, remove the part that is sticking out and pressing on the spinal nerve roots, and then scrape the articulating surfaces of the vertebrae above and below and pack the space between them with bone for grafting, in order to fuse them together so that the damaged disc is supported and splinted above and below with bone. Apparently both orthopedic men and neurosurgeons do this procedure, and neither one thinks the other can do the job right.

Everett's case was fast and rough—just whack, crunch and scrape, with blood welling up out of the hole the entire time. Everett made a halfhearted attempt to stop the oozing, and finally said, "Oh, to hell with it, it'll stop when we get him together again," and shoved a gob of Gelfoam down in there and closed up the incision. Dr. Ronzoni, by contrast, picked daintily at the ruptured disc for over an hour, cleaning out great chunks of it by bits and pieces, and then did the fusion ever so delicately, and then nothing would do but to have absolute hemostasis, a perfectly dry field, before he quit. So he fiddled and fiddled, and looked down into this little hole he was working in, and labored away with bits of Gelfoam and sponges soaked in thromboplastin trying to get the oozing to stop (which naturally it wouldn't) and finally ended up with just about as much oozing as Everett did, only three hours later. I was surprised and said that Dr. Everett hadn't seemed so concerned about the bleeding, and Ronzoni just said, "Well, old Bloody Archie can do it any way he wants to, but I don't like all that chemical irritation around those nerve roots," and we fiddled some more while he gave me a long partisan lecture about why only neurosurgeons should do disc operations.

After that was done Thursday we had another neurosurgical case that was very interesting: a pneumoencephalogram. This is a deal in which the patient is sedated and then placed upright on a chair, leaning his arms over the back for support, and a lumbar puncture is done, and then a bit at a time cerebrospinal fluid is removed and air is injected into the spinal canal in its place; then X-ray pictures can be taken that show where the air has moved to inside the spinal canal and the brain itself. It seems a lot more drastic diagnostic procedure than it is, in a way, although I think I'd have to be in pretty desperate shape before I let anybody do it to me.

In this case, the patient, a twenty-year-old girl named Mary Turner, was in plenty desperate shape, really a tragic situation. When she was ten months old, she had had viral encephalitis, the old "brain fever" that so often leaves the patient gorky or with hydrocephalus—a great collection of water building up in the interior of the brain. Mary's illness had been totally untreated; apparently she'd run a fever of 105 for over two weeks, and her mother hadn't even called the doctor. She recovered from the infection, but in the next five or six years she developed a steadily progressive hydrocephalus which never was treated—the communicating type where the gathering fluid can escape down into the spinal canal, but still exerted continuing pressure on the inside of her brain. As long as her head could expand, it didn't bother her too much, but once the skull bones fused and the fluid kept forming, she started having neurological changes: tremors and spasticity of her muscles and finally convulsions.

For some reason all this hasn't impaired her intelligence—she's a brilliant kid, and has finished high school and is now through two years of college—but the symptoms have been getting worse and worse. She's an odd girl because she has this great big head and this very, very deep contralto voice—she sings in the university choir—and she also has a very mature attitude toward her condition.

I assisted Ronzoni with the pneumoencephalogram, and those films shocked the hell out of me. They showed that the kid has a huge fluid space inside of her brain on either side, with just a thin layer of cerebral cortex about a quarter-inch thick all the way around lining the inside of her skull. She also has a kind of cystic gap in the central part of the brain, and down where her cerebellum ought to be there's just a big hole filled with spinal fluid, with the fluid under very high pressure. I was just amazed; I can't quite see what brain cells that girl could possibly have left to think with, but Ronzoni seemed cheered by the pictures. He thinks the pressure can be relieved by punching a hole through into the fluid space and then running a polyethylene tube from the fluid space into the mastoid area, where the fluid can be absorbed into the general circulation again. Ronzoni insists that this has been a highly successful procedure in a number of cases. Of course, it often fails, too, and the condition is so rare that there aren't any good rules to follow so that each case has to be played by ear. But Ronzoni said that if it worked, this drainage tube business could give Mary the chance of years of fruitful life, while if it isn't done, she will just slowly turn into a gork and then die in a year or two. So Ronzoni will be doing that job next Tuesday. I'll be interested to see how it turns out; everybody in the hospital is rooting for the girl, she's such a nice, bright, unassuming kid, and she surely deserves a break if anyone does.

Then, just to balance off patients like Mary Turner, we have one like Morrie Stein, a patient of Ike's who was admitted on Archie Everett's service because of his low back pain. Morrie, I guess, is a used-car dealer downtown, and he is a real delight. He was admitted on Fourth on Thursday afternoon, and immediately set about reorganizing the way the floor should run to his own advantage. Before I went in to see him I noticed that he was scheduled for Friday morning for Archie Everett to do a laminectomy and fusion on his lower spine, so when I came in the room I said, "Well, I understand they're going to do a little surgery on you," and he said, "Oh, no, they ain't. They just think they are." So I got a little cagey, said maybe I'd gotten him confused with somebody else, and asked if Dr. Everett had seen him yet. "Oh, sure, he's seen me, but he ain't going to get me in any operating room." So I said, "Well, maybe they're going to consider it for a day or two first. Let me go and find out." I knew that they didn't schedule a case unless they were really planning to do it. So this didn't quite add up. I went out and called Everett, and he said they had indeed planned to do the laminectomy, but were canceling it because Mr. Stein had decided that he didn't want any surgery, and would I please just put him in pelvic traction for the time being.

So I went back and reassured Morrie that I'd gotten the word wrong, Dr. Everett was planning to wait, and he said, "Yeah, I know you guys, you can't wait to cut. That's all you guys ever want to do is cut." Well, I obviously didn't appeal to Morrie any more than he appealed to me, so I set about stringing up his traction while he told me all about these goddamn surgeons. He's already complained about the room, the food, the bed, the radio, the nurses, and now (along with complaining about the traction) he explained to me at some length (1) how he was a very nervous sort of person;

(2) how he was a very important person; (3) how he had known Dr. Isaacs for years and years and years and when he said something to Ike Isaacs, Ike Isaacs did such and so; and (4) how he was going to have his girl friend who had trained at Graystone as a nurse see if she couldn't arrange to have a couple of cute nurses who were down on the third floor (where he had been before he'd insisted on being transferred up to the fourth floor) brought up to the fourth floor—so he could pinch them or something I guess. All this, blah, blah, blah, for the three-quarters of an hour it took me to get the traction on him. By the time I finished I was ready to go down and order Mr. Stein onto a salt-free, meat-free, fat-free and sugar-free diet, but with great effort and restraint I refrained.

Have had a little more contact with Frank Gloucester and like him very much. We admitted a little boy Thursday night with a very mean-looking elbow, a great big black-and-blue, swollen thing. Kid had fallen down a flight of stairs. He was a patient of Ike's, and Ike had asked me to take films and call him, and the films showed that he'd broken the elbow but good. The fragments were all out of alignment, but by the time I left this evening nobody had even tried to set the fracture. The kid is lying around with a pillow splint and ice bags on his arm. I don't understand why, and neither does Frank; he took one look at the films and said, "Well, if this were my patient, I wouldn't touch that fracture with a ten-foot pole. I'd call in an orthopod." But Ike hasn't done this yet, and I'm wondering if he's going to.

Monday, January 9

Had a weekend, for once, that was comfortably busy but not frantically busy. I was officially covering both Surgery III and Slater's service; then the night supervisors corralled me with a long, sad tale about how there wasn't any intern at all covering OB this month and would I cover for emergencies? I told them fine, if their idea of emergencies was the same as mine, but I wasn't going to go up there at 3:00 in the morning to watch Dr. Sand deliver babies, and I wouldn't sleep up in the OB room for all the tea in China, I'd be sleeping down in quarters as usual.

Got to work Saturday morning just in time for rounds with Frank Gloucester and Archie Everett. My job on these rounds is to write orders and progress notes as we go along, and Everett also has me do some of the odd jobs, too—dressing changes, suture removals, etc.—even though he may stand by. There is certainly none of this galloping-down-the-hall business.

The main problem of the weekend was a ranch hand who had fallen from his horse and just smashed his right upper arm into fragments. Friday night Everett had hooked the broken arm up in lateral traction at the bedside; the portable X-ray had shown good alignment, but the two main fragments seemed to be about half an inch apart, which isn't too good. So Saturday on rounds Everett asked Frank and me to change the traction angle that evening, and try rotating the arm a little, and then get another film Sunday morning and call him. We did this later on Saturday evening, but found that any movement at all gave this guy terrific pain and muscle spasm. He had big, heavy biceps that tightened up and dragged the bone fragments together so forcefully that he actually got an S-curve in his upper arm, which also wasn't too good. New X-rays Sunday morning didn't look any better than the old ones—fragments still a half-inch apart—and the guy was far less comfortable, so we put him back the way he was. Frank called Everett and then scheduled an open reduction and pinning of the fracture for Monday morning.

About the little boy with the badly fractured elbow: Isaacs finally did ask Everett to see him, so Archie took him up to OR Saturday morning, anesthetized him and put the arm in a traction splint. He'll put plaster on the splint about Wednesday if the reduction holds.

After rounds Saturday I had a flock of little jobs to do: dressings to change, sutures to take out, somebody to hook up in traction and so on. Most of Saturday afternoon I was just going around from one place to another doing little things, seeing patients I hadn't seen all week, writing some progress notes on charts, getting better acquainted with some of the patients. I felt a little more like I was helping run a service again, first time I've felt that way for a long time.

Roscoe Herring, who is on the opposite service now, took double call Saturday night—apparently a very quiet night, since Roscoe doesn't hesitate to call me out if he gets even a trifle busy, in contrast to Luke, who will work his ass off all night long before he'll call me, just as long as he doesn't have to be two places crash emergency at the same time.

Sunday was quiet, too, until about 2:00 P.M., when everything happened at once. First, new admissions started coming in for Monday morning surgery. There were about ten of them expected. Then Everett called to say he was sending in a little boy who probably had broken a forearm, asked me to get X-rays and call when I'd seen them. While I was waiting for the boy to arrive, the OB nurse paged me frantically to come up and catch a baby that was precipitating in the hall. I rushed up there and found the anesthetist already giving the woman cyclopropane. The only trouble was that she really wasn't ready to deliver yet, and she certainly wasn't precipitating. I scrubbed, ruptured her membranes and gave her a little time, but with gas anesthesia I wanted to get that baby out pretty quickly, so I applied the forceps, and I tugged and I pulled and nothing happened. The baby came down a little way, but no farther. I cut a good wide episiotomy and again pulled and tugged and struggled something fierce, and finally, when I was beginning to get panicky about the whole thing, the baby inched its way out, face up. It was a posterior presentation that I had missed completely. At least now I know what a posterior delivery is—it's tougher than an anterior by a good deal—but mother and baby were fine.

By that time Everett's little boy was downstairs, with such an obvious S-curve in his forearm that I decided to take him right up to the OR and let the girl up there take the film. Archie arrived just as we were getting the films. The child was a little two-year-old boy—a blond, blue-eyed little doll, sweet as he could be. The arm wasn't hurting him a bit, but it looked horribly distorted and his mother and father were just frantic. Once upstairs, the anesthetist got him to blow into the cyclo tube until he went to sleep. He had a green-stick fracture of both bones of the forearm, so under anesthesia Everett let me set the fracture. I got it partly set, but he didn't think it was straight enough so he finished setting it, and then we applied the cast. It was odd; with that tiny little arm in my big paws I was afraid I'd just snap it in two, and worked and worked trying to be gentle in straightening the bones; when Archie took over, he just took the child's arm and went *ca-runch!* and there it was, straight as a die. The little boy was downstairs again within twenty minutes, and they took him home that night, I think.

Sunday evening was further complicated by a patient of Dr. John's. The old goat had lanced a thrombosed hemorrhoid for this lady in his office that morning, and then after he got finished she confided to him that she was a bleeder. She was, too. She'd gone on bleeding from this thing all day and finally came into the hospital with two or three pads soaked. She must have been royalty or something; Dr. John himself came in and took her up to the OR and found she had a couple of spurters that were really going to town. So he tied them off; he must have put in seven or eight ties and sewed her up so tight those hemorrhoids were howling for mercy. I didn't hear anything about her all night, but there's one old girl who's going to have a lancinating pain in the ass for the next six weeks.

Monday morning Archie did the open reduction on the rancher's arm, and we found out why the traction hadn't worked: there was a half-inch-thick piece of muscle wedged in between two of the fragments, holding them apart. He pushed the muscle out of the road and used a screw to hold the fragments together, and the guy now has a very nice reduction of a nasty fracture.

After that case, Frank Gloucester and I scrubbed on a prostatectomy with Dr. Martin, and then on a nephrectomy—somebody with a tuberculous kidney that needed removing. I've decided that Dr. Martin is my kind of surgeon; there is no crap about his surgery. When he starts something, he goes ahead and does it and he does it fast. It took him just an hour from open to close on the kidney case, and it went slick as a whistle.

I found ten more new patients downstairs waiting to be worked up for surgery Tuesday morning, so it was 8:30 P.M. before I got home for supper. Ann is getting to be an expert on meals that can be cooked up from scratch in fifteen minutes, any time between 6:00 P.M. and midnight.

Wednesday, January 11

On Tuesday morning I scrubbed with Mel Tanner and Frank Gloucester on a mid-thigh amputation, a little old man with dia-

betic gangrene in his foot. This was the first amputation I've seen,
and I was amazed at what a simple job it is.

After that, we went on rounds together, and then I worked up
some new patients. One of them is going to be an interesting patient to follow, I think—at least she has an interesting history. This
is Mrs. Towne, a fat, roly-poly woman of about twenty-six, just 4½
feet tall, weighing 170 pounds. Some time during the summer when
she had weighed 210 pounds, she'd come in to see Everett with a
huge tumor of the bone in her right upper arm. Everett had biopsied it twice, and in both cases the pathology department had been
unable to make a diagnosis. They thought most probably that she
had somehow fractured the bone without knowing it—though how
in hell anybody could do that is more than I can see—and that this
tumor was just overgrowing callus resulting from movement at the
fracture site while it was healing. But they had shipped slides of this
tumor to pathologists all over the country; seven different reports
had come back, all agreeing that it was some benign bone growth
and not a cancer, but the Armed Forces Institute of Pathology,
which is the national authority in this country, said they thought it
was a periosteosarcoma, a malignant tumor of the connective tissue
lining of the bone.

Well, Everett had decided to sit on this for six months and see
what happened. The surgery for a bone cancer of the upper arm is
too drastic to do unless you're dead certain you're dealing with a
bone cancer. Meanwhile he urged her to lose weight, in case she had
to have surgery. So a week ago he had biopsied the lesion again, and
this time there was no question but that it was malignant. She had
lost forty pounds, so she came in to the hospital and was scheduled
for a forequarter amputation Wednesday morning.

I was assigned to scrub on the case, and I'd never seen anything
like it in my life. The idea is not only to take out the tumor, but
disarticulate the shoulder and remove all the nodes and most of the
bone in the affected shoulder girdle. Everett took out all the
scapula, half of the collarbone, all of the muscles and axillary structures, disconnected all the nerves from the brachial plexus and cut
that free, tied off the great subclavian artery to the arm, and the
corresponding vein, and then just took off the whole damned forequarter. It was a dreadfully bloody procedure—they don't call

Everett "Bloody Archie" for nothing, I guess, but this woman seemed to tolerate the procedure well, at least physiologically. How she is going to tolerate it psychologically is going to be a different question altogether.

This procedure took most of the day. Six or seven patients to work up for surgery tomorrow, none particularly exciting. I put in my bid to scrub on Mary Turner's case tomorrow, the hydrocephalus case, so we'll see. Very tired tonight; that case just shook me up. What is a woman going to do without any right arm *or* shoulder?

Friday, January 13

I didn't scrub on Mary Turner's case after all, but heard that it seemed to go okay. I got in to see her once today; she appeared cheerful but not elated. I guess she fully realizes that the proof of this particular pudding will indeed be in the eating; no one will know for days or weeks whether the operation was a success or not, or what degree of success.

Mrs. Towne, who had the forequarter amputation, has really been a great patient so far. Cheerful as she can be, pleasant, perfectly objective about what had to be done, and appears to be taking her loss and disfigurement with a hell of a lot more equanimity than I would have thought possible. But then how many fat women would you find who could sit down and deliberately lose forty pounds of weight in six months just because the doctor told them he thought it would be advisable and wise? With good physical recovery and no postop complications, and with a good mental state, she may be going home next week sometime.

Speaking of amputations, the cocktail waitress who had her femoral artery tied off by mistake is back in, and I've been seeing her from time to time. Dr. Harlow had done a below-the-knee amputation, and then the girl got gangrene in the stump and they had to do an above-the-knee amputation. This hasn't healed well, and now she's in the hospital again to attempt a skin graft on the stump, with the very distinct possibility that an even higher amputation may be necessary.

This girl is really just about at the end of her tether emotionally; Thursday night when she was admitted and found out she might have to have more surgery beyond the skin graft, she was just literally weeping, and she sits around and does the best she can to keep a stiff upper lip. She has already been thrown to over $3,000 worth of hospital costs and surgeons' fees, and as far as I know this is still being represented to her as one of the regrettable but uncontrollable complications of a vein ligation. There's been no blame cast on the guy that did the ligation in the first place, nor has anybody come forward offering to pay the girl's doctor and hospital bills for her, as far as I know, so there she is stuck with it. Can't really blame her for having low morale, but I still wonder just exactly where medical ethics come into a picture like this. Or whether they only come into it when it's convenient for the doctor.

Had to help on one truly delightful case Thursday night. This was another patient of Dr. Harlow's, who illustrated what can happen to the best-laid plans of mice and surgeons. This woman had an abdominal hysterectomy Thursday morning, apparently a nice, clean uncomplicated procedure. She was returned to her room on Third at 3:00; at 5:30 Olsen's wife called to tell me that the patient was passing large blood clots from her vagina. I knew that she was one nurse in the hospital who could distinguish "spotting" from "hemorrhaging," and I figured if she said this woman was bleeding too much, the odds were good that she was, so I rushed up there, and indeed she was, far too much. I called Harlow and told the OR to set up for a sterile pelvic, and when he arrived we took her up and he found a spurting artery at the vaginal apex. So he put a clamp on it and sent her back down to her room with orders not to disturb the clamp, and went home again.

It seemed to me that this was a slightly cavalier manner of dealing with this problem, but Harlow is a funny guy, definitely doesn't welcome either questions or comments from interns, so I figured, What the hell, he must know what he's doing. The bleeding was stopped, too, so far as I could see at 10:30 when I checked her before going to bed. Then about 1:00 in the morning Miss Foulkes called me up to see the woman, and I found she now had a classical acute surgical abdomen: dreadful pain, guarding, muscle rigidity, all the earmarks of a severe chemical peritonitis, and she was shocky as well.

So I called Harlow out again and we took her upstairs again and this time he reopened her belly and found about three pints of free blood sloshing around in there. He tried to look down in the pelvic area, and something down there started spurting blood all over him and me and the scrub nurse and the overhead light. When he finally got hold of it, it turned out to be the right cervical artery, the major artery to the lower pelvis, which had somehow lost its ligature and had been pumping away in there for God knows how long. This is one of those things that just isn't supposed to happen, but it does, and to a first-rate surgeon as well. I'm just glad he didn't have a flat tire on the way to the hospital.

Scrubbed this morning on a couple of Archie Everett's cases, including the diabetic traffic cop with the broken leg. Apparently he's not been showing any signs of healing his fracture with Steinman pins, so now Archie opened up the leg and literally screwed the fracture fragments together. So they're at least side by side. Whether he'll grow any new bone or not is another matter.

Thursday, January 19th

Had the duty this past weekend, and alas, the ski season is upon us, and there was really no rest. I ended up working right on through Sunday night, thanks to one spooky old Joe that I'll have something to say about later, and by Monday night I was the next thing to dead, and then Tuesday and Wednesday were just packed tight, and I'm not sure I'll stay awake long enough tonight to say anything very coherent. I never saw so many patients wandering through in all my life.

Started the weekend off just right with a big fight with the duty X-ray technician, the tall, skinny girl they call Adeline. Frank and I finished rounds about 10:30 A.M., and as usual on this service I had a stack of little jobs to do that had evolved from the rounds. Frank would say, "See that these stitches get taken out sometime today," or "We'd better get the Russell traction back on today," or some such thing, and then we'd go on, so I keep a little list. This catch-up work took until about 1:30, and I was just having a late lunch when a patient of Flagg's was brought in, a big, fat lady who had been run down by a pedestrian on the sidewalk and knocked on her butt. When I checked her, I was pretty sure she had a fractured hip or thigh, high up, so I called Adeline to come in and take a portable film of the woman before we moved her off the Emergency Room stretcher. She was in a good deal of pain, less when lying very still, but severe any time she moved at all.

Well, while I was working up on the floors waiting for Adeline to come in and take the films and call me, she whisked in, took some pictures, told the operator to tell me I could find them in the tank down in the X-ray, and then lit out for home again. I went down to look at the films, and found one completely blank and the second so massively overexposed that I could barely make out a section of the femur under the spotlight, with no detail at all. A third film was all fuzzy, and showed only mid-femur; the hip and pelvis weren't even on it.

So I called Adeline to come back and take them over again, and she was very snotty over the telephone, said, well, you couldn't expect to get good films of a femur and pelvis on the portable machine. I said, the hell you couldn't, I'd stood and watched her do it before, and Adeline just said, "Oh, shit!" and hung up in my ear. Twenty minutes later she turned up. Meanwhile I'd been thinking, Why have another round of the same old crap? So against my better judgment I got the orderly and we hauled the lady down to the X-ray department and hoisted her over on the table of the biggest, brightest, newest machine they had.

Well, it took that skinny bitch ten successive films before she finally got me a readable film, making one mistake after another—wrong exposure time, wrong angle of exposure, you name it. Finally after nine flops she got me a film that showed that the lady had two fractures through her pelvis. And all this with Adeline getting madder and madder, as though I personally had arranged for this woman to fall down on Adeline's Saturday afternoon on duty. I don't know if she had a boyfriend waiting for her in bed or what; she was sure burning to get out of there. So it took her from 1:00 until 5:00 to get ten minutes' worth of X-rays, and I had to sit down in that X-ray room and ride herd on this damned girl to make sure she didn't go kicking the patient around (this is the babe I've seen treating patients just like pigs when she had to come in to take X-rays on weekends) and also to make sure that she finally did get me a readable film before she sneaked off home again.

Saturday night and all day Sunday were filled with little things, just enough to keep me from sitting down once all weekend. About two o'clock Sunday preops for Monday began coming in—eleven were scheduled to arrive—and if everything else had been nice and quiet, that wouldn't have been too bad, but there were a thousand unscheduled things: a girl with possible appendicitis, another broken hip, a girl with a twisted knee, a woman with a dislocated foot. By suppertime Sunday I was beginning to get punchy with all these things piling up at the busiest possible time of the week.

I finally saw the last of the preops about 10:00, and crawled down to bed on my hands and knees. I got a big, fat hour of sleep, and then the fun began with Mr. Tandberg—a fifty-four-year-old man admitted by Dr. Gillies a couple of days ago with chest pain, diagnosed as a coronary. Mr. Tandberg was spooky before this happened, and he was really spooky after it happened, just scared silly that he was going to shuffle off this mortal coil at any minute, and consequently could not allow himself to go to sleep, among other things.

The nurse on Second called to say that Mr. Tandberg had taken the sleeper that was ordered and couldn't go to sleep, so I went up and tried to quiet him down; he was all worked up because he couldn't sleep, but he didn't want to. I ordered 2 grains of Luminal, told the nurse to do the best she could with him. At 1:00 she called me again: Mr. Tandberg still hadn't gone to sleep, and he was having chest pain, and he was getting frantic, and what could they do? I said to give him a sixth of morphine, and tried to get back to sleep. At 2:00 A.M. the nurse called again and started giving me this long tale, step by step, of what Mr. Tandberg had been doing since she had called me at 1:00. I said, "Look, why are you telling me all this?" and she said, "Well, I thought you'd want me to bring you up to date!" So I told her to go to hell, hung up and rolled over. At 2:30 Miss Wood called and said Mr. Tandberg was insisting they call an ambulance to take him home; if they didn't, he was going to walk out of there in his pajamas and sue them for kidnaping.

Well, aside from the frustration of dealing with a three-year-old mentality, all this froth obviously was no good for Mr. Tandberg's coronary. I got into some clothes and went up and tried to talk *some* kind of reason into the guy. He was just tied up in knots, obviously so silly-scared of his coronary that he was doing everything in his power to keep from going to sleep that night, since he was sure he'd never wake up again, yet insisting that he would give anything to be able to go to sleep. He was so sleepy from the medications he almost forcibly had to hold his eyes open, and so addled by them that he wasn't having any coherent thoughts, even at a three-year-old level.

So finally I suggested that the nurses pour a deep, hot bath and soak him in it for half an hour. The nurse said, "But, Doctor, he's on coronary routine, and that means strict bed rest," so I said, to hell with the coronary routine, that didn't include climbing up the walls at 3:00 in the morning, did it? Put him in the bathtub, and while he was soaking, give him a good stiff 3-ounce hot toddy to drink. And the nurse said, "You mean put *whiskey* in it?" and I said, "Oh, Christ," and went back to bed. I could fight an idiot patient, but I couldn't fight an idiot nurse. So at 4:00 the nurse called me to tell me that at 3:00 she had called Dr. Gillies, and he said he would see about getting rid of Mr. Tandberg in the morning. At 5:00 she called Carey and at 6:00 called the patient's wife; and by then it was breakfasttime.

This week, Monday through today, has been nothing but rush and run, a heavy schedule of scrubs every day, heavy schedule of admissions every evening, and even old Gloucester, who is usually the most gentlemanly and even-tempered party in the whole damned hospital, has been getting irritable. He covers pathology as well as orthopedics on his duty nights, alternating with Garvin. On Tuesday night, I think it was—or really, 1:00 A.M. Wednesday— some old goat died of something, and I went through an hour's persuasion trying to obtain permission for the post, and finally got it, and then called Frank and said that so-and-so was dead, and I had post permission. He said, "Fine, put him in the icebox. The post can be done in the morning." This galled me, somehow; *I'd* had to lose two hours' sleep getting permission, and usually the path resident comes in during the night if a post turns up, in order to get the body off to the funeral home by morning. So I said, "Well, aren't you going to come in and do it now?" There was a long pause and then Frank said, "Doctor, there are limits," and hung up on me.

Tuesday, January 24

I forgot to mention that after the run-in with Adeline, the X-ray girl, on my last duty weekend, I went down to X-ray department on Monday morning and screamed loud and long to Ken Tourney, the chief radiologist, about the whole performance, hauled out the screwed-up films (which I had pulled and saved so that they wouldn't "happen" to get thrown away) and put on quite a performance myself. He said he'd see what he could do, and he did, too. After I left he called the girl in and canned her. I guess that wasn't the first complaint they'd had, and I can't even feel sorry about being the dirty guy that squealed on her. I'm just glad as can be she's gone.

And while they're canning people, it would sure be nice if they'd go to work on some of those scrub nurses. Archie Everett may be no dream to work with in the OR, but he shouldn't have to put up with the kind of crap some of those girls hand him. He always seems to have this big, fat hen named Jeanette assigned as his scrub nurse, and I've just never encountered such a snotty, insolent, sarcastic bitch in all my life. She isn't satisfied with just being incompetent, she deliberately *baits* him, and she doesn't quit until she's rendered him so furious that he can hardly hold his hands still. I just don't understand why he stands there day after day and takes it. I could hardly believe my eyes and ears when I first saw it.

Frank Gloucester has obviously been as disgusted as I have, although he had never said anything; but this morning, when Jeanette had her claws in and was just riding Archie something dreadful in the middle of a tough open reduction, Gloucester suddenly put down his instruments, and looked right straight at Jeanette with those bright blue eyes of his and said very quietly, "Now that will be enough." Jeanette stopped in mid-sentence with her jaw sagging and didn't open her trap again for the rest of the day. I wish he'd do it more often, or I wish Archie himself would rise up like Lazarus and brain her with a bone chisel.

Thursday, February 2

The beginning of the last month on surgical service. And I mean alleluia, too.

Had a funny thing happen this week—funny-peculiar, I mean—that made me feel very good. Medically good, that is, a sort of a morale-booster, of which there have been very few these days. This is what the boys call "pulling a coup" in the vernacular, and it is remarkably nice after a long dry spell to pull a *real* coup.

This one involved a Mrs. Gomez, a big, buxom woman of about forty-five, with a swarthy face and black hair that was dyed a violent yellow-orange. On Monday of this week she had gone to see Dr. Tony Marin because she'd found a lump in her left breast while taking a shower or something. Marin examined her and sent her over to see Jack Barley that same day. He confirmed that the lump was there and would have to be biopsied and admitted her Tuesday afternoon for biopsy on Wednesday and a possible radical mastectomy. He was pretty certain it was a cancer, too, from his own brief admission note.

Well, I saw this woman when she was admitted, and she was just scared silly—knew the lump might be cancer, knew she was the right age for it, and knew that if the biopsy was positive, Dr. Barley wouldn't remove just the lump, he'd take the whole breast off. Naturally, she was hoping desperately that she had come in time. She'd never noticed this lump before and went to the doctor the very next day, but she was also obviously horrified at the thought of having a breast amputated. She was so shaken up and miserable that I talked to her for a while, tried to explain that getting at it early was the important thing, that the chances were all on her side that this was just a benign cyst or benign tumor, but that she shouldn't worry anyway because this early in the game even if it *were* the Bad Disease, taking the breast off was sure to cure it.

The talk certainly eased the woman's mind; I could practically see her relax and cheer up and begin adjusting to the idea of losing a breast. So I went ahead to examine her and found the lump, all right, a tender, discrete mass about the size of a walnut in the upper outer quadrant of her left breast. The trouble was, I also thought I felt a mass in her *right* breast. It was much smaller than the other; I wasn't even sure that I wasn't just feeling the knuckle of a rib until I got her to sit up and lean forward, but finally decided that there definitely *was* a mass there.

So then I started to wonder. All women's breasts are somewhat lumpy and nodular, and I knew both Marin and Barley had gone over this woman and probably had felt that this thing on the right was not significant, but all the same I felt I had to write it down on the physical exam sheet in her chart because it was undeniably there, significant or not. I didn't say anything to the woman, just wrote it on the chart, and then debated calling Jack, and decided I would, but then couldn't reach him. So I printed in big letters on the order sheet: "DR. BARLEY: PLEASE SEE INTERN'S NOTE BEFORE SURGERY," and hoped that would flag him down if I didn't contact him personally.

It did, all right. I ran into him in the OR dressing room the next afternoon just before he took Mrs. Gomez in for the biopsy and he said, "Hey, boy, you pulled a fast one on me; Marin and I both missed that lump in the right breast," and he told me he was now planning to biopsy both breasts. I didn't learn anything more that day, except that I knew she went into the OR about 2:00 and wasn't out until almost 7:00, so I assumed that Jack was doing a radical. Then this morning I found Luke Hamilton and Fred Olsen loafing in the lounge before breakfast, and Fred grinned and said, "Say, I hear you're a big hero!" I said, "That's nice. How come?" So he told me that the big lump in Mrs. Gomez' left breast had been a benign cyst, but the little one on the right was a cancer and that Jack had done a radical. He also said that it had been a small, isolated, discrete lesion and that there had been no positive nodes, and that Jack thought the chances of a cure ran about 80 per cent compared to maybe 30 per cent if it had been missed until it got big enough to be found easily a couple of months later.

Well, it was a good morale-booster, and I'm really tickled that I picked it up when a couple of good men had missed it. On the other hand, I suppose every intern has his hour of glory sometime, at one time or another picks up a breast mass that somebody else has missed, and it doesn't pay to feel too smart about it—just goes to show that the best guys miss things. And also that you can't afford to take a damned thing for granted, ever, about anything in this game, which is a sobering enough thought to keep you from getting too euphoric about it.

Thursday, February 9

I swear this orthopedic service turns up some of the *damnedest* cases. A case came in for Mel Tanner by ambulance Wednesday night, an eighteen-year-old kid with a gunshot wound in his right leg. His two buddies, also about eighteen, were accompanying him. The story was that they had been out hunting and this guy had been carrying his 30–06 rifle with the safety off and put a slug through his own lower leg while climbing through a fence. This in spite of the fact that the only hunting that's open now is rabbits and you don't generally hunt rabbits with a 30–06 rifle. Well, *somebody* put a slug through this guy's leg, and I never saw such a fierce-looking X-ray in my life. Both bones of the lower leg were shattered in mid-shaft; about a three-inch chunk of each bone was just pulverized. But the amazing thing was that the whole damned inside of the leg was just riddled with little tiny bits of shrapnel from the slug, scattered from ankle to hip. The fracture itself was a mess to clean up, digging out old pieces of shredded pants leg from two inches in and cleaning out enough crap in the fracture region so that there might be some chance of the bone healing without a bone infection to help things out.

Then this morning a couple of tall, polite, grim-faced men turned up and spent an hour talking to this guy. They were from the FBI, and they seemed very anxious to take him away as soon as he could be moved. Seems the cops had gotten interested in the car these kids had been in, found a bunch of stolen merchandise in the trunk, plus a few decks of reefers, plus a little of the hard stuff as well— heroin. The guy's buddies, by the way, had vanished in the night as soon as they saw him to the hospital door.

Tuesday, February 15

Quite a stretch with no record here. This is probably a good time to pause and recap a couple of things, too, since my surgery section is moving to a fast curtain, and I will be going over to the Children's Division for the next service—a completely new place, new crowd of people, new kind of patient and everything. Gives me the willies to think about it.

The weekend is pretty fuzzy, don't remember very much about it except that last Friday I got a wretched cold, runny eyes, runny nose and a nice irritative bronchitis, coughed and coughed and coughed in the operating room, until Archie turned me out of there, told me to go cough on something else besides his surgery. Saturday morning I felt like the wrath of God, just ached all over. I thought about trying to con Alec or Luke into trading weekends with me, but then decided to try the All-Purpose Cure first, went up to Second and begged a couple of APCs and 10 milligrams of Dexedrine and took them and presently began to feel at least alive. The nurse offered to give me a slug of penicillin, but I talked her out of some tetracycline instead, being a coward about needles, and by Sunday morning the thing seemed to be squaring away. I just didn't do anything I didn't have to do, and the weekend was relatively quiet, compared with the last couple.

Monday this week wasn't as much of a national Blue Monday as it has been in the past, but it was blue enough. I had come in an hour early because I had to present a case at the Monday morning surgical conference. Herring had originally been scheduled to present the case, but begged off on some excuse or another, so I got stuck with it instead.

A couple of minor cases with Everett Monday morning: a cast revision, a bunionectomy and a knee case—removing a piece of torn cartilage from the knee joint. Shortly after noon L. D. Kaiser admitted a man with a supposedly acute gall bladder. He certainly had belly pain, but it wasn't a typical picture, and when Kaiser got him open he found the gall bladder looked just fine, but there was a loop of small bowel that was caught in an adhesion, what they call a volvulus. So he released it, and the bowel pinked up, and he stood squeezing the bowel for a while and decided the loop didn't need resecting. But then—all this was through a gall bladder incision— he decided to do an incidental appendectomy, and then he fiddled around for another hour or so wondering whether he ought to take the gall bladder out, too, while he was in there. I guess he thought the patient expected it, but he restrained himself. We still don't know how this guy got the volvulus, or why.

That took until dinnertime; I went on to have a free pork chop dinner before the hospital staff meeting, but ducked the meeting and went back up to work up new admissions. I was just finishing up about 10:00 when a patient of Barley's came in by ambulance. This was an elderly man with a marked anemia and a history of throwing up blood for two days. Apparently Jack had been trying to find an ulcer in this guy for about three years, and had never succeeded. Now he was passing blood from both ends, throwing up black coffee-grounds stuff and passing tarry stools. He'd had 2 units of blood at another hospital where he'd gone first, and he wasn't shocky, but Jack ordered another 2 units of blood given during the night, and I had to crawl out a couple of times to see that his blood pressure wasn't going down. You just can't trust the nurses to tell you when it's a GI bleeder; they'll call to tell you the patient just died as often as not. He seemed to settle down, though. Jack was going to get upper GI X-rays this morning, and I haven't heard the results of that yet, but I know he's scheduled for a gastrectomy tomorrow. So it looks like they're satisfied that the blood is coming from a duodenal ulcer. Considering that he's fifty-five, with a long history of intractable ulcer symptoms and now a life-threatening hemorrhage that is sure as hell not going to be his last the way he's going, I think they're probably perfectly justified in laying the knife to him.

This morning—Tuesday—I had a routine round of scrubs. I've been seeing a variety of patients on this service, between the orthopedic cases and the general surgical cases of the outside doctors. With the kind of patient flow that we've been having, which has been heavy almost to the point of the ridiculous, and with rarity of any kind of personal contact with most of them, it is just amazingly easy to fall into the trap that always made me so mad in medical school of regarding the patient, quite sincerely, as a leg, or a shoulder, or a gall bladder. I remember from medical school how the surgeons at Hopkins would bring some doddering old man out for a case presentation to the students and start off by pointing to him and saying, "Gentlemen, this Stomach was admitted to the hospital for the first time the night of November 5th. . . ." If any surgeon ever introduced *me* to a crowd of bright-eyed, wise-guy medical students as "this Stomach," I'd pick up the nearest blunt instrument and brain him with it. Yet I find myself thinking, and even recording in this journal, what we did with this Gall Bladder, and saying how Archie Everett had this Leg to fix.

All this because I was about to say that the orthopedic cases we've been seeing seem to be divided into three categories: the bad backs, which make up about a third; the acute fractures, which cover a good half of the cases; and the rest made up of odds and ends: bunion removals, old fractures with malunion or nonunion, joint fusions or manipulations, prosthetic cases. I should, I suppose, say that *patients* with bad backs made up a third, *patients* with acute fractures make up another half, etc.

Some of the prosthetic work is the most interesting. It's just incredible what can be done in some cases. Sometime last week, Everett operated on a man who had snapped off the neck of his femur about a year ago in a fall, just sheared off the "ball end" of the bone, tearing away its blood supply at the same time. That was eighteen months ago, as a matter of fact, and he never did get a union, and the head of the femur had died and was just sitting in there literally rotting away, so Everett opened up his hip, peeled out the piece of dead bone and replaced it with an Eicher ball prosthesis. This is a device which looks like a polished stainless-steel ball bearing about one and a half inches in diameter attached to a steel shaft the size and shape of a railroad spike; the ball is tilted off at a 30 degree angle from the spike, so that the spike can be rammed down into the shaft of the bone and the ball then becomes a substitute "ball" for the ball-and-socket joint of that hip.

I kept thinking about the Tin Woodsman all through the procedure, and got a good example of why they call Everett "Bloody Archie"—I never saw so much bleeding, or so much indifference to it, in all my life. Other surgeons want the field nice and dry with no bleeding before they close up; Archie seems to be content if there are no large arteries actively spurting. In any event, the case was a mess, and with this device in there the man is supposed to be able to walk on that hip again. I don't know if he's really going to be able to or not, but he sure wasn't going to on that chunk of dead bone, and it's nice to think that he may.

Archie kept telling us all the faults with this device as he put it in. Seems in some people the hard steel pressing into the socket erodes bone so that sometimes the steel ball "wanders" through into the pelvis. They tried coating the ball with inert polyethylene that would be closer to the consistency of bone, but the plastic tends to collect a lot of tiny, microscopic scratches over a period of time, the way a sterling silver spoon develops a patina, and then begins to irritate, and the patient ends up with a hip joint frozen by arthritis. Of course, the only way they can find these things out is by trying, and so far the best they have come up with is none too good.

I've really seen very little of outside doctors' cases, since I'm assigned first to the orthopedic cases, and even when I admit a patient on the outside service I rarely see the patient again. I have been very confused indeed about the patients with acute surgical abdomens that come in; I seem to lack some magic touch in diagnosing them. In fact, I hit them the wrong way so consistently that Gloucester said one night that if I thought a patient had a hot appendix, that was pretty good evidence that he probably didn't and vice versa.

One outside doctor's case I have followed with interest was a nineteen-year-old girl who came in as a joint patient of Dr. Ted Carter and Henry Baldwin. What a pair! They get together in the OR, and there is just a battle royal to see who does what. They'll stand and bicker about whether you do something this way or that way, then snatch instruments out of each other's hands, and fight and scrap and get sore and stamp out and act like a couple of five-year-olds.

This particular girl had come to Baldwin because she'd missed a period, and then passed some tissue with the next period. An unmarried girl who maintained that she couldn't be pregnant, but she came in the hospital with an omnipresent mother, so she didn't have a chance to talk to anybody alone. Baldwin did a D & C, and found tissue that was diagnostic of a hydatid tumor, a possibly malignant growth that arises occasionally from placental tissue that is not completely expelled after a miscarriage. As far as I know, it is prima-facie evidence of a previous pregnancy, although this girl was just wide-eyed about the whole thing; the idea of even an unrecognized pregnancy was simply ridiculous, how could it be possible when she wasn't even married? And Mamma standing around constantly, about as warm and sympathetic as a hawk.

The hell of it is, the girl continues to run a high hormone titer, and Baldwin and Carter both think the hydatid tumor may be the malignant variety, the cancer they call a chorionepithelioma, which next to a malignant melanoma is about the most viciously malignant tumor a woman can have. Grows like wildfire and metastasizes so early that you almost never can stop it by the time it's diagnosed. They will have to open up her uterus and get it out, whatever it is, and it poses a strange problem in human relations: if it is a chorio, this girl's goose is probably cooked, but I don't know in that case what they tell this bitch of a mother—whether they say that it's cancer that can only arise from a pregnancy (which is what I suspect the mother wants to hear—at least that the trouble, whatever it is, arose from a pregnancy) or whether to lie to the mother and let the little girl stick to her story and back her up. I sure would be hard-pressed to know what to do, and I doubt that Henry Baldwin has the native wisdom to come up with the right answer.

This afternoon I had the delight of my first scrub with Calvin Cornell, who is back in the saddle now. The patient was a woman with a history of blowing out a little congenital aneurysm on her carotid artery, clear up inside the skull, on the right. Cornell wanted to do an arteriogram—a procedure in which a big needle is inserted in the carotid artery in the neck, and a radio-opaque dye is squirted in, and then a succession of X-rays are taken machine-gun fashion to try to show where and what size the aneurysm is and whether there are more than one and a few other knotty problems. Cornell was in top irascible form, stamping around and growling, getting real excited at the X-ray people the whole time we were down there (the patient had to be anesthetized in the X-ray department, since the machine-gun-type X-ray machine weighs about four tons and can't be brought to the OR), complaining that they were too damned slow, and generally making a nuisance of himself. I had the strong impression that he was doing this with malice aforethought, since the poor girls were obviously doing as well as could be done under the circumstances.

I think Cornell gets a kick out of being bearish in general. I remember one day when he had done an ulnar nerve transplant and was howling to the nurses on Fourth that they had wrapped the patient's arm in a towel after the preop scrub when he had told them he didn't want the arm wrapped in a towel, although he knows perfectly well that Everett *insists* on having his orthopedic preps wrapped in towels in order to keep the dust off or something. He was growling and howling about this and giving the nurse holy hell that day, and then turned around with a sheepish grin on his face when he saw me sitting there listening to this diatribe, and said, "How are you feeling today? I'm feeling ornery."

The arteriogram on the woman apparently showed that this was a single bubble, so Cornell went in and tied off the carotid artery on that side. Some special pressure tests had shown that she should be able to tolerate this, but immediately after he had tied off the artery she developed almost total paralysis on one side. Cornell was sitting around the fourth-floor desk when I left this afternoon muttering and stewing half-aloud about whether maybe he should take her back upstairs and take the goddamned ligatures off again. Of course, if he does, the aneurysm is going to blow again soon sure as God made little apples, and that will be that for that good woman. It would be nice to think she might live for a while, even half-paralyzed. But Cornell probably won't sleep tonight at all. He's been known to sit there all night long going in and pricking a patient with pins at fifteen-minute intervals to find out if a paralysis of this sort is improving or not.

After having sweat out Barr for so long, I must say it's a breath of fresh air to be working now with Frank Gloucester, one of the most pleasant and even-tempered guys around the hospital. In the OR he's actually fun to work with; he seems to take the attitude that he'd rather have pleasant relations with people than unpleasant, although he admits that many surgeons feel there is a value in being unpleasant, that they get things done more efficiently that way. Gloucester was a GP for quite a time before he started this surgical residency, and expects to go back to practicing general surgery when he is finished here, I believe. And he'll probably be a whale of a success; he's a man of about forty-five, a striking-looking guy, tall, very thin, aquiline nose, very bright eyes, sandy gray hair. When I first met him I thought he was highly arrogant; since then, I've decided that this is just self-confidence. He's in an awkward position here, in a way, because all the staff men know he's been in practice, and knows a lot about medicine and surgery, and has actually done a lot of surgery as a GP; sometimes I feel that they are at a loss to know how to deal with him. But he seems to get along very nicely with everyone.

I barely see Barr any more, which suits me fine.

Thursday, February 16

I scrubbed at 8:00 Wednesday with Archie Everett on Mrs. Bellingham's leg. This was a classic example of what happens when you don't treat a fractured thigh properly when it's first broken. This woman broke her leg two and a half years ago, went to see Ike about it, and Ike did an open reduction—put in a little flimsy plate with four screws to hold it together. Subsequently the plate broke or the screws broke or something, and Mrs. Bellingham developed a nonunion of the fracture. Later she formed a phony joint there about four inches above her knee, so that she couldn't bend her knee more than 30 degrees without the phony joint beginning to bend, too. Somehow, she'd managed to walk on it, but the leg was pretty useless except for minimum support.

So now Ike had referred her to Archie to do something about it. I guess he had seen the woman some while back, in consultation, and recommended amputation of the leg and fitting a good prosthesis. Scared her away—she didn't want her leg whacked off. So now Everett had in mind putting in another plate of some kind instead.

I've heard it said that Everett sometimes looks brilliant in the OR and other times looks as though he doesn't know what the hell he's doing in there. This was one of *those* days, I guess. We went into the thigh through the big muscles in front, splitting them apart with blood spurting all over the place in order to get down to bone. Then he found this big overgrowth of bone the size of your fist above and below the phony joint. Ike's old plate was still in there, broken in half with some of the screws broken off, so Archie fiddled around a couple of hours just getting the present incumbent hardware out of there.

Then he took this new plate, which looked like half of a heavy barn-door hinge, and started chiseling away at the overgrown bone to get the plate to fit. *Whack, thump, crunch.* He didn't seem to have any better idea how to make that thing fit than I did; he worked up a fine sweat, and finally handed the hammer and chisel to me and said, "Here, Doc, you whack away at it for a while." So I chiseled away, and then Frank chiseled away, with chunks of callus flying in all directions, and finally we got the plate to fit at least so-so, and then went up to get some healthy bone chips from the pelvis to pack in around it. The whole procedure seemed just ridiculously crude, but the thigh bone actually looked pretty good once we got the plate screwed on. The woman must have lost two quarts of blood, but I guess Archie thought she had enough left to make out all right.

Spent the rest of Wednesday catching up on patients I'd missed the day before. Finally got to bed about midnight. Had a fine night's sleep up until 2:00 A.M., when I had to go up and see some whiner on Third who had had a thyroidectomy that day and was convinced that he was dying. In fact, he *insisted* he was dying, said he'd had a heart attack. He told this to the nurse and she said, "There, there, I'm sure you haven't," and told the supervisor, and the supervisor said, "There, there, go to sleep," and the man had insisted that he by God was dying and wanted the house doctor to be there to pronounce him. So I went up. I'm afraid I wasn't too sympathetic with this bird; he started giving me this malarkey about how he'd come here because everyone said the nursing care was so good, and how he had a lot of influence in this town, and how when he got home he was going to tell people just how lousy this hospital was, and blah, blah, blah, *blah*. All of which, of course, endeared him to me at 2:00 in the morning. I listened to his chest and then told him to shut up and go to sleep, and walked out.

Before I could get back to bed, a patient of John Gillies' turned up in the Emergency Room, a twenty-one-year-old girl who'd been vomiting and had diarrhea and belly pain. Her husband was a medical student over at the university, and he sort of hovered over me all through my examination. Don't know if he was afraid I was going to violate his wife then and there, or whether he was just clinically curious about what I was up to. I decided she had an acute case of GI flu and called up Gillies to tell him so. He was worried about the possibility of meningitis or polio, for some reason, so we put her to bed with some Luminal and a jug of water going into her, and she was feeling much better this morning.

That hung me up until well after 3:00 A.M. At 4:00 a coronary patient decided that the time had come for him to disobey orders and get up out of bed and go to the john, and since he was on strict coronary routine, this meant that an "unusual occurrence" report had to be made out, which meant that I had to go up and check him. Nothing wrong with *him*; if anything, he looked massively relieved. Probably hadn't had a bowel movement in a week.

By then a patient of Stern's had turned up by ambulance, a diabetic who had just gone home a week before on good control with insulin. Now Mrs. Downey was in a coma or shock, one or the other—convulsing, blue, choking, fibrillating, with her lungs full of water. I couldn't tell if she was in insulin shock or diabetic coma or heart failure, or which combination of these might be the best choice. I called Pete after I'd seen her, and poor Pete must really have been dead to the world; I'd say something on the phone, and there would be this long, long pause, and then he'd say, "Uh . . . what did you say?" So finally I gave up, ordered a slug of injectable digitalis on the woman, got a Levin tube down into her stomach and started pouring water down that, because she was bone-dry but couldn't hold still enough for an IV. I thought sure she was going to crap out on me any minute, but she didn't; she was still very much alive today. Stern said today he didn't know what was wrong with Mrs. Downey any more than I did, probably insulin shock compounded by heart failure. She had a blood sugar reading of 27 this morning, which is about as close to none at all as you can have and still be breathing.

Got back to bed again at 5:30. I'd forgotten that I'd told the operator to call me at 6:45, so she called me. I didn't have a scrub until 11:00, so I just rolled over and went back to sleep until 10:00. I was supposed to scrub with Cornell on a case of his, but Everett grabbed me when I stuck my nose in the OR to help him with a fracture case that had just come in, so Frank scrubbed with Cornell. We finished the fracture just as Cornell was coming out, bloody and sweating but unbowed, from his case, and he gave me hell for allowing myself to be seduced into helping somebody else when I was supposed to scrub with him on Thursday mornings. "If they try to get you to scrub with them on a Thursday morning again," he said, "tell them to go to hell." So next week I'll tell them to go to hell, I guess.

I've really gotten more kick out of scrubbing with Cal Cornell than with almost anybody else. At least he's got a little life, and he obviously takes joy in keeping people on their toes. He puts on this tyrant performance, acts like a real horror, but I'm convinced this is an act he deliberately puts on, mostly because it amuses him. Sort of a ridiculous parody of the "Horrible Surgeon" which he can get away with because he *is* a surgeon as well as one of the original clinic founders, and when you catch him at it he just gives you this cadaverous grin and says, "I'm really not so bad . . . when you get to know me." I've heard both Herring and Schwartz liked him a lot, too, so he's not singling me out for favor.

I managed to finesse an emergency scrub this afternoon. I was still working with Everett when they paged me to see a new patient with a perforated ulcer, so I passed down the word that I'd be tied up for a couple of hours. Somebody else saw her, and by the time I got free she was already on her way up to the OR, so I made myself scarce down in the bowels of the hospital somewhere, figuring that if they wanted me bad enough they could come and get me. They didn't, so I had time to catch up on rounds and admit a couple of preops for tomorrow and still get out of that place at just eight minutes after 5:00.

Friday, February 24

Yesterday was an interesting day, following the deadest duty weekend I've ever had, and a quiet week. Dr. Everett had a man with a slipped disc he was going to remove. He'd taken a myelogram on this man, and there was surely a big disc defect showing up on the films. Old Bloody Archie reached his sanguinous heights that day, I think. As always, he succeeded in achieving a lot of bleeding from down in this hole he'd dug in the patient's back. The blood kept welling up in the wound, and as always he kept muttering about having to operate in the bottom of an inkwell, but this time he couldn't seem to get the bleeding stopped enough to see a damned thing in there. Finally, he went down through pools of blood with his disc forceps, sort of poking his way in, and found what he interpreted as disc, and pulled it out. It must have *been* disc, too, but I don't know how he ever found it. The bleeding kept on and on; we worked for about an hour trying to get it stopped. Finally, Archie took a chunk of Gelfoam an inch long and two inches thick and jammed half of it, dry, down into the hole with his thumb, then quickly closed the guy up before the blood could soak up through the Gelfoam, and packed the guy down to his room pronto. I guess I looked horrified, because later Archie told me a *real* horror story about the time somebody (he didn't say who) inadvertently took a bite out of the abdominal aorta with the disc forceps thinking it was disc he had hold of, and had blood spurting all over the ceiling with *no* way to get it stopped.

Anyway, I checked the guy about every hour, expecting him to be going into shock, but he seemed to be happy as a clam and nothing dreadful came of it. Maybe the neurosurgeons are just too cautious.

Thursday night Miss Wood called me about 2:30 A.M. to come see a postoperative hydrocephalus patient of Dr. Ronzoni's who had just been admitted with a bad ear infection. This seemed to ring a bell, and sure enough, it was my old friend Mary Turner back in again. Mary had gone home after the surgery Ronzoni did to drain her hydrocephalus by means of a polyethylene tube into her mastoid area. Seems she had done poorly from the start, and then gotten infection in the ear; now she'd been running a temp of 103 for three days. Ronzoni thought it was probably a meningitis and asked me to do a spinal tap; I did and found her spinal fluid was full of pus. This afternoon Ronzoni took her up to the OR again and pulled the tube out. I gather this is a common complication of that sort of procedure: the patients get a nose and throat infection that goes to the ear, and from there up the polyethylene tube to the brain. So Mary is a very sick girl and may just not survive her meningitis at this point.

Tuesday, February 28

I'll be leaving day after tomorrow to go over to the Children's Division for two months of pediatrics. I can't pretend I'll be sorry to get off surgery; in fact, I hope I can have as little as possible to do with surgery for the rest of the year.

Mary Turner did not make it. She spiked a temp of up to 106 and

107 Saturday, and Luke Hamilton and Ronzoni spent the weekend keeping her in alcohol packs with fans blowing on her to keep the temp down. She started convulsing all the same, and then just went out. It's probably best; with that kind of temp cooking whatever brain cells she did have left in that quarter-inch cortex of hers, she would have been little more than a vegetable if she *had* survived. So Ronzoni will have to chalk this one up as an unfortunate failure of a procedure that might have been good if there weren't any microorganisms in the world. The spinal fluid culture showed that the girl died of pneumococcal meningitis.

Very few admissions today. One funny old man came in. He apparently had been chewing his dinner the other night and fractured his jaw in the process. He'd had a bone tumor removed from his jaw some four years ago, and apparently it had recurred, and this was a pathological fracture in the site of the new tumor. Painless to the point that he didn't even know his jaw was broken; he came in because people noticed that it was all askew. But the old man was pretty addled anyway; at first he told me he was ninety-nine years old, and then when I objected that he didn't look that old, he said maybe he was sixty-nine; he couldn't remember his name at all without considerable thought, and then wasn't sure he'd gotten the right one. I found myself in the midst of the sort of idiot conversation with him that Alice had with the White Queen. For some reason he didn't have any eyebrows, and I said, "What happened to your eyebrows?" He said, "What's the matter with them?" "Well, you haven't got any." He said, "Oh," and paused, then said, "Well, of course I haven't got any!" So we went round and round.

Of course, I had to end my stint on surgery with a bad taste in my mouth. There was a woman on Slater's service who had had surgery some months ago for carcinoma of the ovaries. Slater had found the disease spread all over, so he had taken out her adrenals, too, in hopes of slowing down the progress of the tumor. With replacement hormones she had limped along for a while, then started sharply downhill a few days ago: intestinal obstruction, metastases in her lungs which filled her chest up with fluid so she couldn't breathe, high fever, all sorts of things. I was called to see her Monday night, and I thought she was going out. Called Hank and asked if he had any magic medicine to pull out of the bag, and he said, no, he'd seen her that morning and just about tossed in the sponge, didn't see anything more to do. He suggested I ask Randy Brock to see her if she was really in desperate straits.

So I called Brock to see her, and she died about the time he got there. Next morning the pathologist remarked that it was too bad nobody had bothered to try draining fluid from her chest, that if they had, she might have made it long enough for the adrenal surgery to have had some palliative effect—in other words, if the people who had been taking care of her had been vigorous about doing everything that could be done, instead of tossing in the sponge, she might at least have had *some* comfortable time left.

Well, I've thought about it. Call it what you will, this was a case neither Hank nor Randy had fought for; Hank, especially, had decided that studied neglect was best, and had followed that course. In this case the studied neglect had cheated this woman perhaps of weeks or months. I don't suppose you can blame Hank, yet this case seems to me to illustrate something that happens to me and to other doctors, too, when they are dealing with patients who seem to be very, very sick. It's almost as if we let ourselves be stampeded into hopelessness.

I know the night that Stern's diabetic woman, Mrs. Downey, came in she looked as if she was just falling apart at the seams, all of them at once. And she *was* sick, and I was disgusted with Pete because he couldn't wake up enough to come dashing over and take the load off my shoulders, because I honestly thought that Mrs. Downey was going to expire any minute, and there I would be with the responsibility on my hands. Well, she didn't die any minute— she hasn't died yet and doesn't look like she's going to. Now, later, I know that she had no more wrong with her than insulin shock (treatable) and mild heart failure (treatable), and I let myself misinterpret and exaggerate what I saw to the point that I all but tossed in the sponge on her, and she might well have died then if I had.

I think Hank did about the same thing in this woman's case. He assumed too easily that her cancer was beyond all hope, and although he agreed with Slater that her adrenals should be removed as a proper surgical procedure a couple of weeks ago, he just gave up on her in his mind when she didn't immediately jump out of bed and scream whoopee. I think he was stampeded into hopelessness by his own expectations of what probably was going to happen rather than a steady, careful, clinical evaluation of the case predicated on the single assumption that *she was going to make it* until she proved otherwise, not just by getting worse or by being in the process of dying, but by *being dead,* and *that* was the time to quit working.

I don't know, but I wonder if it is *ever* right for a doctor to throw in the sponge on a patient. I wonder if it is ever right for a doctor to quit doing things for a patient because he has become convinced that she is going to die anyway. You can not only be fooling yourself in your interpretation of what you see, but also, if you allow yourself to throw in the sponge, you are robbing the patient right then of the only chance she has, namely, the chance the doctor can give her by fighting for her down to and beyond the last ditch.

I think with cancer patients this is more of a problem, and more of an obligation for the doctor, than with almost anyone else. The surgeons deal with cancer more than anyone else in medicine, and to a man they are happy enough to undertake surgical attack on the disease. But too damned many of them flatly reject the patient in their minds the moment they come back with a recurrence, as though they are blaming the patient for having the recurrence. And this is not only unfair, since the patient can't help it, but it's neglecting a duty you assume when you take the patient on in the first place. If you don't want to handle that kind of a dirty job, you shouldn't take the patient on to begin with.

Well, enough of that. I don't know the answer, and other doctors do it as well as surgeons, though not so many. It may be that I should have to make the decision myself a few times before I start feeling too self-righteous about it; I just don't know.

I don't know what to anticipate in going over to the Children's Division day after tomorrow, either. Maybe that's why I'm feeling so gloomy. I think I've been having less and less difficulty running into problems here that I just couldn't handle. The things you do for this crisis or that one have become pretty much of a routine. Of course, there have been a couple of cases that just left me at a total, hand-wringing loss, but for the most part I've managed pretty well in recent months. Now I'm going on to a new place, a new outlook on things, a totally different kind of patient, and I suppose I'll have the same massive insecurity there that I had when I started off the first of the year here, until I get onto the tricks of the pediatric trade.

In this connection, I had a call today from a doctor named Wallace Bernstein at the Children's Division, the senior pediatric resident over there, soon to become an attending man on the staff in charge of the intern and resident training program. He called to say I'd be expected there at 8:00 Thursday morning for orientation, bunking-in and what not, and asked if I had any questions. I said no, except that I had practically no knowledge whatever of pediatric drug dosages, special pediatric procedures, or what I would be expected to do when I got there. He laughed and said, "Well, that's what we're supposed to teach you, isn't it?" So I guess they anticipate a certain amount of dullness when we first get there. The change will be welcome; I think I'll enjoy working with kids, even if some of the procedures are difficult to do—I've heard you have to do dozens of spinal taps on babies, which I can't look forward to with any great enthusiasm—but in general I'm looking forward to it.

Sat around at midnight supper last night chatting with Mort Silver, and he passed on a real gem of medical speculation. He said when he was a rifleman during the war he and an army engineer had calculated that if a man's head were knocked off instantaneously by a 105-mm. howitzer shell, the man would squirt a column of blood eight feet into the air for a period of three and a half seconds. Now there is something to think about.

V

Pediatrics

Five months at a stretch on surgery was too much. Two months on Pediatrics at the Children's Division was not nearly enough. The change from the crowded general hospital to the bright, airy corridors of the Children's Division was like a breath of fresh air; so also was the change in people, the change of patients and the change of job I found there. I liked pediatrics, and my taste for the work shows clearly in the journal entries for March and April. On surgery the intern was nobody, a body in the operating room. At the Children's Division the care of patients from beginning to end depended heavily on the interns. Here, perhaps for the first time, was the sense of fulfillment, the sense of *participating*, that had been missing for so long.

Everything on the pediatric service was not pleasant, by any means. There is probably nothing more dreadful than a truly sick child; the Children's Division was full of them. Some got well, some merely lingered, some died. Looking back now, I suspect that the tragedies outweighed the triumphs during those two months. Many stories had unhappy endings. But from my pediatric service I learned a respect for the courage and bravery of those "little people" we were treating, and for the patient men who engage in their care, which has endured to this day.

THE JOURNAL, MARCH AND APRIL

Thursday, March 1

Yesterday, February 29, was my last day on Surgery III, and leave it to me to draw Leap Year for my internship and then get stuck with the extra day on a surgical service. We had breakfast with Andy, at which Andy did a good deal of whining about how tough it was on all the attending doctors to have a short-handed house staff. I not only had trouble feeling adequately sorry for the poor fellows; I had trouble listening at all. I just felt pretty detached from it all, since I was moving on to the Children's Division so soon.

After breakfast I went up to scrub on a leg amputation with Mel Tanner, then made rounds with him, and spent the afternoon working up new admissions, and that was the day. The only call I had during the night was to see my old friend Mrs. Hammerman, who was back in the house because she had just had a baby, and was complaining of pain in her belly. At first I thought the nurse had the name wrong, but it was the same Mrs. Hammerman. I went up to see her, and she was her usual forlorn self, looked like the weight of the world was on her shoulders. But she *had* had a baby, and even managed a smile on the strength of that. Probably having a baby around the house will do more to help her ills than anything else, particularly if it screams all night. It might get her mind off her colon and onto something else, which couldn't help but be a big improvement. Her belly pain sounded like gall bladder colic to me, and according to her chart, X-rays had shown she has a gall bladder full of rocks, so it figured. Peterson has been working on her for years to have her gall bladder out, but so far apparently has never gotten through. I wrote for some nitroglycerin for the pain, and patted her on the head and told her in my most sincere voice that *everything* was going to be *all right,* and went back to bed. Didn't hear from her again that night, so I guess she believed me.

Thursday morning at 6:45 I walked across the street to the Children's Division, a brand-new, modern building, with 180 beds solely for children from infancy on up to age fourteen or so. Each of the other major hospitals contributes interns to Children's for their pediatrics training, so I was expecting to have the company of an intern or two each from County Hospital, St. Christopher's and so on.

The reports about intern duty there have been varied. Hamilton seemed to like it a lot, Schwartz wasn't unhappy with it, and Alec didn't mind it. Roscoe didn't like it at all, but then Roscoe doesn't seem to like anything at all, most times. Apparently the Children's Division has all sorts of odd little rules arising from the way it is organized. Unlike Graystone this is primarily a charity operation; although it has private, paying patients, at least 50 percent of the beds are reserved for house patients who are treated at little or no cost. The Division claims that it will turn away no child that needs to be hospitalized from anywhere in the state, and it has patients coming in from all over.

When I got to the place I announced myself to the lady at the information desk, stored my bags out of the way and went down for a little breakfast, waiting for 8:00 to arrive. Dr. Bernstein, the senior resident who had telephoned me, met me and the interns from the other hospitals down there and took us up to the house staff quarters on the fourth floor. They're on the northeast side of the hospital, looking out across the valley toward the mountains to the north. There is a very modern lounge with picture windows across the whole wall, a big coffeemaker and—wonder of wonders— a refrigerator well stocked with soda, bread, mayonnaise and cold cuts! The interns' five-bed dormitory is right next door to the lounge, also with a picture window and very nicely appointed. There are lockers for each of us, a big shower room and john, and a little room adjacent to the lounge where the interns on duty can sack out so they don't wake the whole dorm when they get called. Dr. Bernstein told us a little bit about the Division's organization, handed out our floor assignments, and then took us on a grand tour of the building from top to bottom. I don't remember half of what I saw, but I did see the different floors and found out where the elevators were.

My first assignment is going to be on the third floor, East Wing, a mixed medical and surgical floor with some house patients and some private. Not an unpleasant atmosphere, but I felt the old apprehension about diving into a new place again. I guess I never have liked changes particularly. I was uncomfortable most of the morning, especially nervous at the thought of working back to back with interns from other hospitals, all of whom looked far more competent and sure of themselves than I felt, and a little concerned about what might suddenly be dropped in my lap.

Bernstein relieved us of that worry, at least; he told us that we would have our own responsibilities, to be sure, but that the residents would be working with us very closely on everything. For instance, when an outpatient is brought in to the Emergency Room at any time, day or night, the intern checks the patient first, but the resident must also check the patient before any decision is made. To me this sounds like a splendid way to learn; the intern is not left with his bare ass hanging out in the wind, nor likely to pull any really bad blunders, yet at the same time he has the opportunity to make up his own mind about what he thinks is wrong and what he thinks should be done about it, and then see how his ideas stack up with what the resident thinks.

After lunch I got my first taste of what is going to be a real plague around this place: starting IVs. At the Children's Division the interns are expected to do a lot of the time-consuming scut work that the nurses take care of at the main hospital. We are expected to start all IVs, to start all hypodermoclyses and to draw all blood samples for lab work. So at 12:30 the nurse on 3-East called to announce that I had an IV to start on a year-old baby and a blood sample to draw.

The IV turned out to be a real bitch; this little boy had to be totally immobilized in a sheet before I could even get hold of his arm, and he had the tiniest veins imaginable. I tried to get a 22-gauge needle into one and soon found that the needle was bigger than the vein was. I got it in all right, but the IV immediately infiltrated. Finally, at the nurse's recommendation, I tried one of the little "airplane needles" that are specially made for children's IVs, a tiny little needle with a flat metal plate attached to help stabilize it against the baby's skin. Finally got one of these precariously into a foot vein and got the IV running very, very slowly. But when I looked in an hour later it was running much more rapidly, even had to be slowed down some. Apparently the vein had gone into spasm from the needle, and then presently opened up again.

This and a hypodermoclysis took me a full hour and a half of hard work. The clysis wasn't so bad—you just stick the needle down into the fat pad on the baby's thigh and tape it in place, so that the clysis fluid can run in to be absorbed by the soft tissue in the leg. But drawing the blood sample was something else again. This was on an eight-month-old kid with no veins that I could find at all, and the lab needed at least 5 cc of blood. So I waited until the resident could come and coach me in doing an external jugular tap on this kiddie.

Well, I guess I'll get used to it, but I think you have to be pretty damned sure that they really need the blood drawn, and there just isn't any other way to get it, because a jugular tap is about the most grisly procedure I've run across yet. You mummy the kiddie up in a blanket so he can't wiggle, then lay him on his back on a table and tip his head back over the edge, turning it to one side. Then you start pinching the kid until he howls, if he isn't howling already. It's essential that he be screaming at the top of his lungs, because then his external jugular vein bulges out in his neck so that you can see it and feel it very well.

I got the needle into the vein without too much difficulty, but in the middle of things the child stopped crying, the vein collapsed, and the blood immediately stopped running into the syringe. So I snapped his skull a couple of times and pinched him to start him crying again, and finally got the rest of the blood. The resident stood by while I did it, coaching me very matter-of-factly; he even seemed amused at my reluctance to go plunging this two-inch-long needle into this baby's neck. Yet he seemed very gentle with the child, and when I was finished he picked the kiddie up and cuddled him for a while. There was no sense of rush; he waited until the child was happy and gurgling again before we left the room. Later he said, "That's the most important part of the whole procedure, as far as I'm concerned. If you have to do the one, you've got the time to do the other."

This guy's name is Shenk—Joe Shenk—a short, heavy-set, dark-haired fellow who wears horn-rimmed glasses and a big, wide pawnbroker's smile, good-natured but not disgustingly good-na-tured. He's very busy, apparently, covering 3-West as well as 3-East, but I think we'll get along well. He has one peculiar quality that I've noticed in a number of very good doctors: he may be busy as hell, just rushed off his feet, but when he's with you, he's *with* you, not off wool-gathering somewhere else. And when he's with you on some question or problem, he gives you the impression (true or not) that there is absolutely no rush whatever, that he's ready and willing to spend all day, if necessary, getting things straightened out. Or if he is rushed, he says so, and says why. To one question I asked him he said point-blank, "I haven't got the time to give you a good answer to that now, so let's set it aside for a while. We'll come back to it." And I bet we do, too, without my reminding him.

After that in the afternoon I had two admissions to work up—a far cry from the ten or twelve surgical admissions I've been used to, but these were pediatric work-ups: full medical work-ups involving a massively detailed history of the child from conception on, taken from the parents. The first patient came in at 2:00 as an emergency, a little boy three months old with a congenital heart defect of some sort, who had been in the hospital three or four times before during his short life. The last time he had come in with congestive heart failure; now he was in again, coughing and very cyanotic when he coughed, turning almost black all over with every coughing spell. I took a quick look at him and sucked a lot of gook out of his airway and put him into an oxygen tent on the spot. He pinked up pretty well in there and stopped coughing. The history was very confusing; he hadn't had a heart catheterization yet, and I never did learn exactly what kind of defect the Experts thought he had, but obviously it was allowing blood to by-pass the lungs, whatever it was, and the child was in heart failure as well.

I was writing up the history and physical examination when Shenk came by to see the child, so we sat down and discussed what to do about him. He showed me how to set up the initial orders on the chart the way they like them set up there, and then let me tell him what I thought should be done: oxygen, digitalis, other things to get the failure under control first thing, then later a chest X-ray and EKG and so forth. Shenk agreed with just about everything, except he thought the digitalis dose was too small and that we should increase it. So we got those things set up.

The other patient was a baby with a severe eczema he'd had for most of his life—he's eight months old. Shenk and I interviewed the parents together to get the history. The child has had a long-standing eczema, gastrointestinal upsets all the time, apparently some underlying infection process that hasn't been determined (he'd once had an abscess in his thigh, followed by boils all over him), some lesion in the lung that hasn't been diagnosed—a very strange history. We then looked at the kiddie, and he was really a mess, a forlorn, weeping, scratching little creature, just covered all over with this dry, scaly eczema that he scratches until it bleeds and oozes and cakes and then gets infected and full of pus. About the only part of him that wasn't caked was some scraggly hair growing out of the top of this mess, and two sad blue eyes looking out at us. He wailed all through the examination.

Again, I sat down with Shenk and we talked over a program for the kid. He listened to me, too; I even talked him out of smearing anything greasy on the eczema. He had wanted to put on some kind of bland ointment on it, but everything we could think of had some sort of medication or another in it, and it seemed to me we would do better to use warm moist packs on the raw parts and let the rest of it dry up, just put his arms in restraints to keep him from scratching it for a day or so until we got our feet on the ground and found out what was going on. Shenk agreed to this. The boy—his name is Joey McCarran—is going to be in the hospital for quite a while, in any event; this has been going on for so long that it's just not going to clear up by magic. Also, there's a good likelihood of a psychosomatic element in the eczema. He's got a real nervous mother, and a little pipsqueak of a father who kept trying desperately to give us a history while the mother kept interrupting and contradicting every other sentence.

Again, I wrote the initial orders on this child. Both Joey and the heart patient are house patients, so Shenk and I have major responsibility for their care, with a pediatrician named Louis de Shaw assigned as attending man. He will be in making rounds with us tomorrow morning.

At least I've been slightly initiated, and it looks like this will be an interesting service, with lots to learn and not so much pressure that you can't learn some of it. So far the pace seems positively leisurely, none of the constant rush we had over at the main hospital nor the constant screaming for me over the loudspeaker. It's also going to be delightful having my patients assigned to me according to floor rather than by doctor, so that all my patients will be located in one discrete area of the hospital, and I'll have the same crew of nurses to deal with. I think it will be a very pleasant setup all around. Who knows, I may even have some time to read some pediatrics, too. I hope so. I got off at 5:30 today, and it looks as though I will get off pretty much on time on most of my off-duty nights here. Again, I hope so.

Friday, March 2

This was my "businessman's day" that comes once every two weeks, an 8:00-to-5:00 day. I got over to Children's at 7:30, went up to quarters and showered and shaved and drank a cup of coffee. Got down to 3-East about 7:40.

Found one blood sample waiting to be drawn on a baby there, one of two new admissions that had come in during the night. One was a child with a violent skin reaction following the measles. The other was an infant admitted because of vomiting and diarrhea. White, the intern opposite me, had worked them up; both were private patients and both seemed under pretty good control.

This seemed to be pretty much of a typical day, the way I suppose the days here are going to go. I went to get blood from the child who has had vomiting and diarrhea for two or three weeks now and is seriously dehydrated. The lab needed blood to measure salt and potassium depletion, so I had another jugular tap to do. I tried on both sides, and got the needle into the vein each time but couldn't get enough blood on either side, so finally I took it from a scalp vein. The whole business took me almost an hour; I hope I get more proficient at this after a while.

After that I went over to make rounds with Shenk and de Shaw, the attending man, a thin, middle-aged, good-natured pediatrician. We saw patients on 3-West first, then came back around to 3-East to see our congenital heart case and the boy with the eczema. De Shaw recommended a consultant in dermatology for Joey. The boy's face had cleared up a little bit just from the moist packs overnight, and he looked a lot better, but he didn't like having his arms restrained worth a damn. He just sat and glowered at us from under his scabs; he wanted to *scratch*, was what *he* wanted to do, and to hell with us doctors.

The baby with the heart lesion was coming out of his failure this morning, and looking better, too, breathing more freely in the oxygen tent and looking remarkably pink. After rounds were over I went down to the library and looked over the textbook descriptions of the kinds of congenital heart defects that can cause this off-and-on "blue baby" type of cyanosis, and there are several things this baby might have wrong. Very few of them are correctable at all, and the ones that are have appalling mortality rates under surgery. For instance, Shenk said that if the child has a transposition of the great vessels, they just wouldn't consider operating on him out here. They might do it in Philadelphia or Boston, even without a heart-lung machine, but even there they have an 80 percent mortality rate and then only rarely get a good result on the 20 percent that survive the operation at all. On some of the other things, there's just nothing at all that anybody can do, and nobody will even tackle them. Shenk seemed pretty gloomy about this child's prospects and so did de Shaw, but personally I think a diagnosis ought to be established, and fast, to find out if the child's defect is even remotely operable before anybody tosses in the sponge. He's certainly going to die the way he's going, and very soon too, probably.

[*Post hoc:* During the years since that was written, the strides taken in this area have been amazing. Today this same baby might well be operated here, with open-heart techniques and a modern heart-lung machine to sustain circulation and oxygen supply during surgery. Operative mortality may be as low as 25 percent, with an 80 percent chance of at least improving things for the 75 percent who survive surgery. And this we have to hand to the pediatrician-surgeon teams such as those at this hospital who were probing their way through to answers at the time I was there.]

After rounds Shenk and I had a cup of coffee with de Shaw, and then I worked on the ward until lunchtime, taking care of multiple little problems. The intern does everything in this place: I started a couple of clyses, put a tuberculin skin test on a baby's arm, redressed a minor burn and so forth. At 1:00 there was a surgical conference for the interns, dealing with the preoperative medications they like to use on children here, and also discussing acute respiratory emergencies, and how to recognize them and what to do about them. A kiddie doesn't have much reserve when something blocks his airway; sometimes you do a tracheostomy (cutting an artificial air hole in the windpipe to permit unobstructed breathing) on the spot to get air into a child's lungs or he'll be dead in five minutes—which means the intern may have to decide that it is indicated then and there, and then do it. A grisly thought, and it just scares the hell out of me to think of it, but that's the way it is. [*Post hoc:* It still just scares the hell out of me to think of it, but that's still the way it is.]

Back on the ward there was another new patient admitted because of persistent vomiting. All the children on 3-East are under two years old, and this seems to be a favorite affliction in that age group. This kiddie was twenty months old; he'd been vomiting for two days and now was bone-dry and spiking a fever, but no diarrhea. I couldn't get much from the mother to go on; he had just started throwing up after every feeding for some reason, with some vomiting in between feedings. But when I went in to examine him, I was sure he had some degree of neck rigidity and some other signs of meningeal irritation. So I went to find Shenk and asked him to check the child and see if he found anything significant in the stiff neck. He said, "Oh, yeah, the kid's doctor thought he saw it too. He wants us to do an LP (lumbar puncture) first thing."

I did the spinal tap with Shenk holding the child still. It was incredibly simple to do. The spinal fluid looked clear, and the microscopic count showed no sign of pus cells, so I don't know what we're dealing with here. Maybe the child has an early meningitis, or even polio, or maybe just one of these nonspecific middle-ear infections that sometimes cause signs of meningeal irritation. No sure way of telling at this stage of the game; we'll have to see.

After I got that under control for the moment, the nurses had four or five little odds and ends for me to check. One baby's lab reports were back, showing that he needed extra salt, extra potassium and extra water, and he wasn't taking any fluids at all by mouth. I called his pediatrician and we planned a treatment program, to get water and electrolytes in by clysis if possible. I think I'm going to learn a lot about electrolyte balance with these kiddies. I'm also going to have responsibility. The first thing this doctor said when I had read the lab reports to him was, "Well, what do you think the child needs?" And aside from having dosages slightly off, he went along with what I thought.

Over a week since I've recorded anything here—a weekend on duty last weekend and only two week nights off since, and too tired to dictate anything those nights. I was wrong about the pace; this has turned out to be one hell of a busy week, at least as busy as the two months I spent on Medicine at the beginning of the year. It isn't so much the influx of patients—I've been averaging perhaps three to five new admissions per day, with a total inventory of about twenty-five kiddies between the ages of six months and two years on 3-East. This shouldn't be a bad load, except for all the time-consuming tidbits of scut work the interns have to do here, which really fill the day.

But the back-breakers are the nights and duty weekends. Every call night so far the page has started sounding off for me right at 5:00, before dinner, and I've worked straight through, and worked *hard,* until at least midnight without any break. One night it just kept on all night long; I didn't even get to lie down. Not only the patients in the house, but the "drop-ins," as they call the outpatients. It's just incredible the number of mothers who sit around watching their sick babies all day long without even thinking of calling the doctor, and then panic about midnight, become convinced that the little darlings aren't going to survive the night, and pack them frantically over to the Children's Division Emergency Room for the doctor to see them—a steady stream of them from 1:00 A.M. on. I've tried to find out from some of these mothers what the hell they were waiting for all day long, and invariably they insist that "he just seemed to get suddenly worse," but then can't say exactly *how* he seemed to get suddenly worse.

Anyway, we have been running on this service, so far. My opposite number is White, who is assigned to 3-West and 2-East, so on call nights I cover 3-East-and-West and 2-East; two other interns, both from St. Christopher's, cover 1-East, 1-West and 2-East between them; Harry Muldoon is on with me on call nights, and is becoming sort of my buddy. He doesn't get any more sleep than I do on call nights. Muldoon is a great big, hulking, wild-haired bird with cauliflower ears (he used to box Golden Gloves as a heavyweight or something) and a permanent look of menace on his face. He looks so dull and malevolent that my first impression on meeting him was, "Aw, you're kidding!" and I still think if I were a parent with a sick eight-month-old baby on my hands and saw this brute coming at him I'd snatch up the child, scream and run for cover. But Muldoon, I'm learning, is neither dull nor malevolent. I guess he can't help how his face looks. He isn't clumsy either, even though he just about completely covers a wee one with his paw when he goes to examine it.

The other intern, who was supposed to keep our load light, got hurled out of this place about the third day he was here. If Muldoon is ugly, this guy was beautiful, a regular Dr. Kildare type, very smooth, very polite, very complimentary to all the nurses—except that he immediately started giving everybody in the hospital trouble, refused to answer his pages during the day, sat up all night on duty nights studying for his National Boards and just not responding to the telephone and generally ignoring his job. After three days of this Bernstein got his gut full of this guy and threw him out. He has the distinction of being the first intern ever to be canned at the Children's Division.

Most of the patients on my floor have seemed to fall into three general categories. Most common illness is upper respiratory infection of some sort, which can include ear infections, tonsilitis, or laryngitis, or laryngotracheitis, or laryngo-tracheo-bronchitis or pneumonia—just lots of these, and a bad kind of illness for small ones. Then there are the ones with gastroenteritis of some sort or another, with vomiting and diarrhea and the resulting dehydration and electrolyte imbalance. The doctors have usually tried to treat those at home (just as they have the URIs), and so the ones that get to the hospital are the tough ones. With all these kiddies we have to watch out for the communicable diseases—the measles and mumps and German measles—all the time. And then there are the ones with meningitis of one sort or another, which is just all too frequent. Anyway, these are the problems of the bulk of my patients here, and most of these are isolation cases because they're related to infection.

On call nights I've encountered some of the other residents. Roger Pfeiffer is over from County pediatric residency, a pleasant guy but not very approachable. Terry Stone is a great, tall, lanky guy with a very loud, nasal voice and the bad tendency to lecture to you any time a question comes up. He is so convinced that he knows everything there is to know about pediatrics that the other residents laugh at him, which doesn't seem to slow him down any. I get along with him pretty well, but wish he would relax and come off it about half the time.

Finally, there is Saul Weiner, the senior pediatric resident under Bernstein, a little, short, skinny guy who is said to be the brain of the place. He also has a very short temper and a strong tendency to shoot his mouth off, one of these guys who is utterly contemptuous of all attending men at the Division, no matter who they are, and who believes that every child in the hospital is being improperly treated in one way or another. He works hard, but that kind of perfection is hard to get along with.

Most of these days I've started off at 8:00 A.M. on the ward, going over the Cardex order file on all the patients with the morning nurse. This was Ann's suggestion, and it seems to work very well. The nurse briefs me to start with on the problems of the day—that I have to draw blood on this one, that I have some nose and throat cultures to take, that I have this thing to look at and that thing to check: so-and-so has a temperature, and so-and-so farted, and so-and-so spit up his dinner—that sort of thing. Then I dig into this little heap of detail until de Shaw turns up for rounds.

And I'm still trying to get used to these procedures, because we have such tiny victims. I'm beginning to manage some of them better now; I can do an external jugular tap very nicely most times, without any trouble getting blood for lab studies. I can occasionally get blood from a femoral artery in the real little ones if I'm careful about it. I've done a number of LPs, and find that with children this age they are just pea soup, nothing to them at all. Kiddies have only about a quarter of an inch between their outside skin and their spinal canal; I get a heavy-handed nurse to bundle them up and hold them still on the bed with their knees up under their chin and their backs toward me, and find the right interspace between the lower vertebrae with my finger, and then rest two fingers, one above and one below the vertebral column, to use as guides, and run the needle in between them, *pop*, and there I am. I haven't gotten a bloody tap yet. We do a lot of LPs, too, lots more than I had imagined, because meningitis is such a major concern in kiddies this age.

The child with the heart lesion went home yesterday. Heart failure was under control, and the digitalis dose was adjusted, and at Cardiac Clinic, after a long discussion, the Experts decided not even to try to catheterize the child to make the diagnosis unless it survives to be six months old. Their reasoning was that the chances of the catheterization proving an operable lesion were practically nil, and the catheterization itself was too risky unless the kiddie got bigger and stronger first. It seemed like a cold-blooded decision to me. It was also a good example of an odd thing that turns up in some tough areas of medicine: the principle of minority rule and individual veto. This clinic consists of four of the top pediatric cardiologists in the area, plus three crack pediatric surgeons, all of whom reviewed this child's case. Finally, they registered a vote on whether to catheterize or not; two of the surgeons and two of the pediatricians were in favor; one surgeon and two pediatricians objected. So the minority won. Later Shenk said that in a case like that a single opposing vote would have effectively vetoed catheterization; they won't move unless they have unanimous agreement. They might try to convince the dissenter, but if one man felt strongly enough that this was an unjustifiable risk, the rest wouldn't override him.

Anyway, the kiddie is breathing, and not too purple outside of oxygen, and going home. For the time being. Joey McCarran, the lad with eczema, is clearing up his eczema, all right; he just hates everybody is the trouble. We've tried and tried to get next to that child, and he will have none of us. Nor of his parents. He just sits like a little gnome and glares at you. I've almost got Shenk convinced we should have a psychiatric consultation, though how a psychiatrist consults on an eight-month-old baby is beyond me.

Had an interesting case come in yesterday, just a good illustration of how resilient some of these youngsters are. This little boy was brought in by ambulance, and the nurse in the emergency room called me that the child was practically dead, from diarrhea. And she was right. I'd never realized what a roaring diarrhea can do to a fourteen-month-old child. This one had had it for just two days. His name is Jerry Johnson, and he looked like a corpse when I got down there: skin pasty white, his eyes sunk way down in his head and tipped up so you could just see the rim of the whites, so close to unconscious he could barely respond at all, and the skin on his abdomen so dry it was just hanging on him in folds.

I did a cutdown on an ankle vein first thing, didn't even fool around looking for a jugular, since the child had to get water into him fast. Got blood drawn for electrolytes from the cutdown, and started hydrating him. The lab sent back the electrolyte reports in about two hours, and Shenk and I planned the IV fluids and electrolytes he would need to replace what he had lost, and started him off; I went by to check him about every hour all night to make sure he was still alive. And this afternoon, just twenty-four hours after admission, Jerry was up and around, sitting up in a high chair, beating hell out of it with a tablespoon and having a good time. All he needed was salt, potassium and water, and he got it and perked right up. Just a little more dramatic evidence of how important electrolyte balance is. I think that child had about another hour to live when he first came in if he hadn't been treated.

We had planned to go somewhere or do something this weekend, but after Thursday and Friday nights on, and up almost all night both nights, we've scratched it. I'm just going to sleep.

Friday, March 16

I've had a couple of diagnostic coups this week, which were gratifying. One was on a little fourteen-month-old girl named Audrey Carter who came in early in the week with an FUO (fever of unknown origin). Her doctor at home had thought she had bronchitis, and had been treating her with penicillin for about four days, but she hadn't been getting any better. When she came in she looked really sick; she had a temp of 105, and when I examined her I found she had a very stiff neck and didn't want to bend her knees up, and screamed whenever I tried to move her head. Very sore-looking eardrums on both sides, all right, and a red throat, but when I did an LP, I found her spinal fluid was very cloudy. I made a stained smear of it, after sending some down for culture, and found the spinal fluid loaded with a Gram-negative bacteria that looked very, very much like Hemophilus influenzae. This is an uncommon organism to cause meningitis, but a sneaky and dangerous one. Pneumococcus and meningococcus cause a more fulminating disease, but at least they both turn off with penicillin; Hemophilus isn't touched by penicillin.

I couldn't get hold of Shenk right then, but I knew we'd have to get this girl IV fluids, maybe for days, so I got the afternoon nurse to help me do a cutdown. I found the vein in the ankle, all right, but when I went to nick it, it seemed to go into spasm, and I worked and worked trying to get that damned polyethylene catheter into this tiny, tiny, tiny vein, and finally just macerated it trying. Shenk stuck his head in to see how I was doing about then, so he took a look, and poked around a little, and came up with a big fat vein—the one I had thought I had. I just had a tiny skin capillary. So this time when I nicked it, the catheter went in very nicely, and that cutdown has been running twenty-four-hour IVs into Audrey for four days without any sign of getting troublesome. We started her on IV chloramphenicol and IV sulfadiazine, two antibacterials that seem to hit Hemophilus pretty well, and she's responding nicely: temp is down, neck not so stiff, and her spinal fluid clearing. She will probably be in the hospital another six or eight days before she is up and around, but I felt good about her. That was one I picked up and diagnosed strictly on my own, without any coaching from anybody.

But I guess with every good one you've got to get a bad one to match it, just to keep you from feeling too smart. I'd been feeling pretty cocky about fluid and electrolyte treatment of these kiddies we've been seeing with vomiting and diarrhea—there seems to be a viral GI infection in the area that's hitting kiddies—until a little fifteen-month-old-lad named Johnny Beck turned up day before yesterday and delivered me my worst jolt in six months. This lad, a cute little towheaded boy, had just had diarrhea, no vomiting, but he looked in just about as bad shape as Jerry Johnson had when he came in. Shenk saw him with me at admission and told me I should handle the case all by myself unless I got into trouble. So I got electrolyte levels from the lab and then calculated how much water and how much salt the child needed for maintenance in the next twenty-four hours, and how much he needed in addition to make up the deficit, and planned out his fluids and electrolytes for the first twenty-four hours and about 4:00 in the afternoon started an IV on him and began treatment.

Everything went real well; he seemed to perk up as soon as some water got into him, and began complaining that he was thirsty, so I told the nurses they could give him small amounts of sugar water by mouth, too, if he wanted it. But by morning he didn't look so good, and by 2:00 that afternoon he was in trouble. The nurses paged me and said that Johnny Beck was acting very peculiarly; I went down to his room and found him twitching—hands, feet, arms, legs, all jerking spasmodically, almost like a generalized convulsion. He was not breathing very well, and I could feel his liver way down to his navel. I tried to listen to his chest, but he couldn't hold still enough for me to hear anything, yet I heard enough to be pretty sure he was in heart failure, and getting worse.

Well, I called Shenk. I was really scared, and didn't know what was happening. The other kid had come right around on this treatment; this lad was getting sicker by the minute. Joe came down, and checked him over, and we tried running some calcium gluconate into his IV to see if this would stop the twitching, but it didn't change it a bit. Then we tried some concentrated salt solution, and that didn't stop the twitching either. Then Shenk wanted to know how much total volume of water had gone into the boy in the twenty-two hours, and I checked and found the nurses had been giving him "sips" almost all night—with my blessing—and he had very possibly gotten twice as much plain old water in him as he should have. So we cut off his IV and cut off all fluids by mouth for eight hours. Sure enough, as soon as the IV was stopped, he seemed to perk up a little; we gave him a shot of sodium Amytal, which put him to sleep for a while and stopped the twitching, and by midnight we were able to pull the IV altogether and give him carefully rationed fluids by mouth alone. And this morning he was going on all cylinders: liver receding, breathing fine, no more diarrhea.

So by hindsight I knew what I had done wrong: I'd just incautiously loaded him with water, too much water, and he'd gone into heart failure because of so much fluid going into his circulation in a short time, and began having low-salt convulsions. It just gave me a hell of a jolt. Of course, as soon as we corrected what I'd done wrong, he did fine, but in the meantime he had nearly conked out on me. It shook Shenk up, too, but he just shook his head and said, "Well, I guess you have to learn somehow." I guess somehow I do, but that's one mistake I don't think I'll ever make again.

Just to back that one up, I had another patient come in last night that I missed completely, too. This was a child brought in about 2:00 in the morning, with a history of diarrhea for a couple of days, and then suddenly blood with the diarrhea. The mother was a registered nurse who gave me one of these detailed clinical histories that are so difficult to interpret. These girls know too much, yet they don't know enough; they think they're telling you everything that's significant, but they tell you a lot of insignificant things and often miss what is really significant, and they can really fool you. Try as I would, for instance, I couldn't get any objective notion from this mother how much blood the child had passed. Anyway, the history didn't sound too alarming, and when I examined the child I wasn't impressed that he was in any great trouble; certainly didn't think he had a surgical abdomen.

This was a private patient, so I called the pediatrician and told him I didn't think there was anything to worry about. Fortunately, he came in anyway; saw the child and felt its belly and said, "Well, maybe it's changed since you checked him, but I think this baby has an acute belly. Probably an intussusception." He had the X-ray people take a flat plate, which showed suspicious evidence of a complete intestinal obstruction, so he ran him down for a barium enema to see if that would reduce the intussusception (a condition where a section of bowel telescopes into itself and gets jammed), and then called the surgeons and took the child up to surgery around 4:00 A.M. And he was right, too; there *had* been an intussusception, which the barium enema had reduced; since it was reduced and the bowel hadn't gotten gangrenous yet, the surgeons just closed the child up again.

But that one I had missed high, wide and handsome. And felt all the more foolish because it was the child of a registered nurse.

Of all the treatment procedures I had had to do, the two that still bother me a lot are starting IVs on these little ones and drawing blood for lab work. Both things just plain have to be done on these small kiddies, especially in dealing with the vomiting and diarrhea problems; you've got to have the blood to find out where you are starting, and then you have to have access to a vein to get fluid and electrolytes in. But starting the IVs is always a fight, even with the little airplane needles: you have to try to find a vein on the scalp, or get one in the foot, or the hand, or the wrist, and then try to make it stay put once you get it, and it's just an awful job. I've spent as much as two and a half hours straight on one youngster getting an IV started, and it was torment to the kiddie all that time, but I couldn't quit, because we had to have fluid going into him or he was going to die.

Drawing blood can even be worse. The other night it took Shenk and me an hour and a half to get 5 cc of blood from a newborn baby that had suddenly started vomiting blood. Its obstetrician had sent it over from St. Christopher's, where it had been born. We started out by doing an external jugular tap, but couldn't get anything. Then we did a femoral tap—sticking a blunt needle straight down into the groin, by guess and by God hoping to hit the femoral artery, after locating the artery by its pulsation—and got into the vessel but only got ¼ cc of blood before it stopped coming. Tried the other femoral, and again got just a bit of blood. Then Shenk tried to get into an internal jugular on one side, a really deep vein in the neck, and couldn't hit it. He tried the other side and gave the child a pneumothorax by nicking the apex of the lung with the needle. Finally, Shenk patiently tried one of the femorals again, and at last got the requisite amount of blood. After one and a half hours of trying.

I thought sure that baby was just going to die before we got finished, and Shenk himself was a lot less calm and collected about it than he had seemed. He pointed out that you could thrombose a femoral artery very easily with a femoral tap and cut off circulation to a leg, or kill a child with a pneumothorax while groping for an internal jugular, or hit a carotid artery and obstruct it with resultant brain damage; but he also pointed out that any condition in which a newborn baby is vomiting blood, bright red blood at that, means grave trouble, and probably surgical trouble, and the surgeons simply wouldn't go near it without laboratory information. This youngster had had an abnormal opening between his windpipe and his esophagus—a tracheoesophageal fistula—and would have been dead of suffocation at the first feeding if the surgeons hadn't gone in that night and repaired the defect.

So anyway, I've kept good and busy with these patients, and have had a pretty good time with them. This is the end of my first two weeks, and tomorrow I shift floors, and take over assignment on 2-East and 2-West, both primarily surgical floors. The interns don't scrub in surgery here, just help with the preoperative and post-operative care.

And I have the weekend duty coming up. The one weekend I've been on I was run ragged, and I heard from White that last weekend was a real horror, so this one will probably be, too. We'll see how it goes.

Monday, March 19

The weekend was a horror, all right, in just about every possible way. Weekend duty is a long enough stretch under any circumstances; here at the Children's Division the duty starts at 8:00 Saturday morning instead of 10:00 or 11:00 as it does over at the main hospital, and this particular weekend we seemed to have mothers with squalling children coming in the doors, in the windows, up through the cracks in the floor, everywhere. They were just all over the place in a long, endless stream. Add to that a big, fat, weekend-long conflict with Roger Pfeiffer, who was the resident on duty (Shenk was off for the weekend), and it added up to the worst couple of days of duty I've had yet.

The only redeeming grace was that Muldoon had it with me; there was so damned much work that we just worked at it side by side, splitting the house down the middle for the sake of formality, but each of us going ahead with what came up next on either side of the house if the other was busy. Formally he covered 3-East and 3-West and 2-West, while I covered 2-East and 1-East and 1-West. This worked out pretty well, boiled down to about an equal distribution of work, except that Muldoon had almost no experience yet working with the small babies he found on 3-East and 3-West so it was a little rougher on him. He found himself spending almost all Saturday evening just starting two IVs and drawing some bloods for the lab work on patients on 3-East; at least on 1-East and West and

2-East most of the kiddies are two years old or older, so I didn't have so much problem with venipunctures and fussy little-baby procedures. On the other hand, those floors between them take a hell of a lot of surgical admissions, especially on a Sunday.

Saturday morning I started the weekend off by making rounds on each of the wards to see what sort of idiot work was lined up to be done. Two-East had a whole stack of little chores for me. One that took half the morning was changing the burn dressings on little Ronnie Petroni, a two-year-old lad who some time ago had pulled an electric deep-fat fryer full of boiling oil down off the stove onto his head, sustaining terrible third-degree burns of all his scalp and neck, part of his back and all of one leg. Ronnie has been undergoing grafts, a bit at a time, while his burns have been healing, a long, dreary, painful process. He is up on a Stryker frame, a gadget that keeps him immobilized but can be turned over, frame and all with him in it, to avoid bedsores, and still leave most of him hanging out in open air so dressings can be changed. So far his scalp has been grafted, and his back has been grafted, and they're using continuous moist soaks on his leg to get that ready for grafting sometime in the next few days.

Anyway, the burn dressings have to be changed on this little guy at least once a day, and I had the joy Saturday morning. In spite of the moist packs, the burns ooze serum and the dressings cake and stick. In the beginning, dressing changes were so terribly painful that they used general anesthesia to do them, and then later gave him morphine and Thorazine; now they just give him a grain of Luminal half an hour before dressing change time. Still painful, but not terribly so—except that Ronnie doesn't believe it. He is a very reasonable little fellow. He practically never smiles, but he will lie there and converse with you quite sensibly for a kid his age, and he will say, yes, he knows it won't hurt to change the dressings, and no, he won't cry, and yes, he knows you're trying to help him—and then, just as unreasonably, he starts screaming at the top of his lungs, absolutely terrified screaming, the moment you actually begin the dressing change. If you ask him in the middle of all this howling if you're hurting him or not, he stops screaming and says, "No, you're not," and then goes right back to screaming again.

I don't pretend to understand it, except that I know that his burn and the long, agonizing treatment since have done something to this kid that doesn't show on his skin. Every day the guy doing the dressing change has taken lots of time to talk to Ronnie, and every day we tell him that the dressing change will be easier today than yesterday, and that tomorrow it will be still easier, and I think we have him half-believing it, but only half. He's an awfully cute little guy, but pathetic; he's anchored down in that frame so he can't even wiggle. And he's had a long siege, and a great deal of pain and punishment for something that from his point of view couldn't have been his fault. And something is funny inside him now. Thinking about it, it seems to me that it's just wrong that a boy this age should have this much pain and this sort of pain; he's got plenty of time for that sort of thing later. He's been introduced to something at the age of two years that he shouldn't even have had to know exists for a long time, certainly at least not until he has had some warning and some chance to build a defense against it. At this age, he can't possibly have any defense against it, and I don't know what kind of change this brings about in a two-year-old boy. I wonder if this kiddie ever will learn to smile.

After that I went to see some of the other patients on 2-East; there are two or three wild little boys, about nine or ten years old, who have had surgical treatment for megacolon, had to have an obstructing segment of colon removed, and then the upper end pulled through at the rectum. Mike Long is one of them; he's had a lot of scarring of the pull-through area at the rectum, so the intern has to dilate his rectum with a glove every day. And Mike doesn't like it for beans. He's wild enough and energetic enough anyway, and when he sees you coming after him with a rectal glove, he just takes the attitude, "Well, okay, Doc—but you're going to have to catch me first," and that takes some doing. Saturday was one of the days when Mike just didn't like anything at all, started his day by hurling his cereal bowl at the nurse, and so forth. But the nurse called me about 10:00, worried because all of a sudden Mike seemed so subdued. A few hours later he was spiking a fever, and then broke out with a rash. I couldn't tell if it was measles or if he was just having some kind of drug reaction, but everybody on 2-East hoped he'd stay a *little* sick for a while. He didn't, though. By Sunday A.M. the fever was down and the rash subsiding.

Another child on that ward is a real mess, a little boy aged two and a half who was born with a cleft face. Some kiddies have a cleft palate; some have a cleft palate and cleft lip. This child has no palate at all, and a cleft lip on both sides with the cleft on one side extending clear up through his upper jaw and through the base of his eye socket so that his eye was just sort of hanging down into the cleft. I gather he had the same thing on the other side, too, at birth, but that side has had some plastic repair so that at least the eye socket has been closed and the eye located in place. I saw some pictures of him that were taken before any plastic work was started, and they were really hideous. You were looking at his face, but actually were just staring into this great gaping hole right down into his throat, with his eyes separated far apart and hanging loose on their stalks.

Well, now that they've done some of the repair—it has to go slowly, a little stage at a time—I can't really say that he looks much better to me than he did before they started. Maybe somewhat better. The general impression seems to be that he is entirely *compos mentis*—in fact, some of the ward personnel think he's really a pretty smart little boy. God knows he'd better be smart. He's probably going to have to be a hell of a lot smarter than he really is to get along very well in this world, unless they do a whole lot better job on his face than I think they can do. I know the nurses on the floor favor this child a lot, and I'm glad they do. I know it sounds dreadful, but I find him so physically repulsive that I just have to brace myself every time I go near him. It's a horrid sort of affliction for an innocent child, or his innocent parents, to have to endure.

One thing I've learned: not all of the patients around this place are exactly sweet little darlings or delights. I know I felt the first few days that you couldn't really blame a sick child for being nasty, and had to fight down my own negative reactions to some of them. I'm not so damned sure, now; I think maybe it's possible sometimes for a natively nasty child to happen to get sick and come to the hospital and sort of be handed *carte blanche* to exercise his nastiness to the hilt.

The first admission Saturday afternoon was a real dream, a private patient of Dr. A. C. Bell's who came in with a history of vomiting and diarrhea. She was a little bitch, a four-year-old girl who was strictly Mamma's little darling. She started screaming and fighting everybody and everything from the minute she walked in the door. She hadn't had a *lot* of diarrhea or vomiting; it was mostly that Mamma had been bothering Dr. Bell every hour on the hour about it until he had to get some relief some way and told her to bring the child in for admission. The girl wasn't badly dehydrated, but Bell wanted her to have some fluids by IV, so I gave them to her, and had to literally tape her down to the bed in order to anchor her enough to get a needle into a vein. She had been screaming and kicking before; this procedure made her mad, and she started vomiting, and the madder she got, the more she threw up. After the IV had run in, Bell wanted me to get her to drink fluids by mouth, and she just wouldn't drink. So after much, much coaxing I called him and said, "Look, this kid isn't having any, what do you want me to do?" Bell said to put a Levin tube down her and get 500 cc of fluid into her through the tube over a thirty-minute period.

So I had the joy of anchoring her to the bed again and sinking a Levin tube. She began vomiting and screaming and choking in the process of getting it down, and smeared me and the bed and everything else with vomit, screaming at the top of her lungs. Well, I got that damned tube down all the same; by that time *I* was getting ready to scream, and I watched while the nurse put 500 cc of fruit juice and water down in the course of thirty minutes, and in the course of the next thirty minutes we got about 2,000 cc back up again. So I said, the hell with it, and the hell with Dr. Bell. I pulled the tube out, just didn't give her any fluids at all. I'm not sure where we ended up in that shuffle. She must have been drier when we got through than she was when we started out, but that couldn't have been very dry. I just figured that any child with all that howling and kicking in her couldn't be too damned sick, and told the nurses to let her get good and thirsty and then give her small volumes of fluid by mouth only if she promised to behave herself, and then I left. I guess she made it; Bell sent her home again Sunday morning.

By late Saturday afternoon I was already tired and irritable and sick of screaming kids, with a long Saturday night coming up—a favorite "drop-in" night for mothers with children who have been sick since Wednesday morning and who can't locate their doctors at midnight on Saturday. A patient of Dr. de Shaw's, a fourteen-month-old boy, came in on 1-West just at suppertime, and I got into a big flap with Roger Pfeiffer, the resident on duty, about him. Maybe I was just spoiling for a fight, but this one ground me the wrong way. The child had been vomiting and was pretty dry; de Shaw called in orders to start IV fluids on the boy and get any studies we wanted. Pfeiffer was up in the OR doing an exchange transfusion on a newborn Rh baby, had been there all afternoon, so I didn't bother him. Just went ahead and worked the kid up, drew blood and ordered electrolyte studies done stat, and got some glucose and saline started by IV pending return of the studies. The lab reported a fairly sharp imbalance in salt and potassium, the old story we have seen so much of, so I sat down and figured carefully what the first twenty-four-hour requirements should be, bearing in mind my experience with Johnny Beck and his failure and convulsions a few days ago. I wrote the orders, most conservatively, and got the first jug of water and electrolytes started. Checked with the mother to be sure the boy had voided recently before ordering potassium, since you don't dare load that in if there's any chance of a kidney shutdown.

Well, that was all lovely, until I told Pfeiffer about this and the shit hit the fan. I caught him just coming from the OR, and it was an inauspicious time, I suppose, because after three hours of exchange transfusion, the baby had died, and he had been working to resuscitate it, without success, and so he wasn't in too fine a mood. I told him about the patient downstairs and the orders I had set up, and he said, "Did you see the baby pass urine with your own eyes?" I told him, no, the mother had given the history. So he said, "Well, go down there and stop that goddamn potassium until I can get down there and see for myself that he's voiding."

I went down to the floor, annoyed enough, and found that the boy had voided twice since the IV had started, a total of about 300 cc. So I went back up and told Pfeiffer this, and that I'd let the orders stand. He didn't say anything at all, but he went down to check later, and when I walked into the nurse's station he had just finished rewriting all my orders—scratched out the whole page and wrote it over himself. I asked him what was wrong with them, and

he said, "Oh, nothing, really, I just made some picayune changes
here and there."

I looked, and they were certainly picayune. So I got sore and said,
"Look, why change them at all? Why not just let my orders stand?"
Well, we went round and round. I had ordered 40 milliequivalents
of salt in those IVs in twenty-four hours and he thought 30 was
enough. He maintained the child might start retaining water with
that much salt. I pointed out that the last case of this sort I'd seen
we'd had an identical situation, and I'd suggested 30 milliequivalents of salt and Shenk had thought 40 would be better. I tried to
get through to him that with his changes, if the baby came around
fine, I wouldn't have any idea in the world whether the child would
have done as well on my program as on his, that the only way I
could get any real concept of treating kids in this sort of trouble was
to do the balancing myself and be prepared to pick up any trouble
anywhere along the line as it came up. So he said you couldn't be
sure of picking up the trouble in time, this dire thing or that dire
thing might happen.

He was really getting ridiculous now, and I carefully pointed this
out to him, and he said, "Well, goddamn it, the resident is supposed to be responsible for this sort of thing, and I'm not going to
let any intern's orders stand if I think they can be improved on
even a little." So I said, "Well, why bother the interns with it at all
then? All I'm getting out of this shifting around is massive confusion, and I can read about fluid balance until I'm blue in the face,
and still I stay confused. If you don't want the intern meddling, I'd
rather keep hands off the problem altogether, just let you wrestle
with it 100 percent by yourself, including starting IVs and everything else."

Well, we broke it off then; there were other things to do. He said
he thought I was taking a very one-way attitude, and we were at
loggerheads for the whole rest of the weekend. I would see children
in admitting that he had to check, and would take a history and
come up with certain physical findings, and make a diagnosis, and
then he would either minimize or fail to confirm my findings, or
would find something else that he maintained was present that I
hadn't found, or ask me questions about this thing or that that I
hadn't elicited in the history, or one thing or another.

There was a kid who came in with a severe upper respiratory infection and bright red eardrums that I thought were bulging. High fever, no rash; I thought the child should be admitted. Pfeiffer came and looked at him and said, well, the eardrums weren't bulging, and they didn't look too red to him, and anyway, he saw Koplik spots in the child's mouth, so he obviously had measles and couldn't be admitted. Said he'd have a rash by morning. I went back and looked in his mouth again and couldn't find anything that looked like Koplik spots to me, but the child went home. God knows, maybe he had measles, but there's no way I'll ever know.

Well, we went along like this the rest of the weekend. I suppose I just should have kept my mouth shut and cooperated with him instead of making a big fuss, but I was good and damned sore. I know I didn't encourage any cooperation from him, but I also suspect that Roger Pfeiffer is one of these residents who is neurotically compelled to change anything the intern writes down in some way, whether it be orders, or diagnostic impressions, or physical findings or what not. No matter if the change is picayune or not, he has to make some sort of change. I don't know if he's trying to impress the attending man that he, the resident, has been there keeping close control on things, or whether he feels he has to do this to exert his authority, or whether he's just massively insecure and trying to prove that he isn't, or what the hell the story is. But it seems to me if I had to spend much time under this kind of tutelage I would soon end up with no confidence whatever in any physical findings I might make, or impressions I might have, or orders I might write. I finally just kept out of his way, and tried to have as little contact with him, or to cooperate with him as little, as possible all weekend.

I did establish my diagnostic coup for the weekend, though, on another private patient of Dr. de Shaw's. This was a six-year-old boy who had come in with a high fever, headache, photophobia and some signs of meningeal irritation. He'd been admitted Wednesday and an LP had been done and the conclusion was that he had a nonbacterial meningitis of some sort, possibly viral, or even possibly polio. He'd been strictly isolated and observed for polio, and the more studies were done, the more the consensus was that he probably did have polio and that paralysis was going to turn up any minute, but they couldn't definitely be sure. He's stayed this way for three or four days without any change—temp came down with aspirin and such, but spiked right back up again.

Anyway, the nurse called me Saturday evening because the boy had been complaining that his neck was very sore. This was at 10:00 in the evening. I'd seen him about 7:00, and he'd said nothing about his neck and had looked pretty good. But now when I saw him to find out about his sore neck, it seemed that it wasn't his neck that was sore at all but the angle of his jaw, and his right cheek was puffed out twice the size of his left. I didn't feed him a pickle; if I had, he might have told me his own diagnosis once he stopped hollering. I called de Shaw and told him I thought the mystery was solved, except that I'd never heard of a meningitis-like syndrome as the beginning of mumps. But de Shaw said, oh, yes, not meningitis, but encephalitis, and that sometimes it is very tricky to differentiate between mumps, encephalitis and polio until you have a swollen parotid gland staring you in the face. He sounded massively relieved about the whole thing, and I felt that I'd gained something from that miserable day at least.

Saturday night things slowed down about 1:00 A.M., and I got a pretty good night's sleep. Muldoon and I alternated drop-in calls; he got two and I got just one. Then Sunday was a perfectly horrible day. I woke up at 8:30, to my disgust, too late for breakfast, so I ate some stuff from the refrigerator, and then went down and made rounds and checked for idiot work. There wasn't an awful lot of that, but it took me until 10:30, and by then the first admission for the day had arrived: a preoperative for Monday that the nurses wanted me to check right away because they thought he had a runny nose, and that might mean the surgery had to be canceled.

That started it off, and from then until 2:00 A.M. Sunday night I was admitting patients just as fast as I could run, taking time off to gulp a sandwich for lunch, and again taking fifteen minutes to gulp down some dinner about 6:00 when Ann came in. I had a total of nine surgical admissions, plus four or five medical admissions, and was really running my ass off all day long. So was Muldoon; I got up to the lounge for a cup of coffee around 1:30 A.M., and found him sprawled in a chair with his head on a hand, snoring, with a cup of coffee half-finished on the floor beside him. He looked like he was just out on his feet, and when the loudspeaker sounded off with, "Dr. Muldoon, Dr. Muldoon," he jerked awake and looked up at the loudspeaker and said, "Oh, shit, I'm coming," and wandered off toward the elevator without even answering the page. I don't think he even saw me.

I got to bed at 2:00, but was up again at 2:30, and spent most of the rest of the night getting in and out of bed like a yo-yo. A patient of Dr. Simon Sheffield had been admitted about 11:00 P.M., with a bad case of hives and fever. Sheffield had left orders for the nurse to call him if anything happened during the night. So at 2:30 the child started vomiting, and the night nurse on 1-East called me to come see the child. I rushed down thinking something dreadful was wrong, but found that all she really wanted to know was if it was all right for her to call Dr. Sheffield and tell him the child had vomited. I said, "Well, did he want to be called?" and she said, "Yes, that was what he said." So I said, "Okay, then why don't you call him?" Well, she didn't know whether she should or not. So I pounded my head on the desk for a while, and decided there was no fighting it, and went and saw the child (who was now sleeping soundly) and then told the nurse to do anything she chose, I couldn't care less, and went back to bed.

There were two more idiot calls for one thing or another, and then at 5:00 A.M. Monday morning they called me to come down to the Emergency Room and see this drop-in patient, a little hemophiliac boy who had had a tooth extraction a month before, and had been bleeding from the extraction site since sometime on Friday. So now at 5:00 A.M. Monday morning his mother had decided that the time had come to see somebody about this. He'd been bleeding quite heavily, or at least this was the general idea I got; the mother was operating with an IQ of about 10—well, let's say 15; give her the benefit of the doubt. She was about as bright and helpful as a block of stove wood. She couldn't even tell me when the bleeding had started for sure.

The kid, who was about ten, had a great big clot sitting there in his mouth hanging down from the extraction cavity up above. Looked like a gob of dark red jelly half-filling his mouth. I didn't see any fresh blood around it, and I wasn't about to touch the clot, just checked his blood pressure and pulse and found them okay with no sign of shock—in fact, the kid seemed angry and embarrassed to be there at all. I called the resident and told him about this, and he agreed for God's sake not to touch the clot, let it be. He said if it wasn't actively bleeding, send the mother and child home and tell her to bring the child back to the Pediatric Outpatient Clinic when it opened at 8:00; they could get a hemoglobin then, and advise her.

So I suggested this, and she didn't live far away and seemed to understand, so I sent her on home and went back to bed. Hadn't any more than gotten my head down when the nurse was calling again to say that the lady was back again with the boy, insisted he was bleeding again and would I come look at it? I thought, Good Christ, and wondered if the mother remembered that she'd just left here. I asked the nurse how much bleeding there seemed to be, and she said, "Well, not much." I said, "How much is not much? Do you see any at all?" and she said as a matter of fact she didn't.

All this was in a fog of bone weariness; I knew I had a bitch of a Monday coming up, and talking with that nurse on the phone was like wading through knee-deep mud. Finally I said, "Look, if you really think it's necessary for me to come back down and look at that boy again, I'll come down, but I just looked at him ten minutes ago and I don't think I'd see one damned thing different than I saw before." She puzzled over that one, and said, well, let her go look at him again. A moment later she came back and said she still didn't see any bleeding, the boy was happy as a clam, and the clot looked just the way it did before. So I told her to offer the mother her choice: take the child home until 8:00 clinic time or go sit with him in the lobby, but I wasn't going to roll out of bed again unless there was some damned good reason. So I hung up and rolled over for a big hour's sleep before Monday started.

Today was a fast-moving day, lots of admissions, but none of them very exciting. Ronnie Petroni, the burn boy, went up for more grafting today. Joey McCarran, the boy with the horrible eczema, is almost clear; the only thing that seems to set him back is when his mother comes over to visit him—takes him three days of scowling and scratching to catch up afterward. Can't remember much I did today except that I was very, very glad to get off duty tonight. If

somebody calls on the phone tonight at 2:00 A.M. and asks for
Mabel, I'm going to tear the phone out of the wall by its bloody
roots.

Sunday, March 25

The past week on 2-East and 2-West has been ragged, something
going on all the time and busy almost all night on duty nights. The
busyness is insidious: it doesn't seem busy, and the work is interesting and fun for the most part; you just discover along about midnight that you've been going without a break since suppertime, and
have gone all day before that since breakfast without a break to
speak of, and there is still work to do. And there's always something
special that takes time and attention. I catch myself thinking, Jesus,
this has been a rough week, but there was this case and that case
that made it so rough, and next week things will get back to normal. The only trouble is that things *don't* "get back to normal";
they haven't yet, and I don't think they are about to. This ragged
pace is as normal as it's going to get. There's enough everyday
patient maintenance work to keep me steadily and unremittingly
busy anyway; all it takes is one really rough case, or one strange
one, or one really sick one, piled on top, and you've got a "normally" busy week turning into an around-the-clock rat race, and
there is always a really sick one on your doorstep around this place
somewhere.

The real blessing on this service has been Harry Muldoon; we've
been working back to back on duty nights and have gotten to be
good friends. It's amazing how much more fun this game is when
you're working with somebody you like and trust, who is going to
hold up his end without a lot of crap and complaint, as opposed to
somebody who is trying to do as little as possible, or dump his work
on you, or cut corners on you. Muldoon is a work horse, and he's
got patience I can't even approach. He's incredibly good with the
same kids that just irritate me. He's so thorough and careful that he
makes me ashamed of my own sloppiness sometimes, and he doesn't
make any big fuss or fanfare about it, just quietly goes about his
business and gets it done and some of mine, too, if he sees I'm busy
with something else. He's the only man I've run into yet in this

internship who, drinking coffee with me at 11:00 at night when the page came for me, would say, "Why don't you sack out and let me take it? I got forty winks this afternoon, and you look ragged," and then go ahead and do it.

And it was especially good to have Muldoon around a week like this past one, when we've had the Klein girl on our hands. This was a girl who came in about 6:30 P.M. Tuesday evening, a nice-looking child about eight years old, brought into the Emergency Room by her father because she'd been getting sick all afternoon. And I suppose Jeannie Klein was a diagnostic coup for me that I should feel very good about. I did nail the diagnosis, and right under Roger Pfeiffer's nose, too, and I probably would be glad about it if it weren't such a dirty diagnosis to have to make. The kid had complained of headache all afternoon, said her neck hurt at supper-time, and that her eyes hurt and her cheeks hurt. I saw her in the Emergency Room—she didn't have a doctor and was to be a house case—and knew something was funny. She couldn't bend her chin down to touch her chest, and I couldn't bend it down; she had a fever of 100.6, which I thought was too low for a meningitis, and I had an awful time getting a look at her throat. It wasn't that she wouldn't cooperate; she just sat there and cried and didn't want to turn her head, said her cheeks hurt too much. She seemed nervous as a cat, too. I got a nose and throat culture then and there, and drew some lab work while I waited for Pfeiffer to come down and see her; I thought she was an early meningitis, and should be admitted, and have an LP done pronto. She certainly looked sick to me.

So naturally I had to argue Pfeiffer into admitting her at all. He thought it was another prodromal mumps with some meningeal irritation; he thought he found some neck nodes I hadn't found, and thought her throat was red (which I didn't) and wanted to pack the kid home and have the parents bring her in next day. Anyway, he said, we were short on house beds. It seemed to me he was more interested in pooh-poohing what I thought than in looking at the kid, and finally I said, "Look, you can sure send her home if you want to, but I think this kid is sick, and I think she should be admitted until we know what's wrong with her. And I'm going to write that down on the outpatient record whether you send her home or not. She could have bulbar polio just as well as anything else."

Well, Pfeiffer pooh-poohed that, too, spending five minutes telling me why this was a ridiculous idea, but he did admit the kid, all the same. Put her on 2-East. We got busy with something else for an hour or so, and I then went in to do an LP on the girl. I had polio on my mind so strongly I couldn't even think of anything else, even though I'd just pulled that idea out of the hat when I was arguing with Pfeiffer. The more I thought about it, the more sure I was. Had trouble with the LP; Jeannie couldn't or wouldn't straighten out her back very much, and wept all through the procedure (we had to send her father out while we were doing it) and seemed even more nervous and jerky than before. The spinal fluid was crystal-clear, though. I wrote orders for the nurses to check temps and respirations at half-hour intervals, still watching for polio, and went on to work up another admission, planning to check in on Jeannie again in an hour or so.

But the tip-off came about 11:00 when the floor nurse from 2-East called me and said: "Doctor, I think you'd better come look at this little Klein girl. She's so nervous she flinches every time I go near her, and she just bit a thermometer in half when I went to take it out of her mouth."

I went down to see the child, thinking the nurse was surely exaggerating, but she wasn't. Jeannie had snapped a temp stick off clean with her teeth. And she was more than just nervous; she nearly jumped off the bed when I opened the door to the room. I looked at her, and then I tapped her cheek with my finger and watched her jaw go into spasm and her teeth clench. I'd only seen a thing like that once before, in an old Italian gardener in Baltimore, and it wasn't polio that caused it. I asked the father if the girl had cut herself or hurt herself in any way recently; the father said, well, no, not really, except that she's stepped on a nail out in the yard a week or so ago and hadn't said anything about it until today because she was afraid she'd have to go to the doctor and have a shot. And then I knew we were in the soup for sure, and I knew what kind of soup. I got out of that room and onto the phone and called Pfeiffer out of bed and said, "Roger, you'd better take another look at this little Klein girl right now, because I think she's got tetanus."

For once Pfeiffer didn't argue with me. He got down there fast and looked at the girl and said, "Well, I'm afraid you're right this time," and went out to call Dr. Michael Adair, the attending man, and then called the surgical resident to come down and put a tracheostomy tube into the girl's windpipe.

We started an all-night stand—really, an all-week stand. There is so pitifully little you can really do. You can give antibiotics to kill the bug, so that no more of the toxin is produced, but it's the poison already in the system that you're fighting. You can give antitoxin, and we did—60,000 units of it at 1,500 units per cc in horse serum, and sweat out acute serum reaction all night, giving 3,000 units every half-hour or so, trying to find enough places to stick it into her. But the antitoxin only neutralizes the poison that's not yet fixed in the central nervous system. Nothing touches what's already anchored down there, and that's what kills the patient.

Jeannie's spasms got worse all night, a sudden clenching of her jaws, arching of her back, stiffening of her arms and legs, gasping for air and then turning blue; they only lasted twenty seconds or so but they seemed to last forever, and each one was twenty seconds of unadulterated hell for that girl. A sudden movement in the room would trigger them. A sound would trigger them. A touch would trigger them. A bright light would trigger them. We loaded her up with Seconal, and she slept a little between spasms, but mostly she was with it every minute. We tried muscle relaxants, and Demerol for pain, but we were sending boys to do a man's work and we knew it; there wasn't anything but curare or general anesthesia that could really block those spasms and you can't keep a child under anesthesia or curare for ten days. We sweated Jeannie out all week, and it is a dirty disease to sweat out, and we are still sweating it out now. She's still alive, but she's not getting much better.

And through it all I have a cold, growing anger that these parents could ever have allowed this God-awful thing to happen. Jeannie had had her first DPT shot at age two months, but they'd never seemed to get her back to the doctor for the rest of her baby shots, nor for any boosters since, and they now have the joy of knowing that because they never got around to that, they right now have a 50-50 chance of having a dead child out of this, and if she dies, of knowing that she suffered a week of pure agony before she went.

We'll know better by next week if she's going to make it; at this
point every day won is a day to the good, and it won't go on forever.
At least the experts say it won't.

Dogging this girl, I've spent a lot of the night time up and
around this hospital; so has Muldoon. We keep running into each
other up in the lounge at 3:30 in the morning. I've discovered that
it begins getting light over the mountains at approximately 5:32 A.M.
this season of the year, and I have very curiously mixed feelings
about certain places and things around this hospital. The lounge is
a resting place, we always go in there and sit for a few minutes
before turning in, no matter when we are called out or why; I don't
know why, but we do. You can get amazingly hungry for coffee and
a salami sandwich at 4:00 in the morning, which I never would
have believed for a minute before. And then you lie down and go
dead asleep before the second bounce, which I also wouldn't have
believed.

There are other things, too. Walking off the elevator onto the
floors at night you can see the light shining into the dark corridor
from the nurses' station, and you can tell which floor it is (if you
didn't already know) by the sound, and the particular intensity of
the light, and the odor that is in the corridor, characteristic for
every floor, even though what the odor is I can't say. You can sit at
the chart desk and hear a nurse coming back down the corridor,
and you can tell from which room she is coming, and whether she's
coming after you or not, and whether there's trouble there or not,
all from the squeak of her shoes on the corridor floor. It's just
amazing what you can hear in a hospital like this at night and what
you can tell from what you hear.

Muldoon and I had a good laugh the other night. We get little
tidbits and fragments of gossip about ourselves, coming back to us
here and there. There are the nurses we like and the nurses we
don't like, but the nurses have their opinions about the interns, too.
The consensus seems to be that Muldoon is "sweet," and the nurses
universally like him, ugly as he is, and feel very sad and put out
because he's married. And the consensus also seems to be that I am
a bastard and a cranky, ill-tempered, sharp-tongued son of a bitch,
and the nurses all wonder how I ever managed to find a girl who
would marry me at all. So Muldoon said it must have been because

I was so handsome, and I asked him how did he figure that, considering that he, too, had snagged one, and he allowed that he must have had *some* kind of vibrations that got through at one time or another. And we speculated on which of these nurses we could most satisfactorily fix him up with, and went down the roster of their sundry amatory attractions and repellencies and finally decided that the pickings around this place were really a hell of a lot slimmer than you would think at first glance, like practically nonexistent. But then we were both pretty tired at that time.

Monday, April 2

Another hard week and another traumatic weekend on duty. In some ways the weekend wasn't as bad as the last one I was on. Sunday of the weekend was Easter, so there wasn't such a heap of preoperative admissions. On the other hand, the surgeons seemed determined to exhaust themselves all this last week before Easter to clean up all the pediatric surgery there was to be done in the whole city. Maybe they just wanted to take Monday off.

Much of the week was taken up with the little girl with tetanus, Jeannie Klein. She is still with us, by the grace of God, though she doesn't seem to be much improved, just getting along about the way she was before. There seems to be no question now that she does indeed have tetanus; the big question now is whether she will outlive the toxin or whether the toxin will outlive her. It gets cleared out very, very slowly, and the muscle spasm and lack of food (she's fed almost completely by IVs still) are exhausting. If she can just hang on long enough, she'll win; if the last of her reserve goes first, she's had it, and that's about the story.

One thing is sure—the hospital has really rallied to the girl and the problem. It's the first live case of tetanus this hospital has had in three years, and nobody is sparing anything. The floor nurses have worked out a round-the-clock special nursing schedule among themselves so Jeannie has a special on at all times, at no charge; we've had every pediatrician in the city in consultation one way or another without a single consultant's fee; we had the girl on curare for almost a day, with an anesthetist breathing for her all the time, during a rough spell early in the week. Like a terminal cancer, this is a dirty disease and a killer; but unlike terminal cancer, you have

a chance of winning, and if they recover, they recover completely—
no brain damage or anything like that. And this is one disease
where live or die lies right squarely in the hands of the ones who
are taking care of the child, in large part. And I think the hospital
is doing itself proud.

There was so much over the weekend that I think I can just hit
the high spots. Things started off at a gallop Saturday morning
when Terry Stone, the resident on with me for the weekend, called
me and told me some doctor was sending in a kid with a fulminating meningitis, probably meningococcus, with an imminent adrenal
collapse—the Waterhouse-Friderichsen syndrome you read about in
the textbooks, with hemorrhage into the adrenals, and skin hemorrhages, and cardiovascular collapse from the poison those bugs
put out. The child was coming in by ambulance, and Terry didn't
have any particulars, but this kind of thing demands crash emergency alert because a few minutes may make it or break it once the
youngster arrives.

When the ambulance turned up, the kid really looked lousy. He
was about six and a half years old, and he was unconscious, back
arched out and head thrown back in the classical meningitis pos-
ture. He was white as death, with little pinpoint hemorrhages all
over his belly and legs and spiking a fever of 105, obviously in shock
and going fast. While we waited, Stone and I had gotten a cutdown
set ready, and IV fluids ready, and an LP tray ready, and lab
materials ready, and Terry took one look at this kid and said,
"Okay, now we're really going to have to move."

First we did a cutdown, got a big vein in his ankle and got a
catheter into it and got fluids started on him. I pricked one of the
pinpoint hemorrhages and took a smear from that—sometimes you
find the organism fastest that way—and then did an LP, got spinal
fluid that was so loaded with pus it looked like milk. Got a nose and
throat culture, and got that plated.

While all this was going on at a frantic rush, we got the history
from the kid's mother—a very brief history indeed. The child had
been perfectly well until suppertime the night before, then got a
headache, threw up and spiked a fever. No cold or cough or URI
before to nail this on—it just hit hard, all of a sudden, boom. And
by this morning he was unconscious and violently ill.

Well, it sounded like meningococcus, all right, and the throat smear was loaded with the organism, and a smear of the spinal fluid also revealed meningococcus—not many, in fact very, very few, but all you need is one to nail the diagnosis. So we started the boy off right then with massive doses of penicillin, a million units directly into the IV, another million by injection, and planned to repeat this in twelve hours, and then we just sat tight. As Terry said, "If you're a praying man, then pray; it isn't up to us any longer."

By Sunday morning the boy was still with us, and the change was almost miraculous. He was conscious; his temp was down to 102; he still had a stiff neck, but he was responsive and talking and even asking to eat some soup by Sunday evening. We still don't know if there was any adrenal hemorrhage or not, but if there was, we got to him with fluids and support and antibiotics soon enough.

This was the first case of meningococcus meningitis that I've seen, and naturally Terry delighted in lecturing me all about it. It's often considered the deadliest kind of meningitis because it moves so damned fast—it can kill in less than twenty-four hours, and can get beyond the point that it can be stopped even sooner. On the other hand, the outlook is good if you get it in time. The mortality rate in this hospital is about 50 percent for kids brought in in the condition of this boy, even with penicillin, which really slugs the organism. It takes the penicillin a good twelve hours to get a really effective blow at the bug, and if the kid dies in the course of that twelve hours there's nothing you can do about it, even with him full of penicillin when he goes out. Fortunately, when they do recover there isn't much residual damage; Stone was pointing out that this at least is a break. With organisms like Hemophilus, for instance, you may kill the organism and cure the patient of his meningitis, all right, but there is a 40 to 50 percent chance he will be a complete gork by the time he's cured—lots of damaged brain tissue, and effusions of fluid, and intracranial pressure and a lot of other ugly things that unfortunately don't go away when the meningitis goes away.

Anyway, that patient set the pace for the weekend; Stone and I kept running, splitting the work between us. Another patient who was having trouble was a little boy of seven or eight down on 1-East. He had a case of measles a month ago, and developed a galloping measles encephalitis with it. It's a rare enough complication of red measles, thank God, but a dreadful one when it turns up. This boy has been comatose, spiking fevers to 107 and having respiratory difficulties for over ten days. Saturday night he started having spasms of muscle jerking—not real *grand mal* seizures, and not Jacksonian seizures either; these were generalized. Just muscles starting to twitch and jerk for no reason, then stopping, then starting again.

I called his pediatrician when this started, and he said they were probably decerebrate fits, the sort of thing that happens when most of the thinking part of the brain gets totally disconnected. It seems likely that the boy hasn't got any functioning brain left up there at all now, and the neurologist who came in to see him sure wasn't very happy or encouraging. But Pfeiffer maintains that they can go like this for days and weeks and then suddenly snap out of it completely one day, and that it's how soon they snap out of it that counts, rather than how bad it looks at any given point. I hope he's right, but I have a sneaky hunch he's whistling in the dark on this one.

Then we had a bunch of admissions: upper respiratory infections, a child with asthma, a kid with a nasty infected hand, all strictly run-of-the-mill. One little girl on 1-East is really spooky, though. I got called to deal with her several times over the weekend. This is little Betty Bartell, about six and a half years old, who was admitted a couple of weeks ago because she was vomiting up all her food, and nobody could figure out why. They couldn't even figure out whether she was doing it purposely or not. Stone thought she had an ulcer or some bowel lesion, but she had GI X-rays and they were all clean. She kept vomiting, and has been getting less and less responsive and less and less interested in what was going on around her. Not comatose, just vacant. Sits and stares at the wall all day. Finally we decided to get a head shrinker to look at this little girl; she has been looking more and more like catatonic schizophrenia. Or else she's putting on a damned good act. So far I haven't seen the psychiatric opinion, nor do I know whether those boys are going to solve her problem or not. Our problem is getting enough food down her to keep her alive, and we had to fight this problem—and her mother, who is enough to drive anybody schiz—all weekend.

But the real headaches, for me, are the drop-ins that turn up in the Emergency Room in a steady stream. Most of these kiddies have monotonously similar problems: fevers, or coughs, or sore ears, that sort of thing. Once in a while a burn comes in that requires dressing or a laceration that needs sewing up. Trouble is that you have to pay tight attention to every one, because it may be the one in a hundred or a thousand who has real trouble that you just plain have to catch. One thing is sure about children: they can get sick faster, and with less warning, than any other age patient, and there are enough thoroughly vile things that they can get sick with that you can't afford to assume anything.

Once we do get to bed on a duty night, we have fewer calls than at the main hospital, but we have the same level of stupidity showing up here and there on the nursing staff. I sometimes wonder if these hospitals purposely save the dumbest nurses for night duty or if it just happens that way. Sunday night I had a big brawl with the night supervisor about a child down on 1-West. This was a three-year-old leukemic boy; about 9:30 I started a unit of packed red cells. Got into a vein nicely, started this half-pint of packed cells dripping in, and wrote orders that it should all go in within four hours. I didn't hear anything about this until 2:30 A.M., when the supervisor called to say that the IV had infiltrated and would I come start it again? I didn't see how there could be much left to run in, so I asked her how much was left, and she said, "Oh, there's over three-quarters of it left to go."

So I went down to the floor, sore as a boil; all that blood should have gone in long since. The supervisor was just full of excuses: they'd been having trouble with the needle, and they hadn't been able to get it to run in right, and so on and so on. They also hadn't said a word to me about all this in five hours. I went to see the child, and the blood had infiltrated, indeed; he had packed red cells infiltrated into his arm to form a lump the size of a hen's egg. There must have been 50 cc of the stuff there in his soft tissue, and it was obviously painful as hell. I couldn't see how the child could have gotten any of the blood at all into his vein where he needed it.

Well, I blew my cork; I pulled the IV, and ordered an ice pack for the sore arm, and then went back to the nurses' room and told the night supervisor to make out an "unusual occurrence" report, there was no excuse for letting this happen. She objected, said she didn't think it was very dignified for the intern to throw a temper tantrum. So I told her that if this was a temper tantrum, it was high time somebody threw one about something like this; the floor nurse down here couldn't even have looked at the IV for hours, and this was par for the course with that babe. She doesn't know enough to grab her ass with both hands, so they turn her loose with a wardful of innocent children. I spelled it all out to the supervisor in large red letters, and wrote out the "unusual occurrence" form, and then went in and restarted the blood in another vein, and sat and waited until it had all run in, and made the supervisor sit and wait, too. It's a wonder to me that half that boy's arm doesn't slough out.

So there was no sleep that night. This morning, Monday, we shifted floors again; I am now assigned to 1-West for the next two weeks. This is mostly a medical floor, and mostly house patients, older children. Lots of morning scut work, and then rounds. Stone will be my resident, and Dr. Adair is the attending man. Stone is a good man, even if he insists on lecturing you every step of the way. And he does know a lot of pediatrics. He also believes in getting kids out of the hospital, doesn't let these house patients languish around in the place when they no longer need to be hospitalized. As soon as they have what he considers "maximum hospital benefit" he shuffles them on home. Of course, this means that the patient inventory is moving faster, with more sick ones and more work to be done, and the nurses don't like it a bit, but Stone is serenely indifferent to this, and I think he is dead right. We have some leukemics on the floor, a patient with nephritis, half a dozen with bronchitis or pneumonia, the youngster recovering from meningitis, and the little girl who maybe is schizophrenic and maybe has an ulcer and maybe is just deliberately throwing up her food for the hell of it. I think it will be good duty.

Tuesday, April 3

Well, this place sure doesn't want to let the troops get bored with dull routine: a new intern turned up from someplace today, allegedly to replace the one that got canned, and a new call schedule was published, and I found myself having my businessman's day today instead of Friday, and I don't know now who the hell is going to have duty what weekends for the rest of this month. The theory is that this will give the present incumbent interns more time off, two nights and two weekends off out of three, but somehow this seems very unlikely to me. I guess we'll have to wait and see.

Spent the day catching up on follow-ups mostly. Stone greeted me at the door at 7:00 A.M. with news that I was to present the little meningococcus meningitis case at pediatric conference at 8:30, so I had to see the boy and check his chart over for details of history and care. He was doing fine, and looked like a complete recovery coming up unless something japs us that I can't foresee. Then I rushed to get bloods drawn before the conference began, and then got called up to X-ray to inject the dye into a patient so they could do an IVP (intravenous pyelogram, a special study that reveals the inside of the kidney and bladder to X-ray examination).

It was a little two-year-old boy whom I had fought to a Mexican standoff yesterday without getting even a blood sample from him, and this was no easier. Finally ended up injecting the stuff into a jugular, which I don't like as technique at all; I don't mind drawing blood out from there, but I get a little nervous injecting iodine dye in. It seemed to work all right, though, in spite of the fact that these goddamn people just will not lay a heavy hand on these children for anything. When you have a wriggling two-year-old and you're trying to get a needle into a jugular vein without going on in to spear the carotid, somebody has got to hold the child still, and these nurses just won't do it. They wrap him up in a blanket and put a fingertip lightly on his chest and say, "Now, hold still, dear," and then wonder why he flops halfway off the table and why the doctor uses foul language.

The case presentation went without any difficulty, except that I was proudly recounting what had been done, and Stone was sitting there looking pleased with himself, and then Dr. de Shaw and Dr. Adair and half a dozen other attending men just gave us hell, picked the case to pieces. According to them we were damned lucky the boy survived the first six hours, because we put all our eggs in one basket—penicillin—when we should have been loading him up with sulfonamides, too, because they get at the meningococcus just as effectively as penicillin and several hours faster. The trick is to load them up with both, which I'd never heard of before, and which Stone had apparently chosen not to do. We both felt we'd had our ears pinned back somehow, but leaving the conference Terry just grinned at me and said, "Well, at least we had a live patient to present, that's something," and I didn't feel so bad about it.

Back on the floor I ran into the psychiatrist who had been consulting about little Betty Bartell. Yesterday we took her off all food by mouth and fed her by IV; she was just losing weight and getting dry the way she was going. The head shrinker said he didn't think she was psychotic, but that the vomiting was at least psychosomatic, and the withdrawal we've been seeing could just be that she is slowly starving to death. He said he thought the best thing we could do for the girl now was to send her mother home and see what happened then. So I talked to Stone about it; apparently he had tried on Sunday to talk the girl's mother into going home for a couple of days but hadn't pressed the matter. So now we decided to press it, told the woman point-blank that Betty was getting sicker rather than better, and that the psychiatrist felt that she would do better if her mommy wasn't around for a while. The mother reluctantly agreed, and went on home, told Betty that she was going and wouldn't be back for several days.

That was about 2:30 this afternoon. At 5:00 just before I went home, Betty's IV infiltrated and the nurse snagged me to restart it. The girl saw me come in the room, and looked me in the eye and told me in so many words that she'd quit her vomiting if I didn't put the IV back in again! Well, I considered that a reasonable bargain and told her so. I said, okay, we'd try it tonight. The last I saw of her she was sitting up in bed as alert as you please, slopping down about a pint of chicken broth by mouth without any trouble at all.

Saturday, April 6

A busy week of steady hard work on 1-West. Stone lets me do about as much as Shenk did (with benefit of lectures, however) and a whole lot more than Roger Pfeiffer ever did. We get along well, and he doesn't have this crappy attitude that the resident simply has to override anything and everything the intern does.

There's nothing but variety on this floor. And lots of thoroughly unpleasant illness. Part of it is that these kids are old enough to have personalities, but not old enough to understand their illnesses like adults, nor to behave like adults or respond to care like adults. There's just a lot they don't understand, and no way you can tell them. For instance, I had a bleeding leukemic admitted during the week, a kid about five years old with a terrible hemorrhage from his nose. The boy had been perfectly well until three and a half months ago, when all of a sudden he started breaking out with purple blotches all over his legs, and his hemoglobin fell from 95 to 20 percent in about three weeks. By now he has had two almost fatal nosebleeds, and I could certainly see where "leukemia" gets its name. It looked as though he was draining pink water out of his nose, until I realized that that was *blood,* just so depleted of red cells that you couldn't recognize it. Stone and I got his nose packed with Gelfoam plugs soaked in topical thrombin, and then got four units of packed red cells into him, and he turned pink overnight, literally. Not for long, though; he has an acute lymphatic leukemia, and Stone says that with the poor response to treatment he's shown so far, he will be very lucky to live another couple of months even with transfusions every other day.

There was another sad little boy admitted Wednesday night, Teddy Conklin, aged eight. I had a very strange experience with him; I'm not sure what to make of it. He'd been in another hospital for the past six months, mostly because he had some kind of a congenital heart defect—he's got a huge, misshapen barrel chest, with a heart in there the size of a watermelon. They sent him up here because he was beginning to show up traces of blood in his urine, and having pinpoint skin hemorrhages, and spiking fevers up to 104 or 105. Stone saw him with me, and the lad was quiet, but reasonable and cooperative. We thought that everything pointed to a subacute bacterial endocarditis, the kind of infection of the heart lining so many of these kids with heart defects get.

So I went into his room to draw blood for a blood culture, which is the only way to nail down that diagnosis, and this boy looked at me and said no. Just like that. He didn't cry, and didn't beg or wail or thrash around; he just glared up at me and said no needles. I sat down with him for a bit, talked to him—he was a very reasonable and bright little guy—and explained that we had to take blood from his arm, and that I'd do it as carefully and quickly and gently as I could, and if he'd look the other way he'd hardly know I was doing it. He didn't say anything, he just looked at me. He watched while I took his arm, and put on the tourniquet and found a good vein, and cleaned the skin with iodine, and then without warning he bent over and sank his teeth into my hand. He was not fooling; he drew blood. I dropped the syringe and cuffed him hard and said, "*Stop that*," and he disengaged and looked at me and I never saw so much hate and rage in my life as in that kid's face right then. I said, "Look, boy, I am going to take some blood from your arm if I have to tie you down to the bed. Don't do that again." Then I got another syringe, and prepped his arm again, and he bit me again. So I went out and got restraints and put them on all four limbs and stuffed a wad of gauze in his mouth and drew the blood culture. I was so mad I could hardly stop shaking enough to stick the needle in. And I spent the rest of the night feeling sick about my own rage.

Teddy Conklin is a thoroughly nasty little boy, but how can you blame him? He's been sick for six months, he's had a lifetime of needles stuck into him, and he can't fight back—what can he do? Stone says he is probably going to die; certainly he hasn't shown any exciting response or improvement so far on massive doses of antibiotics, and he hasn't got much reserve to work with, and the blood culture was positive for Staph aureus, which nails down his diagnosis. The pity is, he's not even going to die fast the way the leukemic boy will.

The meningitis boy is going home Monday. So is the girl who had tetanus; her recovery is complete. So at least there are some rough ones we can salvage.

Friday, April 12

Finished my stretch on 1-West with Terry Stone today; Monday I go up to 3-West, prematures and infants, to work with Saul Weiner, the senior pediatric resident. Sorry to leave 1-West; it has been rough duty, but good duty—so much going on I can only pick out a couple of things. Such as the bad burn case that kept us going half this past week. A nine-year-old girl who tripped and fell into a bonfire, clothes caught, and she ran. She had about 80 percent of her surface area burned; we nursed her along for three and a half days, and then last night she finally died in kidney failure and pulmonary edema. It was probably the fire she sucked into her lungs that tipped it more than anything, but I think maybe she was lucky. With all that burn she'd have had two solid years of torment healing it up, if she didn't die of infection or half a dozen other things in the meantime. Maybe she got off easy; it's hard to tell.

We had another sweetheart in, back to back with Teddy Conklin, a red-haired boy with true hemophilia. He has been bleeding into his knee joints, one of the hazards these kids live with, and had to have a long leg cast on one side to keep him from moving the knee. He has been in and out of this place from birth on, and hates every part of it. This time he was brought in because of acute belly pain, just a classical picture of acute appendicitis except that the pain was on the left side. We had the surgeons and everybody else in to look at him. The surgeons didn't want to touch him with a ten-foot pole, and I couldn't really blame them—this kid starts bleeding from the gums just by chewing up a piece of raw carrot, and then bleeds for a week. The experts finally decided that he'd had some kind of internal hemorrhage, and treated him with fresh frozen plasma for three days, and he got better so they sent him home.

This kid was real strange; I swear he did everything he could think of to make everybody around that place hate his guts. Dr. de Shaw said this is characteristic of true hemophiliacs: they get their personalities as twisted up as their clotting mechanisms, often deliberately do things to make themselves bleed, refuse to cooperate, get arrogant or obstreperous or just plain nasty. Part of it is the parents, I guess. It came as a shock to me to discover that this boy's parents really didn't give a damn whether he lived or died. The only reason they brought him into the hospital was because he hollered so loudly with his belly pain they were afraid the neighbors would call the cops. They live with a miserable disease like this for years and years, and pretty soon they just get tired of it, they don't care any more.

Of course, they aren't all as thoroughly nasty as Teddy Conklin or the hemophiliac. Most of these kiddies are at least halfway sweet, and some are plain lovable. One of my duty nights, a pair of twins came in, both of them with pneumonia. They were a real pair, about three years old, a boy and a girl and both towheads. The mother and father were both deaf-mutes, and we had a gay time getting a history out of them. Then we discovered that the children could understand sign language perfectly, but couldn't understand English. Not that *they* were deaf-mute; with a little sly trickery we soon established that they could hear, all right. They just couldn't understand anything but sign language. They were cute, and responded to antibiotics in a couple of days, but family conversation in that crowd was really a wonder to observe. We were sorry to see them go home so soon.

I finished off the stretch on 1-West with a real shocker, one of the most tragic things I've run into in this internship, and all the worse because Stone and I between us compounded the tragedy. I don't know what we should have done; Stone is always so worried and concerned about the whole family of these kids, parents as well as children, and it seemed right. It just turned out terribly wrong. We had just finished supper Wednesday night when the nurse on 1-West called us in tears to tell us that she had just found little Georgie Michaels dead in his bed. Georgie was a long-term patient, a two-year-old colored boy and hands down the favorite of the hospital. He was born with a defect in his windpipe—a part of it was pinched closed—and nearly suffocated at birth until the surgeons put in a tracheostomy tube so he could breathe. This was done in his home town up north in the state; he was then flown down to the Children's Division for the step-by-step surgery necessary to rebuild that section of windpipe for him. And he had been doing fine until that night, for some unknown reason, a plug of mucus blocked off the tracheostomy tube and he just quietly suffocated in bed before anybody even knew it.

Well, Terry Stone was shocked, and he dreaded to call the child's parents at their home upstate. He sat around, practically weeping himself, and we talked about what to say to them on the phone. Always break bad news gently, is the thing we're always told. But how could you break *this* news gently? Or prepare these people for the blow? Finally we agreed, Stone and I, just to tell them that Georgie had taken an unexpected turn for the worse, and that they should come down to the hospital as soon as possible that night. Then when they arrived we could tell them the really bad news, in person instead of over the phone.

So Terry called them, and they said they would drive right down—a distance of about eighty miles. This was about 8:00, so we waited for them to come. And waited, and waited. About midnight Terry called again, but there was no answer at their home. We sat and dreamed up all sorts of things that might have gone wrong—a flat tire, taking the wrong road down through the mountains, a washout, you name it. At 2:00 A.M. Stone finally called the State Patrol and learned the answer. Their car had gone off the road coming down the mountains into the desert. The Patrol said they must have been doing ninety in their rush to get to the hospital, and hit a bad curve, and both of them had been killed instantly in the crash.

I don't know the answer. I don't know what we should have done, probably dropped it cold in their laps over the telephone. All I know is that a hospital like this gets some wicked ones, and I've been living on a steady diet of them for two weeks. And you do what you think is right, and if you're wrong, then you're wrong, that's all. It'll be nice to be up among squalling infants for a while now, I think.

Saturday, April 21

Somebody waved a magic wand, and all of a sudden it is slow, very slow. After the hectic rush on 1-West, this week on 3-West has been dull indeed; I might have transferred to a different hospital. This floor has prematures, newborns and infants up to six months old, both medicine and surgery, mostly house cases, with a few private admissions, but we've had about a third of the beds full, and admissions have been exceedingly slow, so I've had a very quiet time of it and spent most of the week loafing.

Almost all my admissions have been of the annoyance variety rather than anything very exciting: colds, croup, prematures that are perfectly healthy little citizens except that they weigh under five pounds, that sort of thing. Saul Weiner is now resident in charge of this floor and 3-East, spends most of his time on 3-East just as Shenk did. Saul isn't a bad sort of guy to work with, except that he doesn't like inactivity. I'm just bored by it; it makes him nervous. He will suddenly appear out of the blue in a great burst of energy and want to make rounds and write progress notes and do this and do that, and then everything will sort of die again.

Actually, most of these tiny little ones need nursing care more than they need doctors, and the nursing staff up here is good. They don't bother me with a lot of needless trivia; maybe that's why I think they're good. I was worrying about procedures on such tiny babies, but so far about the only procedures I've had to do were LPs, which I do pretty well on little kiddies. I had to pump 80 cc of packed red cells into a one-month-old baby last night, using a scalp vein about the width of a hair, and that took half the night but wasn't particularly tough. The youngster didn't even know anything was happening.

I went down to follow up on little Betty Bartell, even though she's out of my care now. I still think she's schiz. She keeps going into these periods when she hurls up everything she eats; then she's got to be fed by IVs and tubes; then she gets tired of that and quits vomiting and starts to eat again. She doesn't seem to me to be improving an awful lot, nor does anybody really know what the hell she ought to be improving from. In the long run, I'm beginning to think that she's either going to end up starving to death or else going to the monkey house somewhere; she is losing weight slowly but surely, day by day.

A couple of interesting cases have turned up on 3-West, mostly by way of oddities. There was a child that was admitted with pneumonia, about three months old, not too sick, really, but Weiner and I both were impressed with how completely flaccid the baby was; it flopped around on the bed like a fish out of water, and felt like a wet bath towel when you picked it up. Weiner ordered a muscle biopsy done, and found the child has a true amyotonia—one of these congenital, incurable conditions in which one of the metabolic gears is missing and the child has no muscle tone or strength to speak of, and never will have. They think that's why he got pneumonia—so little muscle strength he never takes a deep breath, nor coughs up mucus, just lies there while secretions puddle in his lungs. I don't know what happens to a kid like this; probably it will go home, and then die before long. It will get pneumonia two or three more times, and sooner or later they won't get it to the doctor soon enough, and that will be that.

Weiner was all for telling the mother all about this, but de Shaw said, no, not now, not to say too much about the condition except to tell the mother that the baby has had trouble with its lungs and probably will have more trouble as time goes along, just not specify exactly what kind of trouble. "She'll find out soon enough, a bit at a time," he said. "Slug her with it now all at once and she won't either understand what you mean nor believe you. With something like this, the mother has got to convince herself first; then she'll hear what you say." I don't know what I think about it, I think if it were my baby I'd want to know, but maybe I wouldn't either. And de Shaw strikes me as a pediatrician with a lot more experience and wisdom and compassion than some of the young wise guys that come around this place, the ones that know all the answers, as long as it's somebody else's kid.

Oh, yes, prophecy was fulfilled. Somebody had told me long before I got to the Children's Division that I could count on having at least one aspirin-eater to pump out before I left here, and, sure enough, Wednesday night I did. Mommy brought this two-year-old girl in about 8:30 in the evening with the usual sad tale: she had come on the baby sitting with a bottle of aspirin spread all over the living room floor, with baby quietly munching on a few of them. Adult aspirin, too—how can they eat them? Mother didn't know how many the child had eaten, whether it was a dozen or fifty. The bottle had had one hundred in it and there were fifty or sixty left on the floor. So I had the great job of popping down a stomach pump tube and pumping water in and out of this brat's stomach. The child didn't like it at all. I must have pumped for three-quarters of an hour, in and out, getting this gunky white stuff out of her stomach. Weiner saw the child and called the pediatrician, and they decided they'd send her home after she was pumped out, so home she went. Sadder, I'm sure. Wiser, I don't know.

That same night we had a slightly wild half-hour with another kiddie in the emergency room, brought in with croup and laryngo-spasm, just croaking with each breath and very gray in the face. Child had had a slight cold all day, and then this suddenly turned up. I had them call up for Weiner while I started digging out a tracheostomy tray, hoping he'd get down there before I had to do one myself. He turned up, but we went through three sterile tracheostomy sets and couldn't find a knife in any one of them. He finally had to use a penknife to cut a nick in the kiddie's throat and get a tube down into its airway below the obstruction. Weiner was the big hero, got it done in time, and the baby's okay, but I guess the heads really rolled in Central Supply about that one.

The next day an ENT man gave us a very good conference on laryngospasm, and doing tracheostomies with or without the proper equipment. It was a stimulating conference, almost made me think there might be some justification for ENT men existing. He made the point I've heard so many times before, that the time to do a tracheostomy is when you think the child is going to need one desperately half an hour later, not to wait until he obviously needs one because by then he may be dead before you can get it done. Dr. de Shaw, who attended the conference, put in his two cents' worth, said that the single thing to watch out for the most in these children is restlessness. If you have a child with a little breathing difficulty, even if not much, who won't sit still, wants to sit up or lie down or roll around all the time, that's the kid to get a tracheostomy into right then because that's the child that's already getting oxygen-starved and is all of a sudden going to be blue in the face and choking to death very soon. Well, it still gives me the willies to think about it; these guys go around dropping these little pearls of wisdom, but I still don't know if I'd have the nerve to open a baby's trachea just because he acted restless. Sure as I did, somebody would find an open pin in his diaper or something, after I got done.

Saturday, April 28

Somebody has sure got the call schedule screwed up, and in my favor for once. I think. I was off last weekend, and am off this weekend, and next month's schedule says I'm off next weekend at Graystone, too. There has to be a sleeper in this pack somewhere, but I don't see it right now.

Another very slow week on 3-West; about the only interesting thing that turned up was an exchange transfusion on a newborn that came in last night, which Weiner did with my assistance. Baby came in yellow as a pumpkin, five days old. There was certainly Rh history—mother was Rh negative and father Rh positive, with an Rh positive baby—but titers taken all through the pregnancy had shown no sign of trouble ahead. I'd always thought that the titer would at least be up a little, but Weiner said no such thing. At any rate, he found the baby's bilirubin level was way high, and getting higher hour by hour, so he sent blood over to the blood bank for typing and cross-matching. And we had things set up for an exchange transfusion by 2:30 in the morning. So Weiner and I did the exchange on this little peanut.

He found the umbilical vein without any trouble—they always keep a moist pack on it when Rh problems are possible—and got a cannula into it, and then it was just a matter of pushing new blood in and pulling old blood out, first 10 cc at a time, then 20 cc. You squirt 500 cc of donor's blood into the baby this way, a little at a time, and at the same time pull 500 cc out, and the book says you have exchanged its total blood volume. You have to be most careful, because the blood you push into the umbilical vein pours almost directly into the right side of the heart. Anyway, we started the procedure at 2:30 this morning and finished up about a quarter to five, finally. Baby didn't seem to have a bit of trouble. I caught a couple of hours' sleep, and then Ann picked me up at the hospital for my weekend off.

Wednesday, May 2

Back across the street at the general hospital now, but this will catch up on the last couple of days on the pediatric service. After two months there without an exchange transfusion, I got rung in on two—the one Saul Weiner did Friday night and another my last night, Monday night. I should say Tuesday morning, early Tuesday morning. I was hoping to get a little sleep before trekking over to Graystone at 8:30 A.M. Tuesday, because I was scheduled for call Tuesday, Thursday and Friday nights there and that is rough the first week on a new medical service where you don't know any of the sick ones. And Monday looked promising all day, nothing much doing on 3-West, only a couple of admissions in the afternoon.

Then at 10:30 P.M. a three-day-old baby came in, a private patient of Dr. Sheffield's. The child had a deep jaundice, and Sheffield called and wanted this test done and that test done, and then wanted to do an exchange transfusion. Weiner was the resident on duty; I drew blood for the lab tests and the typing and cross-match, but I didn't want to sit up all night doing an exchange, particularly with Sheffield, who has been one of the most consistently bitchy and nasty pediatricians we've had to deal with around here. Anyway, the resident customarily helps with the exchanges that the private doctors do on their own patients. So I got the lab work set up and went to bed, figuring just to make myself scarce and dodge it.

It didn't work. About 11:30 the night nurse called me and told me that there was going to be an exchange transfusion, did I know? So I said that was nice, so what? Well, Dr. Sheffield wanted someone to help him. I asked her why she didn't call the resident, and she said she'd called Dr. Weiner and he had told her to call me. Well, I was sore, but there was no use fighting it; I told her okay, when the patient was in the OR, and Dr. Sheffield was on hand, and the blood was on hand and everything was ready to go, call me back and I'd go up and help; and I rolled over and went back to sleep.

She called back at 2:00, and I went to the OR and the baby wasn't there, and the blood wasn't there, and Dr. Sheffield wasn't there, and I sat around for a half an hour cooling my heels and drinking some coffee and trying to get awake and feeling very put upon. Everything arrived at once at 2:30 and we got going. Or rather, we tried to get going. Sheffield started hunting for the umbilical vein, and we fiddled around and fiddled around, and he couldn't find it. He is sure as hell no surgeon; he was about as skillful as a hippopotamus with boxing gloves on. He dug and fiddled and tried saline in a tiny little vein he found and got nothing back, and spread the umbilicus and went deeper and found nothing, and I got sleepier and sleepier and just wished to hell he would find it and get it over with. Finally, Sheffield decided that he just couldn't find the umbilical vein, he'd have to cut down on the baby's femoral vein, so what does he do but go and call one of the big-cheese pediatric surgeons out of bed to come over and do that. He couldn't call out a surgical resident sleeping one flight upstairs or anything like that; it had to be the big bazoo who had to come in to the hospital from Desertview Heights, half an hour away.

So when the surgeon arrived it was a quarter to 5:00 and the exchange transfusion hadn't even been started. I was dead-tired, and mad as hops at Weiner taking his ease upstairs in bed, and I knew damned well what I was walking into across the street on Medicine II. One of the rules is that the intern never bows out of any procedure he starts on when it's half done, but I was about to tell Sheffield I had to leave, when friend Weiner stuck his head in the door, apparently assuming that we were just finishing up. He found that we hadn't even started, but before he could get his head back outside again I said, "Say, I'm sure glad you came down to relieve me so I can get a couple of hours of sleep before I go back to Graystone this morning." Weiner's jaw sagged, and he was reluctant, but he went and put a gown on, and I told him thank you, very sweetly, told him how much I appreciated this, and got out of there fast. Went back to bed and slept until 7:30, then came across the street.

And that ended the pediatric service.

VI

Medicine II

One of the major things that sustained me (and all the other interns working with me at Graystone) was the certain knowledge that a year is only a year long, and that presently, inevitably, however slowly, that internship year would be over.

When I returned to the general hospital for my last two months on the second medical service, I could see the end in sight. In many ways I was glad to leave the Children's Division and be back in the familiar bustle of "my" hospital; for all the work on the pediatric service, I could never quite shake the feeling that I was an outlander there, a visitor there on sufferance. Going back to the main hospital, and especially going back on a medical service, was like going back to my natural home.

Medicine II was the best service of my internship. It was busy, as the journal shows, but it was a different kind of busyness. There was none of the apprehension I felt at the beginning of my internship; I knew what I was doing, I knew the men with whom I would be working, and I knew some part of my own capabilities and limitations.

I suppose that every intern feels, toward the end of his training year, that he is at last hitting his stride. For me, Medicine II was alive and active and challenging. And it was there, I think, that I first began to discover what I know so well today: that with all its demands and trials and problems and annoyances, the practice of medicine could be fun; and that there were rewards and satisfactions in the work that had only been hinted at before. You had to experience them really to know they were there.

And that, too, is a part of an intern's training.

The Journal, May and June

Saturday, May 5

Back to the general hospital and the medical service Tuesday. It was like old home week: familiar places, familiar faces. Pete Carey is my medical resident again. This service has the reputation of being the man-killer of them all, about half again as heavy as Medicine I; certainly this is the one everyone has howled about being so tough. Among the clinic doctors the service covers are Drs. Jacob Compton, Ned Stern and Dick Rivers, all endocrinologists with a heavy diabetic service; Fred Kidder, with a heavy chest service; Andy Case, with his hematology service; and a number of the outside doctors as well. I couldn't be sure how heavy it really would be, but Pete promised me faithfully that it would be heavy, all right, and I believe him already.

Still, it was a real pleasure getting back to the main hospital, surprisingly enough. Somehow the atmosphere in the Children's Division weighed on my soul or something; it was good to get back on the fifth floor here, back into the stream of things.

It's a funny thing, though, how much different I feel starting out on a medical service now compared with last July. Same resident, same kind of work-ups, same kind of problems, same hospital, same intern—only not really the same intern, and that, I suppose, is the big difference. I was scared before, in the beginning. I was scared silly. I didn't know anything, and I didn't know what was expected of me; I was afraid of making awful mistakes; I didn't know what to look for, what mattered and what didn't, what I could do and what I couldn't—there was an awful lot I didn't know.

And now I'm not scared; it's as simple as that. I don't mean that I know it all, not by a long way; there's still a lot I don't know, but I know what I can *do*. I know what to do about some of the awful, catastrophic things that can happen. I know that I'll spot trouble when it's there. I know when to holler for help and I know what help to holler for and what to do before it gets there. Most important of all, I know now that I don't miss very much, and I think that was the thing that scared me the most back in the beginning. I walk in to take a history and do a physical examination on a new patient, and it takes me only half to three-quarters of an hour in a tough case now compared to two hours in the beginning. I pick up more in that short time than I ever began to pick up in two hours in the beginning, and I walk out pretty damned sure that nothing *important* has slid through my fingers, most times.

I don't know what the difference is. Experience, sure, but that's not all of it. Recognizing certain patterns of illness, recognizing the *meaning* of things patients tell me and the meaning of *how* they tell me, that's part of it, too, and still not all of it. Confidence is part of it; even not being scared is part of it. But not all of it. Another part of it is the things that I see, the red flags that drop, the warning signals, from the minute I see a patient until I'm through with the work-up. It used to be that little things, only half-recognized, would bother me, but I'd shove them aside and ignore them. I don't do that any more. I pay attention. I see a certain yellowish pallor in a patient's face and a certain drawn look around his eyes, and I may never have seen him before in my life but the red flag slams down and something says, "Watch it, he's got the Bad Disease somewhere, sure as Christ crucified, the only question is where." I catch a whiff of an indescribable sweetish odor on a patient's breath, and I know right then that patient's liver is shot. I smell a trace of a sort of dead-mouse odor when I walk into a woman's room, and I start looking for pelvic infection right then, I don't care if she's in for a broken arm. I listen to a patient tell me about his illness, and I watch his face as he talks and I know he's lying to me. Sometimes there's nothing to pin anything on at all; I just have a bad, uneasy feeling that there's something about this patient that stinks, figuratively, not literally—something that's there but just isn't right on the surface, and I start to dig until I find it. And I almost always do find it, too.

Well, anyway, I'm back in the saddle. The service had an inventory of forty patients, and seven new medical admissions on Tuesday. I hardly saw Pete all day long Tuesday or Wednesday, I was too busy working people up and finding out who was around. It looks as if I'll only see the really sick ones already in. It's almost impossible to pick up pieces on patients you haven't worked up, at least on the ones already under control. And Pete and I have started dividing the work, too, as we did before. If some admission

isn't very sick, he'll read my work-up and go see the patient for five
minutes and just write a three-line resident's admission note; if it's
a new patient Pete has seen before I get to him, I use his work-up as
a guide, hit the high spots and only flag discrepancies if I run into
them. I was plenty glad to have this weekend off; we're back on an
every-other-day, every-other-weekend call here, and next weekend is
going to be a sweetheart. Pete says the weekends on Medicine II
grind you down farther and faster than any other part of the service. We'll see.

Friday, May 11

A fast, hard week. A lot of these admissions have been real medical diagnostic problems, and they take time and more time; this
service seems higher in them than anything I can remember on
Medicine I. And some have been real bitches.

Tuesday afternoon, for instance, Morton Silver admitted a
twenty-nine-year-old woman with a fever, muscle aches, malaise and
a terrific stiff neck—she could hardly move her head. I did an LP on
her; no pus in her spinal fluid, but she certainly had a clinical
meningitis, which is quite bad enough for a kiddie and a real death
trap for an adult. We got her stored away in a room, and Mort and
I agreed that we were committed to treat her as a meningitis even
without definite diagnostic proof. But there was another angle to
the case. It developed this woman had a history of psychiatric treatment in the nut ward over at County recently, and there was the
big, fat question of how heroic you wanted to get in treating a
meningitis that wasn't proven when every damned thing you saw
could just as well be put on, or a manifestation of a psychosis.

Not only was the woman in pain; she had a really queer husband.
Jesus, but he was a strange guy. He just hovered over her bed, or
over our shoulders, with this sweet little smile on his face and this
nice, precise way of talking, and he was right there every minute of
the time. I hinted that it would be nice if he'd go away and let me
examine the woman, but he didn't take the hint. Then when I had
the LP to do, I said, "Look, you'd better step out of the room for a
while." He did, but only just *barely* outside the room; I got paged
as I was getting ready to put gloves on for the LP, and I went
barreling out of the room to find a phone, and smashed right into

the guy standing *just* outside the door. Knocked him right on his can. Got back to do the LP and he was back in the room again, smiling sweetly. So this time I took him by the arm and personally led him down to the alcove to sit and wait, and told him to sit *there* and wait, and told the floor nurse to see that he sat *there* to wait, nowhere else.

And then the whole thing fizzled out overnight. Before I went off Tuesday evening, I checked with Silver and started the woman on penicillin and chloramphenicol, and Wednesday morning every sign and symptom of meningitis had disappeared and she was sitting up in bed complaining loudly about things and wanting to go home. I saw Silver on rounds and said, "Say, what goes with that spooky woman, anyway?" and he just shrugged and spread his hands, and said, "Who knows? I don't know." I don't think he ever found out either; he either sent her home on Thursday or she signed herself out against medical advice, I never found out which.

Had another mean diagnostic problem this week, a little girl named Kathy Jenkins, fourteen years old, a real sick cookie when she came in. She was a patient of Dr. Max Gerhard's, one of the outside GPs. He sent her in with an admitting diagnosis of acute rheumatic fever, with severe joint pain. I went up to see her Tuesday morning when she was admitted, and she sure enough had joint pain, all right. Her wrists hurt so much that she couldn't even move them; she just screamed out when you even touched them. And this pain had come on almost overnight; she'd never had anything like it before.

Which was all consistent enough with rheumatic fever, except that these were not the hot, red, swollen joints you see with rheumatic fever. I'd seen enough of those to know them when I saw them. This girl's wrists really hurt, but they looked perfectly normal, with no sign at all of *why* they should hurt. And except for a pallor and some fever she looked perfectly normal, too.

Well, this was one of those cases I was talking about where something just didn't smell right. The history she and her mother gave was just as strange as those wrist joints. She's been having headaches for the past few weeks, and they'd been getting worse and worse. She got them when she walked upstairs, and she got them when she played, and she'd been feeling just generally lousy, no pep or spunk at all. Mother had taken her to Dr. Gerhard a couple of days before she was admitted, and he had found that she had a heart murmur, they said, and that her red blood count was down to 7 grams of hemoglobin. She'd also been running afternoon fevers. Gerhard had been going to treat her at home until this wrist joint business started.

The story didn't make sense; it seemed to me the anemia was the thing to worry about, rather than the joint pain; those wrists just didn't impress me very much, although they seemed to be giving her a hell of a lot of trouble. But no fourteen-year-old girl has any good reason to have a hemoglobin of 7 grams, when 14 grams would be more normal. When I examined her she had a heart murmur, but it was a faint one that could be there just as a result of a severe anemia. I thought of a whole flock of things that could be wrong: I thought of SBE, thinking of the little Conklin boy in the Children's Division; I thought of leukemia; I thought of lupus; I wasn't ready to put my money on a damned thing.

I saw from her chart that Pete had already seen her and ordered some lab work, including a blood count and a couple of tests to rule out or confirm an acute rheumatic fever. I paged him and asked him what *he* thought was wrong with the kid. He was as baffled as I was, but he thought we had to assume rheumatic fever until proven otherwise, and suggested I order up massive doses of aspirin for the joint pain until we saw what the lab work showed and how the patient behaved.

I wrote the initial orders. That was about 11:00 Tuesday; at 1:30 I met the lab girl on my way back after lunch. She had a blood count slip in her hand and a worried look in her eye, and she said, "Well, we've sure got one here."

Just on a hunch I said, "You mean Gerhard's patient?"

"That's right. Kathy Jenkins."

"Leukemia?"

"And how." She showed me the slip, and it was a horrible-looking blood count: over 90 percent abnormal white cells with 40 percent of them the very young cells that flood out into the blood stream in a leukemia. And her hemoglobin was 7 grams, all right. Her bone marrow was making white cells at such a wild rate that there wasn't room for any red-cell formation at all.

The girl asked me if I was planning to do a bone marrow on the kid. "If you were, you'd better do it right quick, because Gerhard is going to turn this case over to Dr. Case the minute he sees this report, and Case will want to do the bone marrow himself."

I got Dr. Gerhard on the phone and told him the story. He said to go ahead with a bone marrow biopsy. I took the girl off the aspirin that afternoon and put her on codeine—she wasn't fooling about those joints hurting.

Wednesday morning we met with Case and went to see the child. The bone marrow had nailed the diagnosis beyond any doubt, an acute leukemia and probably a galloping one. Case started treating her with 6-mercaptopurine, one of the violent bone marrow depressants that sometimes slows this disease down for a while, but his guess is that she has two years at the very most, and far more likely six months.

Quite late last night I found Kathy's mother wandering around looking distraught. Gerhard and Case had both begged the question to her of what was going on early in the day, and then Case had told me I should break the news when I saw her. I sat down and talked with her for a half an hour or so, tried to break the word gently that everything pointed to leukemia, and tried to tell her something of what that implied without letting her have it right in the face. She was really thrown for a loss. She'd heard of leukemia, as all mothers have, knew that it was a fatal disease and that children die quickly from it. I didn't tell her just how quickly some of them die. And I didn't really tell her much about the disease itself, just bore down on the idea that Kathy was going to be very sick for a while, and was going to need all the support she could get from her mother—her father is dead. I figured there was plenty of time for her to learn more about what she was up against. And we'll have some clues in a few days whether Kathy is going to respond worth a damn or not. Case says the response to 6-mercaptopurine can be so dramatic you can hardly believe it, and can hold for weeks or even months before the damned thing breaks away again, but you know in a few days how it's going to act.

Well, that was Tuesday, the first half. In the afternoon I had a multitude of picayune problems, several admissions. Grabbed some supper about 5:30, chewed the fat with Pete. He thought things were quiet enough that he would go home for the evening, which was fine; we were caught up and I thought we might have a quiet evening. Then about 6:30 the nurse on Fifth called to tell me a pregnant lady of Dr. Howard Bensen's was in the house, a Mrs. Bonnino, who was having an asthma attack and Dr. Bensen had asked if I would see her. Nothing urgent, they said, she was just wheezing a little, but Dr. Bensen had sent her in to get the asthma attack under control, and they didn't have any orders for her.

So I went up to see her, and walked into a nightmare like I never hope to see again. She was a very pleasant lady, thirty-two years old, seven and a half months pregnant. Her husband was there with her; there were two other young children at home with a baby-sitter, I guess. Mrs. Bonnino had never been sick in her life, except for a case of flu about six weeks ago, and then this asthma had started a few days before. She'd had some wheezing once in a while before, but never anything like this. She'd seen Dr. Bensen in his office, and he'd given her some pills that almost stopped it but not quite. Then that afternoon it had started up suddenly and severely; she had gone to his office, and he'd given her a shot of adrenalin and tried to get her to come into the hospital, but the shot relieved the wheezing so dramatically she had gone home instead. And started wheezing even worse about 6:00 in the evening, at dinner, so she called him, and came to the hospital.

She was in worse shape than I'd expected from what the nurse had said, but she thought it had gotten worse just in the last half-hour. She was sitting up in bed the way asthmatics do, leaning forward a little bit, and you could see her work to push the air out and could hear her wheeze clear across the room. And she had a gray look that you see in people who just aren't getting quite enough oxygen. I listened to her chest, and it sounded like a typical, tight asthma; I asked her to cough, and she coughed and coughed and coughed and coughed and damned near turned black in the face, but she got up a little plug of mucus with some blood in it. Then I listened again, but the coughing hadn't cleared anything. Her heart was going at about 90 per minute, and she was really working for her air. I'd seen asthmatics before, and the more I saw her, the more I didn't like it. She was in trouble.

I went down to the nurses' desk and called Bensen and told him that this woman was just plain having trouble breathing, and it seemed to be getting worse. He said, "Oh, yes, she's got that damned asthma. Why don't you order something for her and see if you can't get it cleared up? At least get her clear for the night." I asked him if he meant adrenalin or aminophylline or what. He said, "Well, try adrenalin, or anything you want."

So I went down to her room armed with adrenalin. Sometimes people in asthma attacks get perfectly amazing, dramatic relief from an adrenalin injection; it seems to work like magic. You inject 4 or 5 minims under the skin—they can be gasping like a fish out of water and straining their guts out to push out the air trapped in their lungs, and five minutes later the bronchial spasm relaxes and they're breathing free and easy and you can hardly hear a squeak anywhere in their chests. Like a miracle. I said to Mrs. Bonnino, "Well, I talked to Dr. Bensen and I'm going to give you some medicine here that will open up your chest like magic," and gave her the injection, rubbed the injection site a bit to stimulate circulation, and then just stood around for a few minutes waiting for the miracle to occur.

It didn't. Instead, she got worse. In five or ten minutes she was showing the side effects of the adrenalin—pulse racing, a feeling of warmth and lightheadedness, all of that—but her breathing was even more labored and she got a coughing spell that didn't seem to want to stop. I listened to her chest again—the husband was standing there expectantly waiting for the hard breathing to ease up— and she was still wheezing like a leaky bellows. But there was more than just wheezing in there; there was a change in her breathing. She was pushing air out better, but she was still gasping to get more in, couldn't seem to get enough air, and her face looked even grayer than before. I didn't know what the hell was happening, but I knew she needed support, so I told the nurse to get an oxygen tank in there chop-chop, and got a mask on her and got her propped more upright in bed.

By now it was about 7:30 P.M., and I went down to the nurses' station to call Pete. I'd had the horrible thought, while I was rigging up the oxygen mask, that maybe I'd been snookered. Who said this woman had asthma? The diagnosis on the admission slip said that, and the nurse had told me she had asthma when she called me,

and Dr. Bensen said she had asthma, and I just took it for granted
that she had asthma. Now it was dawning on me that something
else might be going on. I was just ringing Pete when he strolled into
the nurses' station, so I hung up and told him there was a woman in
528 who was admitted with asthma, and seven and a half months
pregnant, and she looked bad, and asked if he'd take a look at her.
Told him what I'd seen and what I'd given her. So we went down
there together, and he looked at her, and listened to her chest and
listened, and took her pulse and listened again, and looked up at
the husband and listened again, and then said something inconse-
quential to the woman and adjusted the oxygen mask. And then he
took me to the side of the room with a funny look on his face and
said, "This is no asthma. This woman's in heart failure. Her lungs
are full of water."

"Well, that's what I thought," I said. "But I don't get it."

"Does Bensen know about this?"

"He doesn't know she's sick like this," I said.

"Well, he'd better know about it. Have you listened for the
baby?"

"No. But what's the baby got to do with it?"

"Look, this woman is starving for oxygen, and if *she's* air-hungry,
that baby is in worse shape than she is."

I thought, Oh, my God. I hadn't even thought about the baby. I
listened, and got good fetal heart tones, fast but strong enough. Pete
thought a Bennett valve might help the woman's breathing, so we
got that rigged, and it seemed to give her some relief, and she
colored up a little. Then Pete told me to give her some morphine
and some aminophylline, and also some digitalis IV, and went
down to tell Bensen to get into the hospital.

The woman rallied a bit, and we tried to get more history from
the husband. No history of heart disease, or previous heart failure,
or rheumatic fever. The only illness had been a viral pneumonia
she'd had a couple of months before. She'd been pretty sick with it,
in bed for a week and a half, then got up too soon, had a relapse
and went back to bed until just a few days ago at Bensen's orders. I
listened to this and I thought, Good Lord, do you suppose this
woman lying around in bed for two months with a baby in her
pelvis got a deep thrombophlebitis in one of her legs, and then

threw a clot to her lung when she got up? She was obviously in heart failure now, going into frank pulmonary edema right before our eyes, and after about ten minutes' rally she started getting gray and fighting for air again.

Dr. Bensen turned up, and he was obviously shocked at what he saw. He finally talked the husband into getting out of the room, and then stood around looking helpless with his gray hair and his gold-rimmed glasses and his old-maidish manner, mostly reassuring the woman over and over that everything was all right when any ass could see that everything wasn't all right, while Pete and I went to work on the heart failure. We got tourniquets on both legs and one arm, rotating them every ten minutes. She was only half-conscious now, and the tourniquets irritated her, and she kept thrashing around and shaking the Bennett valve mask off, and jerking it until the oxygen hose unplugged. She began having paroxysms of coughing and bringing up blood. We told Bensen what we'd done so far, what medications and so forth, and he just fluttered his hands and okayed anything we wanted to do, listened to the baby every five minutes or so and said, "Good heart tones, good heart tones . . ."

And she got steadily, unremittingly worse. I've sweated out heart failure and pulmonary edema before, and you can almost always turn it if you get to work early enough and really dog it. We'd gotten to work as early as most times, and we were really dogging it, but it didn't turn. By 10:00 it was obvious that what we were doing wasn't going to turn it. I was convinced we were fighting a pulmonary embolus as well as heart failure; we *had* to be fighting something else. Then Bensen said maybe we should call Lou Franklin to take a look at this girl; I called Franklin and briefed him, then said Bensen wanted him to come over right away, and Franklin said, "You mean, before she dies, huh?" but he suggested over the phone giving her a hundred and fiftieth of atropine IV and doing a phlebotomy, draining off 500 cc of blood or so, while he was on his way over.

The phlebotomy didn't seem to give the woman any relief, and neither did the atropine, but I listened for fetal heart tones this time, and could at least hear them—the baby was still with us. Then Bensen took me aside and told me to ask the night nursing supervisor to get an emergency surgical tray ready on a stand out-

side the door so that if the mother were suddenly to die he could try
to get the baby. I didn't think she was going to make it long enough
for Franklin to get there, but she did. Franklin went over the story
with us, and went over the woman, and couldn't suggest anything
we hadn't done that could be done, but she was marching steadily
downhill. He listened for heart tones and heard them, and then he
turned to Bensen said, "Howie, she's probably going to go out. If
you want that baby alive, you'd better get it out of there right here
and now."

Bensen stared at him and said, "But she might make it?"

Franklin said, "I don't think so. But sure, she might."

"But if I do a section now, it'll sacrifice the mother for sure."

"Yes. I'd guarantee that."

Bensen stared at the woman, and listened for heart tones again.
He told me to get the emergency tray in. And he stalled, and he
wrung his hands, he literally wrung his hands, and got the tray
open, and sent me down to get a gown, of all damned things, and
then some gloves, and he waited while this woman gasped for air,
and then at 11:30, after she had marched steadily downhill for five
and a half solid hours, her heart quit and she stopped breathing
and she was gone. So then Bensen opened up her belly; he had to
use a pair of scissors, there wasn't even a knife on the tray, but other
than that it was flawless technique. There weren't any fetal heart
tones then, but he got her uterus open and the baby out, and there
were tears streaming down his face behind those glasses when he
found the cord wasn't pulsating and the baby wasn't breathing, and
we had a bloody mess of a dead mother and dead child to go tell the
husband about.

By midnight there wasn't anything left for me to do. The husband
gave permission for a post, so I went down to bed for an hour. I
didn't sleep. At 1:00 I had to go see a patient who had been
admitted with belly pain; that took an hour or so, didn't amount to
anything. Back to bed for another hour, and got called to come up
and admit a patient of Dr. Isaacs' who was in with pulmonary
edema. I saw the man, and wasn't impressed, no great trouble;
Isaacs had seen him at home and started medications there, and
already the man was feeling better. He'd had a coronary seven years
before, and recently had been waking up in the night with shortness

of breath, especially bad this particular night. I went down to write an admission note, and tangled with the patient's wife. She was one of these twittery ladies who was just all over the place, didn't know whether she should go home or stay at the hospital, just didn't know. I said I thought the man was certainly seriously ill but he didn't look critically ill, and I thought she could go home, she could be sure we'd let her know if anything went sour.

I was pretty abrupt with her, I was just wrung out, but she trotted off down the stairs. She couldn't have been gone ten minutes —I was still writing up my admission note—when the nurse came rushing out and said the man was in trouble. He let out a holler I could hear all the way down the hall, and was clutching his chest and writhing in pain, blue in the face and gasping by the time I got to the bedside, and then there was no heartbeat, no respirations, nothing, he was dead—boom, like that. I figured he must have blown out an infarcted heart wall, or had a pulmonary embolus, or had a new massive coronary on the spot—probably the latter. Called Isaacs, and he said he'd call the wife at home and tell her the man had died, and also ask for a post. (I learned later that she refused the post, and had been very abusive toward the house staff and the hospital. Can't really blame the lady. I suppose it should teach me not to go telling people things; I don't know.)

Wednesday morning I went down to the morgue and watched the post on Mrs. Bonnino. It didn't tell us much. She had massive pulmonary edema, which we knew, but there was no sign of a pulmonary embolus, and nothing else to account for what had happened to her. This didn't make her or the baby any less dead, however. Lou Franklin came up with a cheering thought when we were talking about it over morning coffee, said the history and progress of the thing made him wonder about the plague, which none of us had even thought of. The idea gave me a chill for a while, but I understand they didn't find any *Pasteurella pestis* in the cultures they took from her lungs.

But last night it caught up with me, and I couldn't get it out of my mind that it just should never have happened. There should have been some salvage—should have been and could have been. And I keep seeing Howard Bensen in my mind, with tears pouring down his face, opening that dead woman's belly—a sad little man, mild, scared, helpless, ineffectual, desperate, bewildered.

And cowardly, let's face it. The chips were down, and he knew what he had to do, and he just didn't have guts enough to do it. I swear to Christ I would have taken that baby. But that isn't fair either; I say that now when I know the woman died. Retrospect makes the answers easy. I just hope to Christ I don't ever have to make such a decision. Who could ever be wise enough for that?

Wednesday, May 16

A follow-up on Kathy Jenkins. There was no question of the diagnosis; blood smears and bone marrow studies both showed acute leukemia, and Andy Case was called in to deal the cards, since this kind of trouble is in his special field. He gave her some packed red cells and pushed her hemoglobin up to 10 or 11 grams, then gave her some more, got it up to 14 grams where it belonged. He also started her on 6-mercaptopurine, hoping this would poison her bone marrow enough to slow down the wild white cell production that was going on. Her joints were still troublesome; the left wrist cleared up, but the right one was still very painful and Andy finally gave her some ACTH to help that. It wasn't long before she was actually looking pretty good and feeling immensely better, so yesterday Case packed her off home again. But it was strictly *auf wiedersehen*, not goodbye. Andy had talked to the mother and told her the story, namely, that the child was going to be chronically and recurrently ill, and very soon critically ill, and that six months was about all she could expect, even though some of these kiddies have been known to live for as much as a year or two sometimes. Privately he told me that there wasn't nearly the response to the 6-mercaptopurine he had hoped to see by now, which probably means that one of the major weapons against this disease is going to go out the window very soon.

And after watching Kathy during this week or so I have a sneaky clinical hunch that this girl is going to go sour right from the start. She may get along okay for a month or so, but then I'll bet it's going to be all downhill, and downhill fast, and right out of the picture. She's a cute little gal, and a bright one, even though she's spoiled rotten, and very sassy to some of the floor nurses. You can't get mad at her; personally, I'd be willing to put up with a whole lot of crap from a little girl like this because she's not going to have very much time to be sassy to people.

There were a couple of other admissions last week I had intended to mention. One was Mrs. Callahan, a cheery little lady of about fifty who came in with a blood pressure of 240 over 180, with headaches, failing vision and nausea, and literally reeking from her uremia. I worked her up and made a guess from the smell of her breath that her blood urea was over 100; the lab reported 107 against a normal of 12, so her kidneys are all beat to hell by the hypertension, or getting beat to hell in an awful rush. So are her eyes—half a dozen fresh retinal hemorrhages. She was a patient of Dr. Isaacs', who sort of dumped her into Pete's lap and thus also into mine. Together we got her started on antihypertensive drugs, and by early this week she seemed to be responding: blood pressure down to 140 over 90, and all her symptoms relieved completely. And through the whole week she was cheerful as could be.

I couldn't help but be reminded of Hattie Stevens; this woman is probably going to go out just the way Hattie did, but then you never know. We chewed the fat with Lou Franklin about these galloping hypertensions and he claims that there is some point in the natural history of the disease where it reaches an irreversible stage. If you get at it before then, you can maybe turn it, at least enough to prolong life for years. If the irreversible stage has already been reached, you may get temporary reversal but you're really just fooling yourself, the game is already lost. The trouble is, you never know which side of the line you're on. With this gal I keep hoping that we are halting the progress of a dreadful disease process that we just don't understand very well; I wish she could spend about two months in the hospital so we could follow her closely and see how far out of the woods we can get her, but that's too costly. We'll have to settle for whatever follow-up we can get from Isaacs, who will be seeing her in his office.

One of the weekend delights was fat old Mr. Herman Grossman, a diabetic patient of Ned Stern's who was admitted with severe chest pain and possible coronary. He was very belligerent, didn't think he'd had any coronary, and on Saturday his EKG didn't show anything very exciting. He didn't want to be in the hospital, and refused to follow any coronary routine of care, and he fought the nurses and he fought me and he fought everybody. Then Sunday, over loud protest from Mr. Grossman, I took another EKG that showed unmistakable changes. He had a coronary all right. So Ned Stern came in Sunday afternoon and just laid down the law to Mr. Grossman.

Ned pulled a very neat trick, I thought. We went in to Mr. Grossman's room, and Ned told the old goat what the EKG showed and told him what it meant. Then he said, "Now, I'm going to let you mull this over for a while, because if I'm supposed to be responsible for your care, I'm going to write the orders and you're going to follow them. I'll be back in a while, and you can tell me what you've decided—to do what I say or to get another doctor. You're the one with trouble, not me." We left his room and went down and drank some coffee, then came back up to get the guy's answer. Mr. Grossman must have been pretty shaken up to hear a doctor lay it on the line, I guess. He was all sweetness and light and jolly-good-fellow by the time we returned. So Ned looked grim and just gave the guy hell for not doing what he was told and for acting like a simpleton; he was going to lie on his back and behave, and shut up and do as he was told, and that was going to be the law for the next thirty days if he lived that long, and that was all there was to it. Then after we left, Ned grinned at me and said, "Just gotta get tough sometimes with some of these meat-heads." It worked, though. I guess he scared the bejesus out of Mr. Herman Grossman—he's been meek as a lamb ever since.

The rest of the weekend was taken up with little chores, enough to keep me busy but not enough to overwork me. Then Monday the ax dropped: ten admissions, two that were especially interesting. One was a thirty-year-old housewife who had been complaining of funny pains in her legs and arms off and on for five years. Three years before, she'd gone blind in one eye for a few hours, went to the doctor, but the sight had come back by the time she'd sat in his waiting room for an hour. Then later the same thing happened with the other eye, and she started to see double from time to time. Then off and on leg pains, cramps, etc. Listening to this story, it seemed to me she might have been reading me the textbook description of early multiple sclerosis paragraph by paragraph. Physical examination showed some characteristic neurological changes, too. Calvin Cornell saw her today and agreed that she was MS. Apparently she went to Dr. Case because a couple of other doctors had tried to weasel out of saying what was wrong with her, which made her sore. Case talked to Cornell and then went in and told her straight out, which is the only thing to do, it seems to me, especially when the patient is an intelligent, capable woman like this. She wasn't happy at the news, but at least now she has something to grapple with instead of "ghoulies and ghosties and long-legged beasties," as she put it.

The other interesting admission Monday was an eighteen-year-old girl with pain and swelling in her ankles and knees, together with sporadic fevers. She was a very strange girl. She'd just seen Case in the clinic prior to admission, and when I went in to see her, she was extremely hostile, didn't even want to say hello. Of course, lots of people are bored or annoyed at having to give the intern the same story they told to their own doctor just an hour ago, but it was more than that with this girl. She was a very lush-looking girl, too, but so flat in her responses that she reminded me of some of the young schizophrenics we had to deal with in medical school. I worked her up anyway, decided she probably had an early rheumatoid arthritis, but also wrote on the chart that I thought lupus had to be ruled out. Then on rounds with Andy Case today he saw my note on the chart and said, "Well, Doctor, you should have the courage of your convictions." Seems that lupus had been his first choice, and the lab today reported that they had found LE cells in her blood smear, which are pathognomonic of lupus—you never find them with anything else. It's not a very cheery outlook for an eighteen-year-old girl, even with the steroid hormones; Case seems to think that two years is about all she can count on now. He also agrees that she's schizy as hell, so she may be spending the two years locked up in a nut ward somewhere.

Yesterday was a horrible day, something like fourteen medical admissions in all. It was just as well I had the duty; I was working up new patients as fast as I could run from 2:00 in the afternoon until midnight without even time out for supper. Some of them were sick, too. One was a little ten-year-old boy with a history of fever, sore throat, headaches and nosebleeds. He came in because he'd suddenly developed pinpoint skin hemorrhages all over his body. When I first saw him I thought, Oh, Lord, here we go again, another Kathy Jenkins. The boy was white as a sheet and had a big, tender, enlarged spleen and black-and-blue marks all over him. Also some big mushy nodes in his neck. I thought sure he had leukemia. When Case came in after supper to check him, we made some blood smears, and then went down and peered through the microscope at them for half an hour or so. There were abnormal cells there, all right, but Case finally decided pretty definitely that it was infectious mononucleosis, not leukemia. We still have to get a heterophil test to be sure, but for everybody's sake I hope he's right. At least you get over mononucleosis.

A little let-up today, and I got off on time. So far this service is about twice as lively as it needs to be to keep me happy. But Andy Case isn't nearly as bad to work with as I thought he might be, and I haven't really seen much of Fred Kidder. Maybe he's just avoiding me.

Friday, May 18

Got off to a slow start yesterday morning. I met Pete on Fifth to see who was going to make teaching rounds with us, and this time Fred Kidder caught up with us. He walked off the elevator and gave us his little weasel grin and said, "Well! The Bad News Twins again, huh?" We spent a good three hours with him on rounds, seeing a variety of patients, including two consultations on patients he had never seen before, which took him an hour apiece. He is very slow working up a patient, just painfully slow, utterly meticulous and perfectionistic; and he kept throwing questions at me or Pete throughout both these consultations which he knew damned well we couldn't answer, and then either just grinned or made sarcastic remarks in that nasal voice of his. No fun at all, but you have to admire him, in a way. He is surely a smart boy, and he has a lot to teach.

After Fred finally left us, Pete and I caught up on rounds on other patients we've been following. The boy's heterophil test was back, positive to a titer of 1:6500. A titer of 1:21 or more is diagnostic of infectious mononucleosis, so he really has it and not leukemia. He's had no more nosebleeds, and even though he feels like hell and looks like hell, Case says he'll be okay, just will have to stay down and inactive until the virus that causes that disease gets tired and goes away. "As long," he added, "as one of you guys doesn't go poking his spleen too vigorously and rupture it for him." This evolved into a discussion of how people get infectious mono; it's one of these mystery virus infections that nobody knows too much about except that it's benign, just annoying, and it's known as "the kissing disease" because it turns up so often in prep school and college students following Thanksgiving or Christmas holidays. Pete remarked in his stuffy, deadpan way that this didn't seem too likely an etiology in this boy's case, and Case grinned and said, well, maybe not, but you couldn't always take things like that for granted.

After lunch we met with Compton and Stern for their weekly diabetic conference—they spend a couple of hours reviewing problem cases they've had. There was one boy there who had handed them a scare: a thirteen-year-old boy who had come in to see Gillies because he'd been losing weight for about six weeks without any apparent reason. No history of diabetes, and Gillies hadn't even given it serious thought, started looking for tapeworms in his stool and signs of lymphoma and other things, but he also drew a blood sugar and sent a urine specimen to the lab before the boy left the office. Report came back that the urine had 4-plus sugar in it, and the blood sugar was so sky-high the lab girl thought it was drawn from a new patient in diabetic coma. Gillies and Stern both thought if the boy wasn't in coma he was likely to be damned soon, but when they tried to call his home they learned he was off with his family on a weekend trip. They had to stir up the State Patrol in four counties to finally locate the people and drag the kid into the hospital to get him under control before he just conked out and died.

Then Thursday night we spent half the night fooling with another diabetic, an old man Compton sent in with insulin shock. The poor old goat must have had practically no blood sugar at all; it appeared that he'd given himself his daily 60 units of insulin three successive times in the same hour that morning because each time he couldn't quite remember whether he had taken his insulin or not. He'd passed out by 10:30 in the morning, and the family had thought he was taking a morning snooze and hadn't gotten around to calling anybody until suppertime. The poor old guy had had a coronary in the past, and a series of little strokes, and he just didn't want to pull out of his insulin shock for anything. Just lay there in bed sweating and snoring while Pete and I dogged him until midnight. We didn't dare get too heroic giving him sugar because these people can be very brittle and swing all the way from profound insulin shock to fatal diabetic coma in a couple of hours if you don't just watch them every minute. He finally began to respond around midnight, but was so confused that he got wildly excited, couldn't get oriented, tried to hurl himself out of bed and so on. This morning he still wasn't with it. Compton finally, reluctantly, slugged him down with paraldehyde. He's probably had some cerebrovascular damage, because he surely should have come out of insulin shock more quickly if that was all it was.

At midnight supper I talked to Pete about the state licensure exams which I'll have to take after internship is over—I think they're coming up the week of July 11th, four days of tests. Pete brought over a file of old tests for me to look at, but I'm going to have to study, I'm afraid, much as I don't like the idea right now. Pete says the clinical part isn't bad but the basic sciences exams are vicious. I haven't cracked a physiology book now in over three years; I wonder if I remember anything at all about it.

A busy day today, but not too frantic. Spent the last hour getting some charts up to date, and then left things in Alec's hands and took off for a long Friday-night-through-Sunday weekend. The weather is getting warmer, summer is almost upon us, and the end of this game is getting within sight, and everybody can feel it in the wind, I think.

Monday, May 28

Another very busy and hectic stretch; we are working at a dead run all day and late into the evening whether on duty nights or not. The pressure is beginning to catch up with me and Pete again, too; we're sitting making bad jokes and giggling like schoolgirls on the rare occasions when we both come up for air at the same time. I don't think it's just us; I think the whole hospital is excessively busy, and everybody else has the feeling of immense pressure and the need for comic relief somehow. We've had a rash of silly nicknames for patients lately, nicknames everyone has been picking up and using. For example, there is little Sharon Bibble, the four-year-old girl with leukemia since last August, who has become a sort of permanent resident on the fourth floor. I have to give her packed cells or whole blood about three times a week, a procedure that she hates. She is almost terminal now, and so full of cortisone that her face is puffy and her tummy sticks out because of her enlarged spleen and liver. The nurses on the floor began calling her Little Bubble because she is constantly there, inoffensive but awkward, like a water blister.

In spite of my ministrations, I seem to have scored somehow with Little Bubble; as soon as I come onto the floor, there she is at my elbow. She never smiles, and she won't let me touch her, but I will sit at the desk writing up an admission note and she will stand there at my elbow watching me. It is a little nerve-racking trying to think my way through some diagnostic problem and get it down on paper with this tiny, solemn creature standing there *very* close to my elbow, scrutinizing what I am doing *very sharply*. If I turn to look at her, she backs away one pace. If I say hello, she comes a pace closer. But most solemnly, gravely. Little Bubble is a bother, but we are so glad that she can be out of bed and walking around that nobody wants to speak crossly to her. I don't know why she picks me for her attentions, however.

Then we have had old Mrs. Beady-Eyes to deal with this week, and continuing warfare with her crew of special nurses. Mrs. Beady-Eyes was a patient of Dr. Fuller's who came in early last week, about sixty-two years old, admitted for heart failure and a possible pneumonia. She was having episodic bouts of shortness of breath. Her real name was Mrs. Beadle, but she was the most malevolent-looking old witch I've ever seen in my life. I went in to work her up and she wouldn't say anything to me, just lay there watching my every move with these suspicious little hard eyes of hers. I guess I started the "Mrs. Beady-Eyes" bit, and everybody in the place picked it up. She was sick and she got sicker; the second day she was there she had developed a sea-gull murmur she hadn't had the day before, probably blew a hole through her heart septum or one of the valves of something, and got violently sicker. Didn't respond well to treatment for her heart failure and kept having spells; she turned blue and choked and everybody thought she was going to die.

Finally Armand Fuller ordered round-the-clock special nurses for her, and that was his big mistake, I think. They got the richest crew of special nurses I ever saw in my life. There was one on the 7:00-to-3:00 day shift who got to be known among the house staff as Old Tugboat: a perfectly huge woman, she must have weighed in at three hundred pounds, over six feet tall, just vast in size; she would move ponderously down the corridor and the whole building would shake. Old Tugboat was also a lousy nurse; she wanted more than anything else to be down in the nurses' station chatting with the other nurses, or down drinking coffee instead of with her patient, and when she was in with Mrs. Beady-Eyes, she didn't want to have to be doing anything for the old girl. Consequently, from the first day she came on special duty, Old Tugboat began militating for more and better sedation for Mrs. Beady-Eyes.

For hours the old lady would just lie there in a heap on the bed, and then suddenly have a choking spell and get blue, and then get all excited and start thrashing around the bed and shouting and screaming that she was dying, and have to be taken care of and watched so that she didn't throw herself out of bed. Old Tugboat disliked these unpleasant episodes the most; she asked permission to put restraints on the old lady, and when that was refused, she became determined that Mrs. Beady-Eyes was going to be so slugged out with Demerol and Luminal that she wouldn't have any non-sense out of her. I mean, she wanted her *out cold all the time,* and set about calling interns, residents, anybody she could get her hands on, for special sedation orders. The other specials followed suit; every time Mrs. Beady-Eyes got an episode of excitement, they would track somebody down for a special order.

Well, this began to wear thin. I told Milt Musser that something was going to have to be done, I thought the old girl was being deliberately oversedated by the specials. He looked at the chart and saw how much Demerol she was being given, one way or another, by about the fifth day, and said, "My God! No wonder she's having trouble breathing!" He asked Fuller about it, and Fuller said to cut off all sedation altogether, that the patient didn't need any sedation, she was barely alive as it was.

So we discontinued all sedatives, and for the next four or five days those goddamned specials were just crawling down our throats. If we wouldn't order something for her over the telephone, they insisted we come up and see her, like about every three hours, and of course by the time we got up to see her the choking episodes were invariably over and the patient was lying there snoring like a baby. All day, all night, the same old crap. I was getting so refractory to those nurses, and to Old Tugboat especially, that I wouldn't go see the woman at all if I could possibly help it.

For a while she got a bit better. We could tell, because she started looking around and blinking and screaming that she was dying again. But then her failure got worse and wouldn't turn, and on at least five occasions the specials decided that she had just died and called me to confirm this impression. Three times this happened about 3:30 A.M., and I had to drag myself out of bed and confirm that she was indeed not dead, she's simply quit breathing quite so loudly for a few minutes. On one occasion Milt Musser swore that if Old Tugboat ever so much as spoke another word to him about this patient he was going to rise up and brain her with the nearest ashtray.

Of course, finally Mrs. Beady-Eyes shuffled off, truly and sincerely dead, and the post showed that she had indeed blown a hole through her heart septum. So she was going to have died anyway, no matter what anybody did or did not do for her, but the consensus was that she might have managed it a little sooner, and that it was a living wonder that she'd made it for forty-eight hours with these Florence Nightingales hovering over her bed. Anyway, that was the sad tale of Mrs. Beady-Eyes.

The weekend was rough, a total of fourteen or fifteen admissions, and lots of sick people around the place. I had packed cells to give to Little Bubble, which is an afternoon's work in itself; I had Old Tugboat on my back night and day; we had a weird one come in Saturday evening that I'm too bushed to go into right now except that it was, and is, the damnedest case we've run across yet, and nobody knows what's wrong with her. She took me all Saturday night and most of Sunday running in and out to make sure she hadn't either (1) died or (2) changed in some way to give us a clue as to what was wrong. By the time this morning came along I didn't care whether school kept or not, got up for rounds, then went back to bed about 10:30 and slept until my first admission came in at 1:00. Home by 9:30 this evening, which is about par for the course.

Tuesday, June 5

Very busy, and time is moving very fast. This is the first week of the second month of Medicine II, and of the last month of this internship year. So far this has been by far the most busy, active and interesting service of the year, and I imagine that the rest of this final month will follow suit. The work is beginning to break down into a pattern. I can see how the weeks go and plan accordingly.

Monday is usually the major heavy day of the week; I don't think there's been a Monday yet on this service that there haven't been eight or nine medical admissions at least. When I have the duty Monday nights, we will frequently run up to sixteen or eighteen admissions in a twenty-four-hour period, which is just a dreadful load of new patients to work up. Monday mornings we have teaching rounds with Ned Stern and Jacob Compton from 8:00 until 10:00, and by then I usually have my first new patient in, and Pete and I split up. He makes rounds on all the rest of the incumbent patients while I start seeing the new admissions and working them up. From time to time I run into Pete in a corridor or nurses' station and report to him on who is in with what kind of problems, and tell him which I think he should be sure to see and which don't seem to have any very important problem. Occasionally, when I get jammed up with too many coming in at once, he will see some and work them up, and then tell me he's seen them already so I won't need to bother until or unless I have the chance. Monday afternoons they are coming in thick and fast; a rough diagnostic problem can suck up a couple of hours, but there are so many that it's sometimes hard to keep them straight. But not so hard now as before.

It's amazing how I find I can compartmentalize these people, tucking away their admitting complaint and history and physical findings and how they look in my mind, and later tuck lab reports and other men's opinions and responses to medications and all sorts of other data into the same compartment; I may have twenty-five or thirty such compartments, all "active," going in my mind at the same time, and never get them confused. I know damned well that I could tonight sit down and list every single one of the patients in our service—about thirty-eight right now—and give explicit details of their total history and progress since I first saw them, right down to the time of day they turned up in the hospital, and the actual figures on their lab reports. Given enough paper and enough time to write it, I would have the total detail on at least thirty of the thirty-eight correct in even the most minute and specific detail and the other eight I would have correct in general. I read somewhere that a good doctor has to have an indelible memory for trivia, and I guess it's true. But the data storage and selectability that goes on in this game is hard to believe and damned near impossible to understand. You just take it for granted that it's going to work that way, and so it does.

Anyway, if I'm off duty on Monday, I end up working up the real sick ones and sneak away at 9:00 or 9:30, feeling guilty at leaving three or four unworked up. If I have duty on Monday, as I did last night, I'm generally working until ten or eleven or even beyond midnight just catching up on loose ends. They keep admitting right straight through 9:30 or 10:00 in the evening, too.

Tuesdays are often just as loaded as Mondays, sometimes even worse, but less predictable. One Tuesday I had only two admissions; the next I had ten. Tuesday mornings we make teaching rounds with Dick Rivers, and thereafter any time a new patient comes in I drop whatever I'm doing and go work him up so as not to get behind. Wednesdays tend to be lighter; we make rounds with Andy Case after our breakfast meeting, seeing his patients. He's had a very heavy service since I came on, which I guess is a little unusual. Thursdays are frequently quite light on admissions; we make rounds with Fred Kidder in the morning, which takes more time than usual. Fred, as I've said, takes the long way around, and we seldom break up much before 11:00. Fridays may be very busy, since for some reason a lot of the outside doctors seem to admit patients on Fridays.

And together with the rounds and the work-ups on new patients and the follow-ups on old patients there are always procedures popping up: LPs to be done; somebody's chest or abdomen to be tapped for fluid; packed red cells to be started and nursed along on a leukemic; a bone marrow tap to do; dozens of things which get all scrambled up.

Duty weekends are surely no relief; we seem to have a lot of sick patients that need care, and the attending men are not as readily available, so we have to handle more responsibility ourselves. Usually I've been working all day Saturday and straight through until 3:30 or 4:00 A.M. Sunday, then sleep in through breakfast Sunday morning until they start screaming for me, which is about 9:00. Then back up on the floors to check on lab reports that are back, run EKGs that can't wait until Monday, start blood transfusions—enough to keep me busy until the Sunday afternoon admissions start. And lots of these are scheduled admissions of patients coming in for diagnostic studies, so we have long histories and careful physical examinations to do.

So that is the way the weeks go. It seems like every minute counts, there just isn't time enough in any one day to get half done with what needs to be done; it's just a question of what you can slough off the most safely. Yesterday about 4:00 I sat down for a minute and figured out that with new patients waiting to be worked up, and with the procedures I knew I *had* to do that day, I had twelve more hours' straight work lined up already, assuming no further interruptions of any kind, and assuming I worked at as fast a clip as I could.

I even figured out that I lost five minutes on each new admission just because of the paging system. I hear my page, pick up a phone and dial operator; there is a minute's delay while the operator gets to answering my return call, then she tells me that there is a patient for me on the fourth floor. Then I ring the floor to find out if the patient is dying on the spot or can wait until I get there. One line is busy, so I ring the other line and get a ward clerk who never heard of the patient in question. There is a three-minute delay while she goes to hunt up the nurse who paged me in the first place, and presently, after five minutes on the telephone, I learn that it's a routine admission, nothing crash emergency about it. It seems petty, but with ten new admissions, and this lost five minutes for each one, that's another hour shot in the course of the day. Give me a total of a half-hour for meals, and this also adds up to less work time.

At least I feel more confident now; I can form an opinion about the patient's trouble in a half or three-quarters of an hour per patient. I haven't really missed anything too serious since I came back on the medical service here. I have picked up a number of things that hadn't been picked up before as well. One big help is the series of "routines" I have in mind for most categories of patients—maybe I should call them "screening programs." Any patient over fifty who hasn't been in the hospital for a while (or *any* patient with a cardiac history) is automatically going to require an EKG, a chest film and blood nitrogen levels unless they have just been done in the doctor's office. The same with anybody with hypertension. I have in mind a different screening program for patients with upper gastrointestinal complaints; another for lower bowel complaints; and so forth.

Of course, there are plenty of patients who won't categorize so nicely. Like the patient who comes in about once a week, always about 9:30 in the evening, with an admitting diagnosis of "chronic nervous exhaustion." This is the sort of patient who just kills you at that time of day; you've just finished admitting ten patients and don't feel like doing one damn thing right then that isn't absolutely critical.

I've noticed a big change in attitude in the various attending men in regard to the house staff in general and me in particular, as compared with the beginning of the year. What we used to ask about before, we now just go ahead and do. When I first came on this service I practically had to wrench bone marrow biopsies out of Andy Case's hands by force and guile; now he calls over from the clinic and says, "Look, I'm sending Mrs. So-and-So over, and I want her to have two units of whole blood, but would you do a bone marrow on her before you start the first unit?" and that's all there is to it. Dr. Isaacs, who was so very, very chilly to me when I first came to the hospital, was so pleased with the way I worked with his hypertensive Mrs. Callahan (who is limping along all right, I learn, not getting worse at any rate) that he practically gives me *carte blanche* on his hospital patients now—tells me to go ahead and write what orders I want, just keep him posted on any problems, and often pages me when he comes in to make rounds so that I can join him if I am free.

So we go along. Little Bubble went home for about a week, now is back in for more packed red cells, her usual taciturn little self, although the past few days she's been feeling pretty well and has been following me around on the fourth floor again. The nurses all think this is screamingly funny. She won't say a word to me, and she won't take hold of my hand or anything like that, but she follows me on rounds. She stood by solemnly watching me do two LPs yesterday, peeking through the drapes, then followed me down to watch me write up the charts. What all this attention from this little four-year-old girl means, I don't know. She is a strange-looking creature, with her face all puffy from her cortisone and her large protuberant abdomen; she wears this pink starched dress, a frilly thing that comes straight down behind and sticks out at a 45-degree angle in front, so that she looks as though she is tilting backward; and then she wears a little tweed coat over this. She has also picked a couple of old men on the fourth floor as her special friends, and goes down to watch them play solitaire.

Case is going to send her home again if he can, but fears her next admission she will stay; he thinks she has another three months at the most. She's had her leukemia for a year now, and has responded well to her treatment; she wouldn't have lived more than two months from its onset without treatment. But now she isn't making any red cells at all, and is being kept alive solely on transfusions. Case says soon she'll begin having fevers and begin wasting away and ultimately die of an overwhelming blood poisoning from some minor scratch or bruise or sore throat.

I wanted to say something about the oddball case that came in on my last duty weekend, on the twenty-seventh, I think it was. A real puzzler, and still a puzzler. It was a ragged weekend, and I was just gulping some supper Saturday night when Luke Hamilton called me from the Emergency Room to say he was sending up a patient to be admitted on Dr. Rivers' service. He said the woman wasn't diabetic, nor comatose, but totally disoriented. She lived in the apart-

ment building across from the hospital, and her landlord had found
her walking around the halls in her nightgown banging on people's
doors.

I went up to see the woman—her name was Myrtle Fraser—and I
knew I'd seen her around the hospital. She was one of the maids,
one of these little people who come out of the woodwork at night and
go around scrubbing things. She was lying in bed with her eyes wide-
open, but she wouldn't or couldn't answer any questions whatever.
Her eyes were very, very red, and I thought her tongue deviated to
the left. All through the examination she kept patting my arm and
patting the side rail, and trying to sit up, but she didn't show any
sign of responding to anything I said, almost as though she were
completely cut off from her normal environment.

Well, naturally in a fifty-five-year-old woman I thought she'd had
a stroke, but something didn't add up. Then, while I tried to talk to
her I suddenly realized that she couldn't see nor hear. She didn't
turn when I spoke to her, and her eyes were moving back and forth
in the sort of searching nystagmus that you see in the suddenly
blind. It also dawned on me that the reason her eyes were so very
red was that she wasn't blinking. I watched her for ten minutes
straight, and made passes at her eyes with my hand and then with a
flashlight, and Myrtle didn't blink once in all that time. Other
things were odd: there was no odor on her breath, but there were
black-and-blue marks all over her body, and these looked two or
three days old. I remembered that Luke had said the landlord had
found a lot of furniture knocked over in her room.

So I called Pete to see her. I was wondering about a stroke now,
wondered if maybe she'd been attacked, and cracked on the head
with resulting brain injury; also wondered if she could have been
poisoned with something. Oh, yes, she also had a temperature of 105
when she came in.

I called Pete and he called Dick Rivers and both of them saw her,
and neither one had any better idea of what was going on than I
did. We called somebody in her family long distance and got a
history from a sister that this woman tippled a good deal, in fact
drank quite heavily and had done so for quite some time, and once
had had trouble with her liver from it. Pete thought maybe she'd
gotten into some wood alcohol; we even went over and tried to get a

look in her room but couldn't rouse her landlord. (Later we found out that there was no alcohol of any kind, nor empty bottles, in her room.) We did an LP on her and got perfectly clear fluid, no blood in it at all, as there ought to be if she had had a crippling blow on the head. So there we sat. About 2:00 A.M. after we had sponged her temp down to 103, she at least began blinking her eyes and began looking a little better, but by morning—that was Sunday—she began convulsing, so she's had to be loaded up with barbiturates to control her seizures.

She's been in the hospital a week now, and we still don't have a diagnosis. It certainly looks like a poisoning of some sort. The day after she was admitted she went into kidney failure, passed a grand total of one ounce of urine in thirty-six hours, and everybody thought she was going out on us for sure. Then the kidney failure seemed to stop and she nearly flooded herself out of the room one day, passed two and a half quarts of urine and we thought she would never stop. Rivers' theory is that Myrtle has some kind of mass lesion in her head, and hemorrhaged from it, and then had a vascular collapse that caused the kidney shutdown—which seems to me to be hanging an awful lot onto an awful little. Cal Cornell saw her and thinks she has a Korsakoff's syndrome—sort of massive brain deterioration from long-standing alcoholism, the "gin-soaked brain" which suddenly caught up with her. I don't know what the hell she has; I think she was poisoned with something but I don't know what. She's alive, which amazes me, but she's still utterly disoriented; she can converse, but she can't remember anything you tell her for longer than five minutes and she confabulates all over the place. At any rate, she isn't getting any worse. So at this point old Myrtle is hanging in mid-air. We'll see what happens, if anything.

Wednesday, June 13

Well, this will be mostly to continue the chronicle of old Myrtle Fraser. We have learned a lot about old Myrtle since I last wrote, and talk about a cat and its nine lives—old Myrtle has no right to be with us about five times over by now, but she is still with us. I think God must have made old Myrtle of sterner stuff than he made the rest of us. We have not only learned about Myrtle; we've learned about Myrtle's family, and if old Myrtle is balmy, her family is even balmier. Or else Myrtle is very, very rich and nobody but her family knows it.

As I said, by the first of last week this old girl, who had been a night maid at the hospital, was doing pretty well, but didn't have her wiring connected right. No diagnosis, and nothing to do but sit by and wait for her to get better or something. Dick Rivers took off last week for the AMA convention in the East and left Ned Stern in charge of the case. Myrtle was really not entirely with us; she'd gotten her vision back, and her hearing, but she still couldn't give us a particle of history of what had happened to her. She couldn't remember long enough. You'd go in and ask her a question, and she would scratch her chin and appear to consider a bit before answering, but in the course of about twenty seconds of considering she'd forget what it was you asked her. Or even that you had asked her anything. Then she'd ask where she was; you'd say, "Now, Myrtle, where do you think you are?" and she'd say, "Why, in Graystone Hospital, of course!" very indignantly.

Anyway, in the midst of this confusion last Wednesday morning a couple of Myrtle's sisters trouped in from Los Angeles, and wanted Myrtle to sign power of attorney over to them; apparently there was a safe deposit box or something they wanted to get at. They tackled Stern about this, and Stern said no dice, we didn't even have Myrtle diagnosed, didn't know the cause of her troubles, and he surely didn't think she was mentally competent right then to sign over power of attorney to anybody. So he wouldn't approve or witness any such transaction. This made the sisters mad as hops. They tried to get Carey to approve, and they tried to find out where Rivers was—a very, very snotty crowd of people.

Well, there wasn't anything they could do, but then Wednesday afternoon old Myrtle blew up on us. The sisters were standing around trying to talk lucid sense to this far-from-lucid old girl when Myrtle suddenly remarked that she had to go to the john, and when the nurses slipped a bedpan under her, she poured forth a full bedpanful of bright red blood from her colon, and promptly went into shock. This was a double jolt; for one thing, nobody had any idea that Myrtle was bleeding from anywhere, and, number two, she had developed some phlebitis in her leg and I, in my infinite wisdom, had talked Stern into putting her on anticoagulants, a decision he had agreed to more or less reluctantly. Anyway, when this blood came out in the bedpan, the nurses hollered for me and I hollered for Pete and Pete hollered for Stern. She was obviously bleeding massively somewhere in her GI tract, but we had no idea where, no GI X-rays, no nothing. She hadn't thrown up any blood, but there was that drinking and liver disease history, and there was the awful prospect that she had esophageal varices that were bleeding.

We ordered up 4 units of whole blood and poured it into her and gave her vitamin K to counteract the anticoagulants, and used plasma and dextran and Aramine and everything we could think of to pull her out of shock, and she kept pouring blood out of her rectum just as fast as we poured it into her arm. We'd get her blood pressure up to about 120 and she'd do fine for a few hours, and then it would sag down to 90, and some more blood would come out and she'd go shocky again. We gave her 4 more units of blood on Thursday morning and she quieted down until evening, then started bleeding again and went into profound shock. We were really just waiting for her to stop bleeding, and she wouldn't do it.

Well, her family was much upset with Stern because he wouldn't go along with the power of attorney deal; and now they decided that Myrtle was going to die anyway, so Friday morning they informed us that Myrtle was not to be given any more blood. That same morning I met Ned Stern on the floor and asked him when he was going to get the surgeons in to have a look at old Myrtle. Ned looked a little surprised and said, "What do you think the surgeons could do?" So I said, "Well, if nothing else, they could open her up and find out what she's bleeding from." Ned seemed to regard this as a totally alien thought—I guess it just hadn't entered his mind to have a surgical consultation—but a few minutes later when Arthur Emery came onto the floor, he asked Emery to take a look at the woman.

Emery went down to look at her and reviewed her chart, and came back to tell Stern that she was sure a foul risk for any kind of surgery, but she was going to bleed to death unless somebody stopped her, and if he could be sure she wasn't bleeding from esophageal varices, he would be willing to go in and try to find out what she *was* bleeding from. So I put a Levin tube down into Myrtle's stomach and sucked out some yellow gastric juice but no blood, pretty good proof that she was bleeding from somewhere below her stomach, at any rate.

About this time the nurse came back with the bottle of blood she had gone to start and told us the family absolutely refused to allow her to start it on Myrtle, they weren't going to permit her to have any more blood, and they didn't think Dr. Stern knew what he was doing, and blah, blah, blah. Myrtle was getting shocky again, so we went down to her room and found the family on both sides of the bed determined to prevent anyone from starting another unit of blood. We argued and argued, and finally had to physically eject these two old harpies from the room to get the blood started. Then Ned went down and told them loud and clear that the blood was the only thing keeping Myrtle alive and he had ordered it given, and if he was going to run the show, he wasn't going to have them obstructing him and countermanding his orders. So the family discharged Stern on the spot. Ned said, "Fine! That's delightful. But if she's in this hospital, she's got to have an attending doctor. Who do you want to take care of her?"

They conferred and decided on Dr. Peterson. He came over from the clinic and soft-talked to the family, and finally talked them into letting Myrtle have more blood and taking Stern back on the case again. So an hour after he was fired, Stern was rehired again.

We poured more blood into her, trying to get her stabilized, worked at it all Friday morning and half the afternoon, and Stern then introduced Arthur Emery to the family as the surgical consultant he had called. Arthur told them Myrtle had to have surgery to look for the bleeding source and get it stopped, and again the family balked. They just wouldn't think of authorizing surgery— this was about 5:30 in the afternoon—and then Emery just tore into them. He'd gotten wind of this situation, and I've never seen Emery so mad. He told them point-blank that as far as he was concerned he didn't want to touch this old girl with a ten foot pole because he was afraid she would die on the table and she just wasn't any surgical risk that *he* would ever elect to take unless he had to, but he could guarantee them 100 per cent certainly that she was going to die within twelve hours if he didn't open her up, and that they could just make up their minds, if they had any minds to make up. They could sit there in that room and watch her die and accept responsibility for it, or they could let him kill her in the operating room; it was all the same to him, except that at least that way they could blame him when she cooled. So about then old Myrtle dumped out another bedpanful of blood, and the family finally very nastily and reluctantly agreed.

By 10:30 we had her as full of blood as we were going to get her, and in as good shape for surgery as we were going to get her, so Emery took her upstairs. He had her on the table for four hours and gave her 8 units of blood while she was up there, but he found a huge chronic duodenal ulcer with a big calcified artery running through the base of it which had ruptured, and that was what was dumping out all the blood. Emery did a gastric resection and took out the ulcer itself, and tied off the artery, and sewed her up, and got her back down on the floor again, and prayed. By Saturday morning old Myrtle was sore, but she was still among us and not bleeding any more, and by Sunday morning she was almost back to her old, disoriented self again.

Stern came in to see her Sunday morning, and, much to my amazement told me that Myrtle had me to thank for thinking of a surgical consult, the idea had never entered his mind, and he'd fully expected her to lie there and exsanguinate. Well, that was well and good, but it was still clear this week that we might have taken care of the part of Myrtle below her ears but we weren't making any headway with her above the ears. She still doesn't know who or where she is. She just isn't entirely with us upstairs. Unfortunately, her family are still with us, though, and still thoroughly nasty, as though we were doing something wrong in keeping the old girl alive. Why they don't just go in and choke her to death with a pillow I don't know. She's probably got a strongbox full of gold mine stocks somewhere.

So much for old Myrtle; she merely contributed to a very rough weekend of duty. It seemed that I spent most of the time admitting surgical patients. There was one lady who came in with belly pains that sounded like an acute gall bladder, and she said, yes, it probably was, because twenty years before one of her kidneys came loose and fell over her gall bladder. The kind of history that makes you want to sit down and cry. Ultimately, Hank Ruggles took her upstairs Saturday night and found a gangrenous appendix stuck up behind the cecum and involving the gall bladder, so he took out both appendix and gall bladder in one fell swoop and cured her, I guess.

Sunday afternoon, while I was in the midst of some ten other admissions, Roscoe Herring threw me a curve that really set me back. If ever there was a patient who survived tenaciously in spite of everything her doctors could do to kill her, it was Mrs. Gorman. Roscoe called me from the Emergency Room about 5:00 Sunday evening and said there was a woman down there in diabetic coma that he was sending up for me to take care of, a patient of Ned Stern's. I got the nurses alerted and got the coma cart out and stood by. They brought this woman up and I got her in bed; she was lying there sweating, with her eyes wide-open and staring, hardly breathing, little convulsive movements of her arms and legs, no odor on her breath, obviously in insulin shock, not in coma. Her husband was with her, but he was stone-drunk, and Mrs. Gorman wasn't giving any history. I put a call in for Pete, but he was tied up with something somewhere else. So I pulled blood for a blood surgar and Co_2, and then injected 50 cc of 50 percent sugar water into her vein, and her recovery was like magic; she shook her head and sat up blinking and asked where she was and what had happened, all in a matter of about twenty-five seconds. I switched over to an IV of 5 per cent glucose in water, and within a half-hour she was sitting up eating supper and feeling just fine.

It was only then that I got a history, from her and from Stern, and it gave me the cold chills because this woman had come within a hairbreadth of being killed. She'd been sick for about three days and hadn't eaten much, but she'd taken her insulin just the same, without telling her doctor. Tested her urine Friday and found it positive for sugar, but didn't test it again because, she said, "I was sure it was going to be positive, so why test it?" Unassailable logic— I guess. Sunday morning she and her husband started getting drunk fairly early in the morning, after taking a third day's insulin (38 units for her) without any food behind it. When she started having trouble with her vision and getting shaky, her husband called Stern. He asked what her urine was testing, and the husband said, "Positive for sugar" (as indeed it had been, forty-eight hours before), so Stern advised that he give her 6 more units of insulin. Well, by sheer blind luck that morning's dose had emptied the insulin bottle, and by the time the husband got his coat on to go down to the drugstore for more, his wife was out cold on the floor and beginning to convulse, so he brought her to the hospital instead. Another 6 units of insulin and she'd have been dead by the time she got there—her blood sugar was practically zero as it was.

Which illustrates the dangers of telephone diagnosis, I guess. Stern came in to see her, and I told him the story, and he looked as chagrined as I've even seen him look, and Roscoe had a very red face when I told him how we'd cured a patient in diabetic coma in twenty-five seconds with sugar water. Of course, it wasn't any help that the husband was drunk and the wife feeble-minded; I've talked to her a couple of times since and that woman just doesn't have anything upstairs at all. Anyway, it livened up Sunday evening a bit.

Monday afternoon we readmitted Ruth Callahan, Dr. Isaacs' patient with the malignant hypertension. She's been nauseated, sick to her stomach, having trouble with her vision, and she almost faints every time she stands up—in fact, she passed out in the john Monday morning, which was why she came back in. The Ansolysen has been keeping the blood pressure down, perhaps too far down, but Ruth is in trouble. It looks very much as if we came into the picture too late, that the bridge had been crossed. There just wasn't enough of her kidneys left to start with, and her uremia is worse and getting still worse, and I am quite sure she is going to die in spite of anything we do about her blood pressure. Again we will see. She's now in heart failure, too, I think. She'll take close watching.

Kathy Jenkins is also back in the hospital again. I'm not entirely sure just why yet; she looks better than she did rather than worse. Have to nail Case about that tomorrow.

Poor Matt Meadows finally bit off a bite too big for him to chew, the arrogant bastard. Ted Van Wert has been treating this middle-aged man with diabetes and severe arteriosclerosis of both legs, barely detectable pulses in his feet, and getting worse for months. Ted asked Matt to do a sympathectomy on the man, remove the sympathetic nerve ganglia that control the muscular walls of his leg arteries. The theory is that with them removed, the arteries will dilate and stay dilated, and let more blood through. So Matt went in to do the sympathectomy, and for some obscure reason decided to do a Y-graft, remove the man's lower aorta and both common iliacs and replace them with an artery bank substitute.

The man went into surgery at 10:30 A.M. and Matt finished at 5:00 P.M., but just as they were about to move the man from the operating table somebody noticed that one of his legs had gone white and pulseless, so Matt opened him up again. He ended up doing a thromboendarterectomy clear down to his knee on that side, finally finished at 1:30 A.M. And this morning, twenty hours after surgery, the man is still on death's doorstep, and probably won't survive the night tonight. Something surely went wrong with that one, and I'll bet it's a long time before Ted Van Wert turns another patient over to Meadows for a sympathectomy. The tragic part is that the man's leg circulation wasn't really all that bad before Meadows stuck his thumb in the pie. He could have lived very nicely without any surgery at all, for a few months or years at least. The sympathectomy was supposed to improve that prognosis; as it is, it will be surgery that kills the man for sure.

A bad night last night, up most of the night, and a bad day today, so I'd better quit and get some sleep. A whole houseful of sick patients to see tomorrow. It's getting so I wonder how many I leave limping along when I go off duty will be dead by the time I get back next morning. They can sure fool you, going and coming.

Saturday, June 16

Kathy Jenkins, I learned, came back into the hospital for transfusions. Actually she is doing far better than anybody expected. The one course of 6-mercaptopurine slowed down her bone marrow very well, and it has taken this much time for the leukemia to break loose again. Now she has had 3 or 4 units of packed cells to build up her blood level again, and Case has put her on intensive treatment with 6-mercaptopurine again, as well as on cortisone, and she's going back home again. She's not looking too bad, and apparently has been feeling pretty well. And she's convinced herself that this leukemia business is not as grim as it's made out to be.

I made some comment to Case about living in a fool's paradise, but he said it really wasn't any such thing, that every comfortable

day Kathy has is a comfortable day won; she may have two months'
worth of them, or six months' worth, but that he thought there was
a difference between allowing a patient to fool herself, on the
one hand, and allowing her to enjoy what she could enjoy without a
lot of doom-singing. It seems like a pretty fine philosophical point
to me, but then I don't have leukemia either. I found a half-hour to
sit and chew the fat with this little gal today before she went home.
She's bright, and she's got plans for the summer, and she's at peace
with her affliction, and I didn't say one word to upset it. Maybe
Case *has* got a point.

Thursday night Little Bubble died in her sleep, very quietly.
She'd been running evening fevers to 103, and chilling, obviously in
septicemia. The nurses called me to see her about 11:30 Thursday
evening; she had just broken a fever and soaked her bed, and said
she was "firsty" so I got her some orange juice. She went back to
sleep and a few minutes later heaved a little sigh and stopped
breathing. I'd been dreading it, and then it was so easy for her. As it
should have been, that at the very least. I hope somewhere Little
Bubble may learn how to smile.

Thursday, June 21

It is getting very near the end now, and everybody is very much
aware of it. I have a long weekend duty coming up, from Friday
night through Monday morning, to repay Alec for the long weekend I had earlier in the month. Then just five more days to go after
that. It's a very odd feeling to be so near to the end of a year you
thought would never end. Especially odd that I'm eager for it to
end, but not nearly so eager as I was a couple of months ago.
Sometimes I even halfway like this big dump.

Tuesday evening the clinic doctors threw their big annual banquet for the house staff, in one of the fancy banquet rooms at the
Hacienda. They asked Mort Silver to cover the house solo for the
hours of the banquet, so all the interns and residents could get
away, and they all did except for Hank Ruggles and Fred Olsen,
who were in the middle of an emergency gastrectomy when the time
came. All the clinic doctors were there except for Slater, who turned
up later. There was bourbon and scotch to drink, and then a fine
sirloin steak dinner, and a few speeches—mostly reminiscences by

the old boys who had started the clinic and the hospital some thirty years ago—and then we received our official internship certificates, declaring that we had indeed completed a year of internship at Graystone Memorial Hospital between such and such dates and performed our duties loyally and well. Afterward those of us who didn't have duty were invited to stay and have another drink or two.

There was talk of who was going where and what happened next for us. Pete Carey is staying on for a second year of medical residency; Brock is going out to Illinois somewhere for his second year. Floyd Schwartz has been accepted as a first-year surgical resident here; Alec Ivy is going back East as a first-year medical resident. Herring goes into the Navy, with two years on Saipan to look forward to—that should be the life. Hamilton applied for a residency in medicine here and was turned down, about which he is very bitter, but has found a spot somewhere in Los Angeles. Much to everyone's surprise, Hank Ruggles announced that he is entering partnership with Goodfellow and Boggs, to handle most of the gynecological surgery from their practice. And I will dig in to study for state licensure exams, and then doubtless continue to look for a general practice spot, at least until there is money enough to survive a residency.

It was a good party. I think these men, the clinic men, know that they teach well, and give a lot to their interns in return for what they get, and have a good feeling if the men who move on (or stay on for more training) seem likely to be decent doctors, thanks to their efforts. Even Nathan Slater was halfway mellow and benign, sipping his ginger ale after dinner. His gastrectomy patient must have survived.

The rest of the week has been busy but benign. Old Myrtle Fraser is coming along fine, still some abdominal pain from her surgery, but she is eating now and progressing very nicely even if she isn't any better oriented than before. Ruth Callahan has been going steadily downhill, one labored step at a time. She's having trouble with shortness of breath now, and gathering fluid in her legs; we digitalized her, but that hasn't seemed to help much with her heart failure. She can't eat anything, and is sick to her stomach all the time. If she survives to the end of my internship, I shall be very much surprised, because I think that she's going to go into pulmonary edema and die almost any day or night now.

Otherwise, things have gone on very much as before, perhaps a little lighter load, but patients come and patients go. One thing I've learned to count on, almost fatalistically: every duty night something turns up to keep me up all night. Last night it was a little old lady of eighty-five years with long-standing diabetes, and brittle as brittle can be. She had been having insulin shocks at 3:00 every morning for about a week, and came in yesterday at 4:00 in the afternoon in insulin shock. Compton saw her and wrote for some IVs containing both insulin and sugar, warned me not to give her much sugar to pull her out of shock because she'd flip right over into acidosis if I did. She was doing pretty well when I went to bed last night, but at 3:30 A.M. they called me that she was in shock again. So I went up to see her, and very cautiously stuck about 25 cc of 50 per cent sugar water into her IV, and she popped right out of it. So then I had to sit holding her hand the rest of the night, keeping her just on the edge of shock until breakfasttime, also cut down on her daily insulin dose, and by this afternoon she was looking and feeling much better.

I've seen enough of these people to know what a spooky disease diabetes is, especially in older people and children; I've treated insulin shock plenty of times, but haven't really had to ride out a diabetic coma yet. Disappoints me a little. Ned Stern sneered at this, said, "Don't complain; they always come in at 10:00 at night, and you are up with them all that night and the next day, too, and it's just one big mess." This from the man who should know. I'd still like the experience of riding one through, but time is really getting short.

[*Post hoc:* I never did have to ride out a patient in diabetic coma during internship, but I have had that "pleasure" more than once later in practice, and Ned Stern was right: it really is just one big mess.]

Monday, June 25

A thoroughly busy weekend again, the same as the others on this service except that I cannot shake off the curious detached feeling

that everything now is temporary, and that the new, sick patients
coming in now will devolve upon my successor, whoever the lucky
guy is, so I see them from a certain distance and with a certain
detachment. A patient of Fred Kidder's came in with a bleeding
ulcer, and tending to him took up most of Friday night and half of
Saturday. This guy was particularly obstreperous because he
wouldn't leave his Levin tube down until Kidder himself came in
and threatened to put him in a strait jacket unless he kept his
hands away from it. Finally went up to surgery Saturday night, on
Slater's service, and I lost track of him, except that he seemed still
to be around this morning.

Saturday night Ruth Callahan filled up with fluid, as predicted,
and expired, as predicted. She had a rough hour or two, but no
more, thank God. She was a good patient and a good woman; she
just happened to have an evil disease that whipped her. Sunday
the new medical admissions started in about 10:00 in the morning,
and kept Pete and me running until midnight. Then today we
admitted about ten more, and got word that every bed in the hospital was now packed full, so we may not have so much the rest of
the week. Trouble with that, of course, is that all the doctors then
get nervous about having somebody they *have* to hospitalize and
having no beds for them, so they start dumping the not-so-sick ones
home quicker. I was plenty glad to get off tonight, though, even at
8:30.

Saturday, June 30

A benign week, surprisingly so, although there still weren't any
beds to store people so nobody much got admitted. Pete and I both
managed to keep busy enough with rounds and routine procedures.
Thursday night was very busy, with an aged patient of Fred Kidder's who had been in the house with bronchitis for a week suddenly getting a plug of mucus in his trachea and nearly choking to
death. This one Pete and I managed not to kill, at any rate, for
which Fred duly thanked us. We did have to be up to check the old
goat about once an hour all night. I got a look at his chest film, and
it looked like he didn't have any useful lung tissue left at all, but
Fred assures us that he has a little wedge of good lung tucked up in
each apex that keeps him going.

Then Friday we limped through the day—at least I did—making myself as scarce as possible. Saw two or three new people, did an LP and a thoracentesis (tapping fluid from inside the chest), and mostly waited for the day to get over. A quiet evening, and as I made pill rounds about 11:00 before turning in it hardly seemed credible that this was the last, the very last night I would make pill rounds on this internship. I hoped for a quiet night, but no such luck; Isaacs sent in a woman in pulmonary edema about 2:30 A.M., and I fiddled with her until she was out of the woods around 5:30.

Broad daylight outside, a nice summer Saturday morning, and Ann was to pick me up at 8:00 A.M., so I sat in the library and read until the cafeteria opened. Found Ted Van Wert and Ned Stern both there waiting with me at 7:00, and I blew myself to bacon and eggs for breakfast and listened to them argue about whether a diabetic mother's baby *in utero* makes enough insulin for both mother and baby in the last trimester of pregnancy, and if so how does it get across the placental barrier? Nice, ordinary breakfast conversation. I went down to quarters to shower and shave and change clothes, and then at 8:00 paged Alec and checked out to him, and he said, "Well, you lucky bastard, you get out of here a day early, don't you?" and I said, yes, that was the way it broke, and he said, "Some guys get all the breaks." And I said, "Yes, but only the honest ones," and hung up the phone. Then I went outside to the parking lot to wait for Ann, and she was held up a few minutes in traffic but not very long, and I got in the car, and we drove away from there as quietly as we could.

Postscript

Abruptly as it had begun 365 days before, my internship year was over. I do not know who my successor was on Medicine II; I never saw any of the new interns who began their year of training at Graystone the day I ended mine. I did not want to see them then, and by the time I returned as a practicing physician on the hospital's attending staff, more than one new staff of interns had passed down the road that I had traveled.

During those last few days I remember that Ann and I had thoughts for only one thing: a rest and vacation. I had a grandiose dream of doing nothing but eating and sleeping for a solid week (I still have the same dream, still unfulfilled). Ann read travel folders and figured how we could manage a week on the beach in Baja California for practically no money at all. Neither of us got our way, because state licensure exams faced me just three weeks off. I did not sleep and we did not travel. I studied. A year had been spent away from books, a year filled with clinical medicine of all varieties, but the theory had been ignored. I read anatomy and physiology again. I dug through my biochemistry notes and textbooks. I reviewed my medical school lectures in pathology. Then I went to take the examination, a grim affair four days long.

The clinical portions of the test were duck soup—I rode through in triumph. The basic sciences portions were horrible, and I was certain that I had failed, and saw before me a long six months of study and marking time until the exams were again offered. Each examinee had been assigned an identification number, and on the appointed day a week after the exams a grim little list of numbers was posted on the main bulletin board of the Medical School: the numbers of the men who had flunked.

Some did fail the examination. I passed. Rumor had it that, identification numbers or not, the examination written by an M.D. could be distinguished by the examiners from one written by a chiropractor, a podiatrist, a naturopath or an osteopath, and that no M.D. taking the test would fail to be licensed. Maybe the rumor was true; I did not know then and I do not know now. I had made it, that was all that mattered. In due time a license to practice medicine and surgery within the boundaries of the state was issued to me. Now, some years later, I may overlook payment of a grocery bill or forget my wife's birthday, but I do not fail, each year, to have that license renewed at the proper time. It is all a matter of values.

You would never recognize Graystone Memorial Hospital now. During the years since my internship, an entire new building has been added and the number of beds has doubled. An entire wing of the hospital has been given over to the obstetrical service, and now there are thirty beds available for nonpaying patients who become the direct responsibility of the interns and residents for their delivery. A completely new operating suite with twelve operating rooms and an intensive-care unit was built on the top floor of the new building. Graystone now has a quota of sixteen interns, and fills its quota each year. There are as many as fifteen surgical residents, ten residents in anesthesia, three in radiology and seven in medicine; a residency there today is considered a prize, with considerable competition for each available spot.

Other things, too, have changed. Dr. Tuckerman died of cancer of the lung, and Cal Cornell fell dead of his second coronary one day as he left the operating room after a long and grueling case. John Gillies left the clinic for a more attractive situation elsewhere. Arthur Emery has been gradually retiring for years; he has not yet quite made it, but the consensus is that he probably will before another ten years have passed. And coming up behind Nathan Slater and Matt Meadows are four new surgeons on the clinic staff. There are new faces on the hospital staff every year. Many changes, yet one thing does not change: the training of new doctors goes on just as before. For all the new building and for all the new teachers, the interns starting each July are just as green, just as frightened and just as hapless as they ever were. They work just as hard, doing the same kind of work, with just as many failures and just as many triumphs today as when I was there. But they learn . . . and the work goes on.